A Hands-On Workbook for Physical Anthropology

Lauren Arenson, Ph.D.
Pasadena City College

With contributions by:
Elvio Angeloni, M.A.
Pasadena City College

KENDALL/HUNT PUBLISHING COMPANY
4050 Westmark Drive Dubuque, Iowa 52002

Cover photos supplied courtesy of Tad Motoyama, Los Angeles Zoo.

ISBN 0-7872-7241-8

Printed in the United States of America
10 9 8 7 6 5 4 3 2

Acknowledgements

I would like to thank my students, for whom this book is written. Their dedication to higher learning is truly an inspiration. Also, to my family and friends. I appreciate your support and encouragement. To Robert Bowman, who, without his kind words and dedication to teaching me the ways of the computer, this book may have never reached completion. And most important, to Marshall, thanks for making all of my dreams come true.

Contents

Introduction

1.1 Introduction to Text

The purpose of this workbook is two-fold. The first is to assist with the difficult concepts presented in introductory physical anthropology courses. This workbook is designed to allow the reader the opportunity to improve his/her knowledge of the subject matter by applying critical thinking skills to the interpretation of the fossil record. The second purpose is to enable students to gain a better understanding of the scientific methodology utilized by anthropologists conducting field research. This knowledge will aid the student in being able to critically assess the conclusions drawn from data obtained from field studies.

This book is the first of its kind, designed to be used as an in-class supplement for introductory classes in physical anthropology, with or without an associated laboratory section.

The fossil record is often characterized as fragmented and/or incomplete. Although this statement may be true, we must examine what conclusions may be drawn from the existing data and attempt to form cohesive theories to explain the past. Thus, we may consider the study of hominid phylogeny as being similar to solving a giant puzzle, which ultimately relates directly to ourselves.

To the author, there is no journey more exciting than the one you are about to embark on. Learning about our past allows us as humans to understand why we react, appear, and adapt to environmental forces today.

Your comments and suggestions are very important. Please direct all correspondence to Lauren Arenson, Social Sciences Division, Pasadena City College, 1570 East Colorado Boulevard, Pasadena, California, 91106-2003.

E-mail messages can be forwarded to **ljarenson@paccd.cc.ca.us**.

■ 1.2 Term Project

The following project is to be completed in stages throughout the course. Begin by reading through the following guidelines. The key to this assignment is to establish a well-designed environment in which your species exists. As you proceed through each question, be sure to offer very specific responses. In short, this assignment will be building upon every component addressed in this course. Most important, be creative . . . have fun.

1. Design an imaginary species. Describe all facets of the species, including appearance, reproductive behavior (including courting rituals, lifestyle, food choice, sleeping patterns, care of young, generation span, and so on). Describe in detail the environment in which your species exists. Describe all predators that prey upon your species. Take your time and cover all aspects of your species' existence.

2. Discuss the ancestors of your species. Which traits of your species are primitive? Which are derived? How long has your species existed? Describe physical traits that allow your species to adapt to its environment.

3. Address those evolutionary forces that impact your species over time. How does your imaginary species adapt to environmental fluctuations? Does your species possess generalized or specialized physical characteristics? How does this impact the evolution of your species?

4. Discuss how the changes in your species impact the environment. How are those animals that prey upon your imaginary species impacted? How does your species continue to affect the environment in which it exists?

5. Describe in detail your species after one million years of evolution. How has your species changed? Why? How has the environment changed? Why? Discuss your thoughts on the evolutionary strategies that allowed your species to adapt over this period of time.

6. Look back to your original description of the imaginary species. Is there anything that you would like to change in order to increase its fitness to an ever-changing environment? What benefits would exist if changes could be made to the original description?

■ 1.3 Letter from the Smithsonian

This article has been widely posted on the Internet, and is often claimed to be a genuine letter from the Smithsonian's archives. It isn't. The Smithsonian has no paleoanthropology division, and no curator named Harvey Rowe.

Read and enjoy it anyway. After all, it's the sort of thing that could have happened.

Paleoanthropology Division
Smithsonian Institute
207 Pennsylvania Avenue
Washington, DC 20078

Dear Sir:

Thank you for your latest submission to the Institute, labeled "211-D, layer seven, next to the clothesline post. Hominid skull." We have given this specimen a careful and detailed examination, and regret to inform you that we disagree with your theory that it represents "conclusive proof of the presence of Early Man in Charleston County two million years ago." Rather, it appears that what you have found is the head of a Barbie doll, of the variety one of our staff, who has small children, believes to be the "Malibu Barbie". It is evident that you have given a great deal of thought to the analysis of this specimen, and you may be quite certain that those of us who are familiar with your prior work in the field were loathe to come to contradiction with your findings. However, we do feel that there are a number of physical attributes of the specimen which might have tipped you off to its modern origin:

1. The material is molded plastic. Ancient hominid remains are typically fossilized bone.
2. The cranial capacity of the specimen is approximately 9 cubic centimeters, well below the threshold of even the earliest identified proto-hominids.
3. The dentition pattern evident on the "skull" is more consistent with the common domesticated dog than it is with the "ravenous man-eating Pliocene clams" you speculate roamed the wetlands during that time. This latter finding is certainly one of the most intriguing hypotheses you have submitted in your history with this institution, but the evidence seems to weigh rather heavily against it. Without going into too much detail, let us say that:

   A. The specimen looks like the head of a Barbie doll that a dog has chewed on.
   B. Clams don't have teeth.

It is with feelings tinged with melancholy that we must deny your request to have the specimen carbon dated. This is partially due to the heavy load our lab must bear in its normal operation, and partly due to carbon dating's notorious inaccuracy in fossils of recent geologic record. To the best of our knowledge, no Barbie dolls were produced prior to 1956 AD, and carbon dating is likely to produce wildly inaccurate results. Sadly, we must also deny your request that we approach the National Science Foundation's Phylogeny Department with the concept of assigning your specimen the scientific name "Australopithecus spiff-arino." Speaking personally, I, for one, fought tenaciously for the acceptance of your proposed taxonomy, but was ultimately voted down because the species name you selected was hyphenated, and didn't really sound like it might be Latin.

However, we gladly accept your generous donation of this fascinating specimen to the museum. While it is undoubtedly not a hominid fossil, it is, nonetheless, yet another riveting example of the great body of work you seem to accumulate here so effortlessly. You should know that our Director has reserved a special shelf in his own office for the display of the specimens you have previously submitted to the Institution, and the entire staff speculates daily on what you will happen upon next in your digs at the site you have discovered in your backyard. We eagerly anticipate your trip to our nation's capital that you proposed in your last letter, and several of us are pressing the Director to pay for it. We are particularly interested in hearing you expand on your theories surrounding the "trans-positating fillifitation of ferrous ions in a structural matrix" that makes the excellent juvenile Tyrannosaurus rex femur you recently discovered take on the deceptive appearance of a rusty 9-mm Sears Craftsman automotive crescent wrench.

Yours in Science,

Harvey Rowe
Curator, Antiquities

Genetics and Inheritance

2.1 Introduction to Genetics

Evolution refers to the complex set of processes by which living organisms originated on earth, diversified and adapted through sustained changes in form and function. The earliest living species, one-celled organisms such as bacteria, referred to as prokaryotes (meaning "pre-nucleus"), existed as early as 3.7 billion years ago. Eukaryotes ("true nucleus") or multi-celled organisms with a defined nuclear membrane first appeared approximately 1.2 billion years ago. Since the time of these earliest organisms, evolution has resulted in the successive radiation of new species. While approximately 99% of all flora and fauna species that existed at one time on our planet are now extinct, others have diversified to exist today.

The science of genetics began with the research conducted by Gregor Mendel. Mendel described the patterns of **simple inheritance** in terms of seven pairs of contrasting traits that appeared in garden pea plants. His research suggested that traits are inherited as separate units, each inherited independently from one another. Mendel concluded that each parent has pairs of units (**chromosomes**) but contributes only one unit from each pair to the offspring. These units, which Mendel first described, are now understood to be a section of the DNA that has an identifiable structure or function and are known as **genes**.

Charles Darwin and Alfred R. Wallace observed the process of natural selection operating within the natural world. **Natural selection**, the basis of all biological principles, describes the mechanisms for evolutionary change resulting from the differential rate of survival and reproduction of certain organisms within a given population due to their biological characteristics. Thus, individuals possessing certain physical traits that make them well **adapted** to their environment or that offer them effective reproductive strategies tend to pass along more genetic material to the next generation. **Fitness** is determined by adaptive and reproductive success. Evolution then proceeds by the natural selection of well-adapted organisms over long periods of time. Natural selection refers to a constant but gradual transition of evolutionary change in order to better adapt to the ever-changing environment. This process is called **gradualism**.

Current researchers, including Stephen Jay Gould, have proposed a variation on the theme of species evolution, known as **punctuated equilibrium**. According to this view, species do in fact tend to remain stable (with little variation) over long periods of time.

Sudden physiological changes seem to occur relatively abruptly, either replacing the original organism with a more successful form or resulting in extinction. These adaptations are occurring rapidly in terms of the geological time scale, yet are actually happening over hundreds or thousands of generations.

2.2 Study Guide: Key Terms

Define the following terms:

adaptation:

adaptive radiation:

alleles:

biotic:

DNA:

dominant traits:

eugenics:

evolution: (macro/micro)

fitness:

genes:

genotype:

gradualism:

heritability:

heterozygous:

homozygous:

hybrid:

inheritance:

locus:

meiosis:

mitosis:

natural selection:

paleoanthropology:

phenotype:

polygenic inheritance:

polymorphism:

population:

protein synthesis:

punctuated equilibrium:

Punnett squares:

recessive traits:

RNA:

speciation:

twin studies:

variation:

2.3 How Does Evolution Work?

Ian Tattersall

Ever since the triumph of the Modern Evolutionary Synthesis in the 1940s and 1950s, the received wisdom in paleoanthropology has been that all evolutionary phenomena can be ascribed to a single mechanism: gradual change in genes and gene frequencies within lineages, under the guiding hand of natural selection. Dobzhansky's[1] placing of a "sign of equality between the mechanisms of macroevolution and micro-evolution" has been accepted more or less as dogma, however reluctant the great geneticist himself was to write that sign of equality. So we can start here from a proposition everyone should be able to agree on: Natural selection (differential reproductive success, mediated by the environment) is responsible for at least a substantial proportion of the morphological change in the fossil record.

But can this be all? Hardly. For while natural selection may explain morphological transformation, it does nothing to account for biotic diversity, the other dominant signal in the fossil record. Dobzhansky himself[1] identified three levels at which the evolutionary process acts: in the origin of genetic novelties; in the ordering of those novelties in molding "the genetic structures of populations into new shapes"; and in "the fixation of the diversity already attained on the preceding two levels" (p. 13). Mutations and recombinations account for the first of these, natural selection for the second. But we have to look elsewhere to explain the third level, which relates to the origins of genetic discontinuity among populations. Obsessed as they have been with the problem of tracing the roots of the single species *Homo sapiens* back into the past, paleoanthropologists have largely succeeded in ignoring this last issue—although its central significance was clear to Dobzhansky, who specifically stated that "the origin and functioning of the isolating mechanisms constitute one of the most important problems of the genetics of populations" (p. 14).

This is not to suggest, of course, that natural selection is irrelevant to the accumulation of biotic diversity: of course it isn't. But neither does it achieve everything. Dobzhansky himself put his finger on the problem by characterizing natural selection as one of the levels of action. Virtually every widespread species (*Homo sapiens* is as good an example as any) is geographically variable and straddles a variety of ecological zones. Each local population will be subject to distinctive selective pressures in its own particular environment, and will respond accordingly. This is the context in which any genetic and phenotypic novelties that appear (Dobzhansky's first level) will transfer from the level of the individual to that of the population (his second level)—largely, at least, under the influence of natural selection. However, as long as genetic continuity is not disrupted—as long as, in Dobzhansky's parlance, local variants do not become fixed (his level three)—such variants will remain mere ephemera, which may, through interbreeding, be reabsorbed into the parent population at any time.

The event that produces fixation is speciation, or the acquisition by a population of genetic isolation. I have characterized speciation as the "black box" of genetics[2]: a poorly understood group of mechanisms, at any of a variety of genomic levels, that have in common only that they achieve the same effect.[3] However, it seems that speciation is unrelated either to adaptation per se,[2] or to any specifiable degree of morphological shift.[4] Speciation emphatically is not simply a passive consequence of accumulating morphological change. On the other hand, what this mysterious process achieves is clear: the establishment of new objective historical entities. This is of critical importance, for evolutionary change consists not just of the arrival of anatomical or be-havioral novelties, but of their propagation and conservation.[5] Such novelties will not endure if the "package" in which they are enshrined does not itself persist as a distinctive entity. Endurance in this sense does not simply mean the avoidance of extinction, but the continuation of morphologies which, in the absence of genetic disjunction, are constantly

From *Evolutionary Anthropology*, Vol. 2, 1994, pp. 2–3.

threatened with disappearance (or modification) through reabsorption. Whatever one may conclude about whether the Neanderthals were wiped out[6] or simply swamped genetically,[7] the incontrovertible fact is that they are no longer around.

Thus, species play two roles in evolution: one as discrete, bounded entities, with births, lifespans, and extinctions and the other as dynamic units consisting (usually) of multiple local populations, each itself an individual engine of evolutionary innovation—but historically unvalidated, as it were, until the event of speciation.[4, 5, 8] Species probably vary in time very much as they do in space, i.e. within limits. Further, it is the releasing effects of speciation that allow a population to move beyond those limits.[4, 5, 8] Hence, while the concept of punctuated equilibria as originally formulated[9] might appear a trifle severe in insisting that a lack of any significant change marks the intervals between speciation events, it still remains obvious that any notion of evolutionary change that excludes speciation must be regarded as incomplete.

Although there is no direct relationship between speciation and morphological change, it is nonetheless clear from a glance at living primates that morphological differences between members of closely related species are minor indeed, at least in those parts that tend to be preserved in the fossil record. Among extinct primates, such differences are certainly of much smaller magnitude than those found within the rather few fossil human species normally recognized. And if, as the comparative evidence indicates, within-species morphological diversification is inherently limited, the question obviously arises as to how both the major discontinuities between higher taxa and evolutionary trends (which, though real, are rarer than we often assume), are to be explained. Given what we know about the fluctuation of environments over time, neither phenomenon is plausibly ascribable to gradual adaptation over the eons.

The answer here appears to lie in competition among species, particularly among closely related ones. As Gould and Eldredge have recently remarked,[10] "Most macroevolution must be rendered by asking what kinds of species within a clade did better than others (speciated more frequently, survived longer), or what biases in direction of speciation prevailed within a clade" (p. 224). Species, in other words, may be viewed as individuals,[11] and are sorted over time in very much the same way that individual organisms are winnowed by natural selection. Of course, such sorting need not be strictly adaptationist; in a fluctuating environment, species may become extinct (or find their competitors extinguished) for reasons that have nothing to do with how well they (or their competitors) are adapted for survival in a given habitat—after all, environmental changes are random with respect to adaptation. Nonetheless, certain traits (enlarged brain size among them, apparently) may well, on average, predispose to survivability.

As Gould and Eldredge[10] have pointed out, the sorting of species rather than of individuals "enjoin[s] a very different programme of research from the traditional 'how did natural selection within a lineage build substantial adaptation during long stretches of time?'" (p. 224). It demands that we investigate the reasons for the differential success of discrete species and the histories of diversity within clades. Paleoanthropologists would do well to remember this, for much paleoanthropological practice up until now has consisted of attempts to shoehorn human fossils into a linear framework that projects *Homo sapiens* back into the far distant past in a steadily transmuting succession. Paleoanthropologists, tending to see time and change as virtually synonymous, have focused the bulk of their efforts on attempts to demonstrate within-lineage morphological transformation as the dominant signal of the hominid fossil record, and thus to assign species the status of arbitrary ephemera. This tendency has been facilitated by the existence today of only a single hominid species—which is actually a highly atypical situation, albeit partially disguised by paleoanthropologists' generous-hearted reluctance to exclude any larger-brained hominid from *Homo sapiens*.

All of this is a pity, for we should not believe that earlier humans played the evolutionary game by a unique set of rules. There really is no place in hominid systematics for special pleading based on human "culture" (whatever that is), and most certainly not in the period before *Homo sapiens* declared independence from local ecosystems with the invention of settled agriculture. The sooner the practice of reconstructing human phylogeny is brought into line with what we know of the evolutionary process among mammals as a whole, the sooner we will be able to make sense of the complexities of our own fossil record.

References

1 Dobzhansky T (1937) *Genetics and the Origin of Species.* New York: Columbia University Press.

2 Tattersall I (1993) Speciation and morphological differentiation in the genus *Lemur*. In Kimbel WH, Martin LB (eds) *Species, Species Concepts and Primate Evolution*, pp. 163–176. New York. Plenum Press.

3 Tattersall I (1992) Species concepts and species identification in human evolution. J Hum Evol *22*:341–349.

4 Tattersall I (1986) Species recognition in human paleontology. J Hum Evol *15*:165–175.

5 Futuyma DJ (1987) On the role of species in anagenesis. Amer Naturalist *130*:465–473.

6 Tattersall I (1993) *The Human Odyssey*. New York: Prentice-Hall.

7 Smith FH (1984) Fossil hominids from the Upper Pleistocene of central Europe and the origin of modern Europeans. In Smith FH, Spencer F (eds) *The Origins of Modern Humans*, pp 137–209. New York: Alan R. Liss.

8 Futuyama DJ (1992) History and evolutionary processes. In Nitecki MH, Nitecki DV (eds), *History and Evolution*, pp 103–130. Albany: State University of New York Press.

9 Eldredge N, Gould SJ (1972) Punctuated equilibria: An alternative to phyletic gradualism. In Schopf TJM (ed), *Models in Paleobiology*, pp. 82–115. San Francisco: Freeman, Cooper & Co.

10 Gould SJ, Eldredge N (1993) Punctuated equilibria comes of age. Nature *366*:223–227.

11 Ghiselin MT (1974) A radical solution to the species problem. Syst Zool *23*:536–544.

2.3 Study Questions: How Does Evolution Work? —Ian Tattersall

1. In your own words, describe the process of 'natural selection' and state its importance to the study of hominids through the fossil record.

2. What is biotic diversity?

3. What factors, according to Tattersall, influence the process of evolution?

4. Define speciation and describe its impact on macroevolution.

5. How do fluctuations in the environment impact a species rate of survival?

6. What is meant by species competition?

2.4 *How Does Evolution Work?*

Milford Wolpoff

So how does evolution work? In a word, complexly, and more so than Tattersall suggests. Species competition, his preferred mechanism of change, does not by itself account for biotic diversity, and it accounts for little else. The singular focus on species and speciation addresses only part of the question of how evolution creates diversity; there are more explanations, and very much more to be explained. It is no longer possible for single-cause descriptions of evolution to be considered as all-encompassing explanations.

The last two decades have seen the New Synthesis modified by several realizations, the one important to this discussion being the unlinking of microevolution and macroevolution with the understanding that major evolutionary changes are not always the result of microevolutionary processes continuing for long periods of time.[1] There are many complex causes of change; for instance, selection works at three different levels:

1. the genic level, where inclusive fitness maximization can be important because of the way alleles are distributed within groups of related individuals;
2. the individual and populational level, the realm of traditional population genetics and the models that derive from it;
3. the species level, where both differential survivorship[2] (including the competition between the species that Tattersall discusses) and differential fecundity of species formed by cladogenesis[3] play important roles.

We need not choose which of these is "correct"—they all are valid domains for the operation of differential survivorship and reproduction.

Yet, selection is only part of the picture—there are roles played by the other microevolutionary forces incorporated in the New Synthesis. With the realization that only a very small part of the genome contributes to phenotypic change,[4] the role of mutation in neutral evolution at the molecular level[5] is far removed from the simplistic mechanisms visualized to explain major evolutionary change in decades past. Mutations underlie the neutral evolutionary changes that characterize more of the genome than does directed change. Drift, in disrupting coadapted genetic systems and rearranging them in novel and occasionally quite successful ways, is an important element in explaining the often-observed association of major morphological change with (not just after, contra Tattersall) peripheral speciation. These truly significant reorganizational changes,[6] when they are successful, can accomplish a restructuring of the genome at the time of speciation in ways that could never be the result of these processes on a microevolutionary level.

Species are critical to Tattersall's vision of evolution, not as vessels containing microevolutionary processes but as the vehicles for creating major change. He is quite correct in joining those who question the linking of all macroevolution to microevolutionary mechanisms. The explanation he provides to replace the traditional account for how evolution works is species competition. He reasons that long-term evolutionary trends could not reflect environmental adaptation because environments fluctuate and adaptive variations would be reabsorbed by the parental stock. Instead, ongoing species competition could continue for longer periods, and account for evolutionary trends whose results can become fixed when they are within species. Tattersall argues that paleoanthropologists are blinded to this possibility because by extending *Homo sapiens* into the past, different contemporary competing human species cannot be distinguished.

Only by recognizing species diversity can we hope to explain the important trends in human evolution. Brain size increase is surely foremost among these (Tattersall admits "enlarged brain size . . . may . . . on

From *Evolutionary Anthropology*, Vol. 2, 1994, pp. 4–5.

average predispose to survivability"), but does the contention that human brain size expansion is a result of interspecies competition make any sense? Compelling data show that brain size increased throughout the Pleistocene in all areas of the world[7,8]—this is a reality that must be explained, and not the artifact of "cultural bias" that some had hoped.[9] If the regional populations were actually the different human species that Tattersall envisages,[10] brain size increased significantly in each "species." So to accept this model, we must believe that various human species occupying different geographic areas competed for over a half-million years and reacted to the rivalry by evolving the same unique morphology—expanded brain size. Even if we suspend belief in the competitive exclusion principle, which notes that species competing for limiting resources die off, move to separate area to avoid competition, or evolve different adaptations to eliminate it, this argument is nonsensical. If there was such a competition, would we expect the competing species to evolve the same adaptation to avoid it? Would one not conclude that the presence of the same, unique long term adaptive trend in different regions suggests that the same species occupied these regions? This is not an indulgence to "generous-hearted" paleoanthropology but a consequence of phylogenetic analysis which is based on the notion that synapomorphies are the basis for establishing closeness of relationship, not for proving the existence of differences.

By focusing on phenomena at the level of species and speciation, the important evolutionary implications of internal subdivisions within species[11] are overlooked. Questions about evolutionary processes that cause stability or change within such species are never asked because it is assumed that they are irrelevant.

Multiplication of species is a necessary consequence of Tattersall's model, for to have species competition drive evolution there must be lots of species. Tattersall does not think that internal subdivisions are able to persist unless they are fixed by a speciation. But in widespread internally subdivided species there may be no single large "parental population" that the others continually divide from and reabsorb into,[12] and isolation by distance is sufficient to maintain long-lasting differences.[13] Genic exchanges play an important role in subdivided species, in an aspect of evolution that he does not consider—indeed cannot consider—as part of the balance mechanism that maintains internal diversifications within species.[12] In any event, what some paleoanthropologists have seen to persist over time is not a race or subspecies, but features. There is the rub. As Tattersall says, "whatever one may conclude about whether the Neanderthals were wiped out or simply swamped genetically . . . the incontrovertible fact is that they are no longer around." No doubt, but just as incontrovertibly their features persisted well into the European Upper Paleolithic, and in some cases to recent and modern times.[14] This evolutionary pattern shows exactly what should not be there unless long lasting internal subdivisions are important to the evolutionary process—the persistence of regional features. It demonstrates without question that speciation did not happen; Neandertals were not ephemeral.

Paleoanthropology is an important source of knowledge about evolutionary process. With the proliferation of working scientists and the intensity of funding dedicated to understanding human evolution, it is quite incorrect to suppose that "paleoanthropologists are consumers, rather than producers, of major theoretical insights."[15] To understand what human evolution studies can contribute to elucidating the evolutionary process, however, I propose we begin with an accurate description of what practicing paleoanthropologists actually do. Tattersall makes three assertions about this:

1. [paleoanthropologists are] obsessed . . . with the problem of tracing the roots of the single species *Homo sapiens* back into the past;
2. paleoanthropological practice up to now has consisted of attempts to shoehorn human fossils into a linear framework that projects *Homo sapiens* far into the distant past in a steadily transmuting succession;
3. [paleoanthropologists also attempt] to demonstrate within-lineage morphological transformation as the dominant signal of the hominid fossil record—and thus to assign species the status of arbitrary ephemera.

These reveal a misunderstanding of how paleoanthropologists and other evolutionary researchers approach science. They are not practicing their profession in order to work out their obsessions or to shoehorn data into pre-existing models. Paleoanthropologists, like all evolutionary biologists, attempt to disprove hypotheses.

Generally, it is the hypothesis of no difference that is first examined, but what does this mean in the context of human species? There are two interpretations, and these are linked to the definition of species. One is definitions based on phenetic difference (everybody can see phenetic differences all through Pleistocene human evolution), and the other is genealogical difference. Tattersall and I seem to agree that species can only be defined phylogenetically as "discrete, bounded entities, with births, lifespans, and extinctions." Yet, when it comes to a critical diagnosis of species in the hominid fossil record, Tattersall does not turn to phylogenetic criteria but to phenetics, asserting that "among extant primates [morphological] differences are certainly of much smaller magnitude than those found within the rather few fossil human species normally recognized." This is why he has maintained that far too few species have been recognized in the hominid fossil record.[16] He wants to have his cake and eat it too, on this issue, as he shifts from branching pattern to morphology to define species—even while asserting "there is no direct relationship between speciation and morphological change"—to identify them.

But there is much more agreement than disagreement between us. As he says, the practice of reconstructing human phylogeny must be brought into line with what we know of the evolutionary process among mammals as a whole.

References

1 Charlesworth B, Lande R, Slatkin M (1982) A Neo-Darwinian commentary on macroevolution. Evolution *36*:474–498.

2 Vrba ES, Eldredge N (1984) Individuals, hierarchies and process: Towards a more complete evolutionary theory. Paleobiology *10*:146–171.

3 Vrba ES (1980) Evolution, species, and fossils: How does life evolve? S Afr J Sci *76*:61–84.

4 Marks J (1992) Beads and string: The genome in evolutionary theory. In Dover EJ (ed), *Molecular Applications in Biological Anthropology*, pp 234–255. New York: Cambridge Universary Press.

5 Kimura M (1979) The neutral theory of molecular evolution. Sci Am *241*:98–126.

6 Barton NH, Charlesworth B (1984) Genetic revolutions, founder effects, and speciation. Ann Rev Ecol Syst *15*:133–164.

7 Wolpoff MH (1995) *Paleoanthropology, Second Edition.* New York: McGraw-Hill (in press).

8 Leigh SR (1992) Cranial capacity evolution in *Homo erectus* and early *Homo sapiens*. Am J Phys Anthropol *87*:1–14.

9 Gould SJ (1992) Eve and her tree. Discover (July):32–33: "for reasons of cultural bias, rather than compelling data, conventional views had envisaged the brain power of *Homo erectus* as arising . . . among populations spread all over the Old World".

10 Tattersall I (1993) *The Human Odyssey*. New York: Prentice-Hall.

11 Lande R (1986) The dynamics of peak shifts and the pattern of morphological evolution. Paleobiology *12*:343–354.

12 Wolpoff MH, Xinzhi Wu, Thorne AG (1984) Modern *Homo sapiens* origins: A general theory of hominid evolution involving the fossil evidence from east Asia. In Smith FH, Spencer F (eds.), *The Origin of Modern Humans: A World Survey of the Fossil Evidence*, pp 411–483. New York: Alan R. Liss.

13 Wright S (1943) Isolation by distance. Genetics *28*:114–138.

14 Frayer DW (1993) Evolution at the European edge: Neanderthal and Upper Paleolithic Relationships. Prehistoire Europienne 2:9–69.

15 Pilbeam DR (1989) Human fossil history and evolutionary paradigms. In Hecht MK (ed) *Evolutionary Biology at the Crossroads*, pp 117–124. Flushing: Queens College Press.

16 Tattersall I (1992) Species concepts and species identification in human evolution. J Hum Evol 22:341–350.

2.4 Study Questions: How Does Evolution Work? —Milford Wolpoff

1. How do Wolpoff's points differ from Tattersall's concerning the forces of evolution?

2. What is meant by selection?

3. What is meant by species diversity?

2.5 *Charles Darwin's Obituary*

T. H. Huxley

Very few, even among those who have taken the keenest interest in the progress of the revolution in natural knowledge set afoot by the publication of the 'Origin of Species'; and who have watched, not without astonishment, the rapid and complete change which has been effected both inside and outside the boundaries of the scientific world in the attitude of men's minds towards the doctrines which are expounded in that great work, can have been prepared for the extraordinary manifestation of affectionate regard for the man, and of profound reverence for the philosopher, which followed the announcement, on Thursday last, of the death of Mr Darwin.

Not only in these islands, where so many have felt the fascination of personal contact with an intellect which had no superior, and with a character which was even nobler than the intellect; but, in all parts of the civilized world, it would seem that those whose business it is to feel the pulse of nations and to know what interests the masses of mankind, were well aware that thousands of their readers would think the world the poorer for Darwin's death, and would dwell with eager interest upon every incident of his history. In France, in Germany, in Austro-Hungary, in Italy, in the United States, writers of all shades of opinion, for once unanimous, have paid a willing tribute to the worth of our great countryman, ignored in life by the official representatives of the kingdom, but laid in death among his peers in Westminster Abbey by the will of the intelligence of the nation.

It is not for us to allude to the sacred sorrows of the bereaved home at Down [sic]; but it is no secret that, outside that domestic group, there are many to whom Mr Darwin's death is a wholly irreparable loss. And this not merely because of his wonderfully genial, simple, and generous nature; his cheerful and animated conversation, and the infinite variety and accuracy of his information; but because the more one knew of him, the more he seemed the incorporated ideal of a man of science. Acute as were his reasoning powers, vast as was his knowledge, marvellous as was his tenacious industry, under physical difficulties which would have converted nine men out of ten into aimless invalids; it was not these qualities, great as they were, which impressed those who were admitted to his intimacy with involuntary veneration, but a certain intense and almost passionate honesty by which all his thoughts and actions were irradiated, as by a central fire.

It was this rarest and greatest of endowments which kept his vivid imagination and great speculative powers within due bounds; which compelled him to undertake the prodigious labours of original investigation and of reading, upon which his published works are based; which made him accept criticisms and suggestions from any body and every body, not only without impatience, but with expressions of gratitude sometimes almost comically in excess of their value; which led him to allow neither himself nor others to be deceived by phrases, and to spare neither time nor pains in order to obtain clear and distinct ideas upon every topic with which he occupied himself.

One could not converse with Darwin without being reminded of Socrates. There was the same desire to find some one wiser than himself; the same belief in the sovereignty of reason; the same ready humour; the same sympathetic interest in all the ways and works of men. But instead of turning away from the problems of nature as hopelessly insoluble, our modem philosopher devoted his whole life to attacking them in the spirit of Heraclitus and of Democritus, with results which are as the substance of which their speculations were anticipatory shadows.

The due appreciation or even enumeration of these results is neither practicable nor desirable at this moment. There is a time for all things—a time for

Taken from *Charles Darwin: The Expression of the Emotions in Man and Animals: Definitive Edition* by T. H. Huxley (Oxford University Press, 1882).

glorying in our ever-extending conquests over the realm of nature, and a time for mourning over the heroes who have led us to victory.

None have fought better, and none have been more fortunate than Charles Darwin. He found a great truth, trodden under foot, reviled by bigots, and ridiculed by all the world; he lived long enough to see it, chiefly by his own efforts, irrefragably established in science, inseparably incorporated with the common thoughts of men, and only hated and feared by those who would revile, but dare not. What shall a man desire more than this? Once more the image of Socrates rises unbidden, and the noble peroration of the 'Apology' rings in our ears as if it were Charles Darwin's farewell:—

'The hour of departure has arrived, and we go our ways—I to die and you to live. Which is the better, God only knows.'

T. H. Huxley, *Nature*,
Thursday, April 27, 1882

■ 2.6 Study Sheet: Forces of Evolution

Describe how each of the following forces impacts evolution. Offer an example to illustrate the importance of each. Be sure to read all articles in the chapter first, in order to assist you with completing this exercise.

mutation:

selection:

gene flow:

genetic drift (founder's effect):

non-random mate selection:

■ 2.7 Diagram: Protein Synthesis

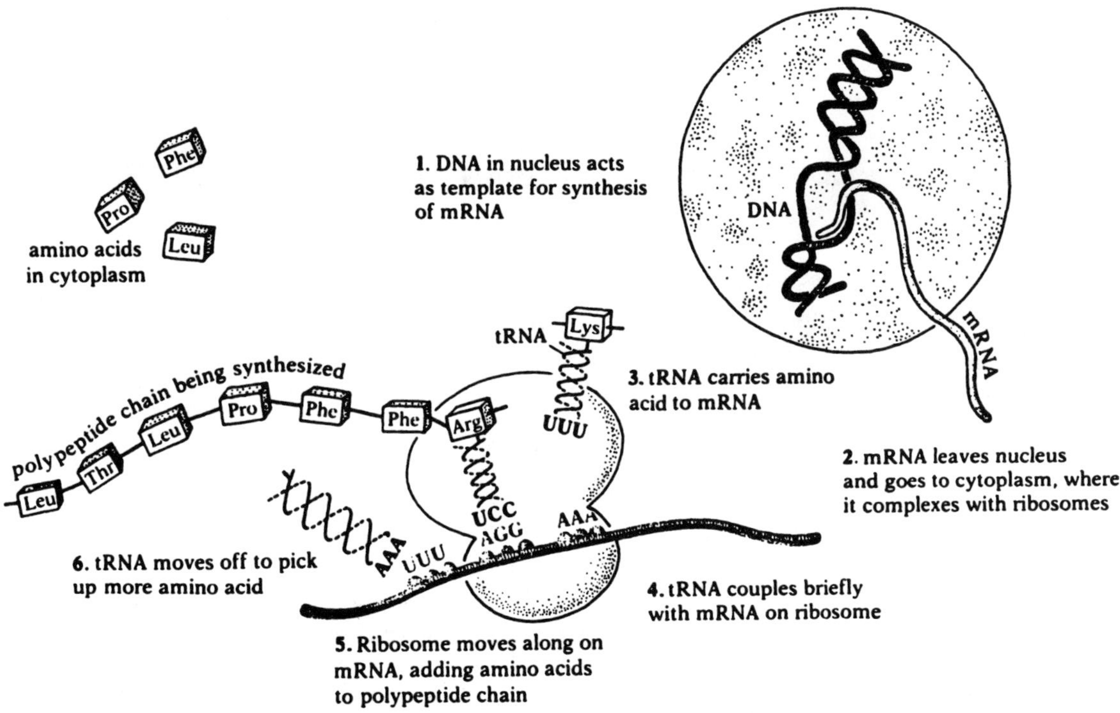

Messenger RNA is synthesized, one chain of the DNA gene serving as the template. This mRNA then goes into the cytoplasm and becomes associated with ribosomes. The various types of the tRNA in the cytoplasm pick up the amino acids for which they are specific and bring them to a ribosome as it moves along the mRNA. (The letters A, C, G, and U each stand for a particular base.) Each tRNA bonds to the mRNA at a point where a triplet of bases complementary to an exposed triplet on the tRNA occurs. This ordering of the tRNA molecules automatically orders the amino acids, which are then linked by peptide bonds. Synthesis of the polypeptide chain thus proceeds one amino acid at a time in an orderly sequence as the ribosomes move along the mRNA. As each tRNA donates its amino acid to the growing polypeptide chain, it uncouples from the mRNA and moves away into the cytoplasm, where it can be used again. (Note that the various molecules and organelles shown here are not drawn to scale with respect to one another or to the cell.)

Note: William T. Keeton, *Biological Science*, 3rd ed., illus. Paula di Santo Bensadoun (New York: Norton, 1980), 647. Reproduced by permission of W. W. Norton & Company, Inc.

2.8 *What We Learn from Twins: The Mirror of Your Soul*

Familiar question: Are we shaped by our genes, or by what life does to us? Possible new answer: It isn't as simple as that makes it sound.

Barbara Herbert, a former council worker living in southern England, discovered after the death of the woman she had thought was her mother that in fact she had been adopted. Among her assumed mother's papers, she found a name and address in Finland. When that produced no answer, she contacted the local newspaper in Finland. A reporter dug up the story. Her real mother had been sent to England, two months pregnant, in 1939. She had given birth, been sent back to Finland, and committed suicide at the age of 24.

Mrs Herbert had a feeling the story was not over. She seemed to recall somebody saying, "There was another one." So she contacted Hammersmith Hospital, where she was born; and, sure enough, there had been twins. The Registrar-General refused to help her contact her twin. She took the Registrar-General to court, and won. That is how she found her sister.

They met at King's Cross station in London. "We just said 'Hi' and walked off together, leaving our husbands standing there," says Mrs Herbert. "It seemed so natural." Mrs Herbert is a bit fatter than her sister, but she can think of no other important difference between them. Their intelligence quotients (IQs) were one point apart. They were tested again a year later; they scored ten points higher, but still only one point apart.

Mrs Herbert and her sister Daphne are gold dust to geneticists. Unlike fraternal twins, who are the product of separate eggs fertilised by different sperm, identical twins are natural clones, produced when a fertilised egg splits in two shortly after conception. Such twins, when separated after birth, are thus a scientific experiment designed jointly by nature and by society. They have the same genes but have been brought up in different environments.

These curiosities are getting rarer. Until the 1960s, twins offered for adoption in the West were often separated at birth, on the argument that two babies would be too much for one mother. That no longer happens. Since only one birth in 300 produces identical twins, and separated pairs are increasingly hard to find, people like Barbara Herbert and her sister are much sought after by scientists eager to study the relative importance of nature and nurture.

These studies provide some of the best clues to the question of how we become who we are—a question which fascinates people in different ways. Ordinary people wonder about the source of their failings and virtues, and would like to know whether they can make their children better, cleverer and happier than they themselves have been. Scientists are gripped, and still largely baffled, by how the human brain and personality are formed. And, in politics, the nature-nurture question lies at the centre of the argument about "social intervention". If our intelligence and our personalities are written into our genes, there is not much that governments can do to improve us.

Since the study of twins generally seems to support the nature side of the argument, it is triumphantly saluted by hereditarians as evidence for their case. "Twins have been used to prove a point, and the point is that we don't become. We are." So writes Lawrence Wright in his new book, "Twins: Genes, Environment and the Mystery of Human Identity". The environmentalists, on the other hand, condemn most studies of twins as methodologically flawed and even dishonest. Actually, what such studies show may be more interesting and mysterious than either side yet realises.

It was Francis Galton, Charles Darwin's cousin, who in the late 19th century first thought of using twins to investigate the differences between people. Galton, who coined the term "eugenics", correctly suggested that twins who looked alike came from one egg, and that those who did not came from different eggs. From that, he worked out a way of using twins to estimate the impact of genes. Look, he suggested, at the similarities between identical twins and those between ordinary ones (who genetically are no more similar than any children of the same parents). Those characteristics which identical twins share more than other twins will, he reasoned, be more caused by the genes the pair brought into the world.

This process, and the study of separated identical twins, are the two main ways of using twins to study the effects of nature and nurture. Galton carried out the first systematic study of twins. The results convinced him of the pre-eminence of genes in human make-up.

Eugenics in Disgrace

The idea of eugenics captivated people on both the left and the right of politics in the first half of the 20th century. Fabian social reformers such as Sidney and Beatrice Webb were delighted to think that they would be able to breed a better working class. Josef Mengele, on the other hand, wanted to breed a better race for Hitler.

As Robert Jay Lifton recounts in "The Nazi Doctors", Mengele was obsessed with twins. When a new group of prisoners arrived in the concentration camp at Auschwitz, Mengele would run out to meet them shouting, "Twins out!" Twins lived in a separate block, and were allowed to keep their clothes and their hair. Mengele gave them sweets, and called them his little friends. He weighed them, measured them and logged the colour of their hair and their eyes. And he gave them diseases, to see how long they took to die.

The Nazis' enthusiasm for genetics did the subject no good at all. The left forgot it had ever had any interest in the matter. So did most academics. For a time it became fashionable, instead, to assume that people are chiefly the result of their environment, what they experience after they have been born. This rival view fitted neatly into the social-engineering optimism of most of the world's post 1945 governments.

The posthumous scandal over the work of Cyril Burt seemed to confirm this change of mind. Burt was the main proponent of hereditarian ideas in Britain. His evidence came from studies of separated identical twins. After his death in 1971, it was claimed that much of this evidence had been fabricated. His defenders' attempts to rescue his reputation have been less than conclusive. At best, he was a sloppy scientist; at worst, a fraud.

Still, despite its embarrassments, the hereditarian school began to reassert itself. In 1969 the *Harvard Educational Review* published an article by Arthur Jensen called "How much can we boost IQ and scholastic achievement?" Mr Jensen's answer: Not much, because IQ is highly hereditary; so money spent on pre-school programmes for poor children is wasted. As Adrian Wooldridge, of *The Economist*, puts it in his book "Measuring the Mind": "The hereditarians felt that the environmentalists had turned into a decadent establishment, smugly self-satisfied but intellectually sloppy."

Hereditarians Ascendant

The new hereditarians were assailed, in print and in person; but they were not squashed. Their research won support from, and gave support to, conservative politicians keen to roll back the costly welfare policies of the post-1945 years. "The Bell Curve", by Charles Murray and Richard Hermstein, published in 1994, is a powerful expression of this alliance. It argues that, since IQ is largely inherited, and people marry people like themselves, the difference between the intelligence of races and classes is liable to grow steadily wider.

The study of twins provided much of the ammunition for the hereditarian counter-attack. Some of it emerged from the first large-scale post-Burt study of separated identical twins, run by Thomas Bouchard, a professor at the University of Minnesota. Mr Bouchard saw an article on a pair of reunited identical twins, and decided to make a study of them. It was fun, says Mr Bouchard. Much research work by psychologists involves grumpy students, doing it for the money. The twins, delighted to be reunited, were a pleasure to work with. Mr Bouchard now has a register of 8,000 pairs of twins, some identical, some not, some separated, most reared together.

Another American scientist, Robert Plomin, has been working with 25,000 pairs of identical and non-identical twins in Sweden. Mr Plomin has also set up a study working with 10,000 pairs of identical and non-identical twins in Britain. He now works at the Social, Genetic and Developmental Psychiatry Research Centre at Britain's Institute of Psychiatry.

Over the past couple of decades there has been a clear shift in science's view of the hereditarian argument. These days, no respectable scientist denies the role of genes in forming our brains and characters. The question over which argument continues to rage is just how big that role is.

Studies of twins have examined a range of physical and psychological traits to try to estimate how large a contribution genes make. Some of the work looks at illnesses such as cancer, schizophrenia and alcoholism. Finding the cause of these could help in learning how to cure or contain them. If, for instance, schizophrenia is something you can inherit, then it may be susceptible to gene therapy.

Some of the studies are curiosities. David Lykken, a colleague of Mr Bouchard's, has inquired into the origins of happiness. He concludes that happiness bears almost no relation to wealth, professional standing or marital status, and is 80% inherited. Some other studies have made sceptics' eyebrows rise because they appear to show that political conservatism and religious fundamentalism have a genetic basis.

But the most contentious work of all is on IQ. Mr Bouchard's studies suggest that the level of one's intelligence is, in the jargon, "69–78% heritable"—heritability being the proportion of the difference between people that is acquired through the genes, not life itself. Burt's disputed figure is within that range.

Some critics, such as Marcus Feldman, a professor of population genetics at Stanford University, says the work on twins is tainted by politics. The Minnesota research is financed by the Pioneer Fund, a foundation set up in 1937 to help research into heredity and eugenics, including racial differences. The fund has financed work by such controversial figures as Philippe Rushton on the relative size of the genitals and brains of different races. It is accused of, but strongly denies, racist motives.

Mr Lykken has played into the critics' hands by arguing that women should be licensed to have children and that children produced by unlicensed breeders should be compulsorily adopted. Mr Bouchard defends Mr Lykken's intellectual freedom. He says he is uneasy about the source of his cash, but insists that the Pioneer Fund has never tried to influence what he does.

What matters in the end, assuming that most of the people involved in this work do it in a properly detached way, is what they find out. It is striking that studies of twins regularly come up with higher levels of heritability than do other sorts of studies. Mr Bouchard's estimate runs up to 78%. That compares with studies of adopted children, and of first- and second-degree relations, which produce figures as low as 30%, and at the highest 50%. A task force of the American Psychological Association, trawling through all the available studies, including those on non-twins, has come up with an average of 50%.

This disparity has led to questions about the reliability of twins studies. One problem is that separated identical twins do not actually provide a perfect nature-versus-nurture template. For a start, they do at one time share the same environment—in the womb. If, as some scientists now believe, those nine months are important in deciding how the brain is wired, this would help to explain why non-identical twins, who are no more genetically alike than any brother and sister, have IQs more like each other's than ordinary siblings do. It would also undermine the claims of the separated-twins studies to offer conclusive proof of what genes do.

Moreover, separated identical twins are rarely separated at the moment of birth, and some of them are then reunited before they come under the scientists' eye. If the first six months of a child's life matter as much as most people think they do, then spending even that short time together could influence the result of a twins study. And, when grown-up twins are reunited, they will naturally pay special attention to what they have in common; they may, the professors explain, "mythologise" their relationship. The twins in the Minnesota study had an average of five months together before they were separated, and nearly two years together after their reunion before Mr Bouchard got hold of them.

A subtler concern—voiced by Mr Feldman, himself a father of identical twins—is that the dichotomy between genes and environment is a false one. His own twins, he says, share professions, ideas and friends; their environments, in other words, are much closer than those of most non-identical twins. Maybe Galton's classic twins study was invalid: perhaps you cannot look at the similarities between identical twins, and those between non-identical ones, and conclude that the difference must necessarily be due to genes.

■ Chickens, Eggs and Babies

Mr Plomin, the student of those 35,000 pairs of twins, does not deny this. One of the ways in which genes work, he says, is through our tendency to select and design a particular environment. A baby, for instance, may be born happy; its happiness may make its mother show it more affection; that may reinforce its cheerfulness. Even though that virtuous circle may have originated with the child's genetic tendency, it can be strengthened by what happens after the baby is born. If the child is taken away from its mother and dumped in a children's home, it may not stay happy. Or, if a child with a tendency to be miserable gets an unswervingly affectionate mother, it may cheer up.

And, just as our genes can affect our environment, so our environment may shape the expression of our genes. Height, for instance, is now around 90% heritable in rich countries. In the past the figure was lower, because not everybody was well-nourished enough for their genes to express themselves properly. Heritability, in other words, is not a constant; it is affected by whether life is giving people's natural tendencies a chance to flower properly.

Turn the results of the heritability studies on their heads, and there is further cause for reflection. If IQ is 50% or so heritable, then up to another 50% is determined by something other than genes. The same applies to many other parts of our make-up, the figures for which are roughly of the same order of magnitude. But some things seem to be markedly less genetic. Despite the talk of a "breast cancer gene", for instance, this disease seems rarely to be the result of genetic programming. When one identical twin gets breast cancer, the other gets it in only 12% of cases.

Look, too, at sexual orientation. Some studies have suggested that homosexuality is around 50% heritable. Yet a recent study of Australian identical twins who had grown up apart from each other appeared to show that homosexuality was only 20% heritable in men and 24% in women.

So where, if these figures are right, does homosexuality mainly come from? Not, apparently, from growing up in the same family. Across a whole range of measures, including the tendency to homosexuality, if you look at separated identical twins and identical twins who have been brought up together you will find that they are pretty much alike. Belonging to the same family does not, on this evidence, have much effect. This seems to be confirmed by an examination of adopted children, born of different parents, who have been brought up in the same family. Do they have much more in common with each other than they do with the kids next door? They do not.

■ There's Something Else

But that is daft, most people will instinctively say. The experiences we had in our parents' house were surely of vital importance in shaping our lives. The families we grew up in—and the families we ourselves are now creating—cannot be irrelevant to the character of the children they produce. Yet, if this scientific work is to be believed, belonging to the same family apparently has little effect on the way people turn out.

To some extent, of course, the explanation is that parents do not treat their various offspring in the same way. Mr Plomin cites a study which compares parents' and children's accounts of whether one child got the same treatment as his brother or sister. Not surprisingly, the children reported a greater level of difference than did the parents. Yet it is hard to believe that parents commonly treat identical twins so differently that one becomes a homosexual and one a heterosexual.

The bigger part of the explanation may be that except in special cases—the loving mother who manages to warm her genetically miserable child into real-life happiness—what our parents do is not decisively important to the way we grow up. That is the view of Sandra Scarr, a controversial professor of psychology at the University of Virginia. She offers the idea of "good enough" parenting. So long as a child has parents, and so long as they are not seriously brutal, she reckons, one set of parents is just as good as another.

If that is so, the really important variable may be chance. Perhaps it is the small, random event—the infant romance by the swings, the bullying in the corner of the playground—that shifts us imperceptibly towards widely different ends. Or maybe, for those who look at the universe in a different light, it is some higher power. Anyway, those who had feared that the scientists would soon have us neatly dissected on their laboratory tables can take new heart. How we become who we are seems as mysterious as ever. Thank God.

2.8 Study Questions: What We Learn from Twins

1. Why are Mrs. Herbert and her sister Daphne "gold dust" to geneticists?

2. What are the different ways in which twin studies fascinate people?

3. How have twin studies been seen by hereditarians? By environmentalists?

4. Be familiar with Francis Galton's reasoning as to how twin studies could reveal characteristics caused by genes.

5. Be aware of the ways in which both the political right and political left might use eugenics to bolster their positions. What was the view expressed in *The Bell Curve*?

6. Why are twin studies seen as important in curing diseases?

7. Be aware of the claims made by hereditarians regarding happiness, political conservatism, and religious fundamentalism. What has Bouchard claimed regarding intelligence?

8 In what ways has the reliability of twin studies been questioned?

9. In what sense is heretability "not a constant?" In other words, how might our environment shape the expression of our genes?

10. If environment plays such an important role in what we become, how important is family as part of that environment?

11. How can it be that family up-bringing is important but not enough to explain the differences between children? What does explain the differences, if not so much heredity or family, according to the author?

2.9 Cartoon Guide to Genetics: Mendel's Theory of Simple Inheritance

MONK FINDS GENE;
WORLD YAWNS!

FIFTY YEARS OF RESEARCH HAD FAILED TO FIND ANY PRECISE LAW OF INHERITANCE. OBVIOUSLY, DISCOVERING THE RIGHT FORMULA, IF POSSIBLE, WAS A JOB REQUIRING SUPERHUMAN PATIENCE, UNLIMITED TIME, AND, AS IT HAPPENED, A MIRACLE OF LUCK.

NO WONDER IT HAPPENED IN A MONASTERY...

GREGOR MENDEL (1822 - 1884) WAS AN AUGUSTINIAN MONK FROM BRÜNN, AUSTRIA. IN HIS SPARE TIME, MENDEL BRED PEA PLANTS IN THE MONASTERY GARDENS.

BUT MENDEL WAS NOT JUST AN AMATEUR GARDENER, BUT A **SCIENTIST** WHO STUDIED HIS PEA PLANTS MOST CAREFULLY— HE CALLED THEM HIS "CHILDREN."

CHOOSING PEAS WAS THE MIRACLE OF LUCK: THEY ARE PERFECTLY SUITED TO GENETIC RESEARCH, WITH A NUMBER OF STABLE VARIETIES WHICH MAY FORM HYBRIDS:

ONE TYPE MADE SMOOTH, ROUND PEAS, WHILE ANOTHER'S WERE LUMPY AND WRINKLED...

THERE WERE GREEN PEAS AND YELLOW; GREY SEED-COATS AND WHITE; WHITE FLOWERS AND PURPLE. THERE WERE DIFFERENCES IN THE COLOR OF THE UNRIPE PODS, THE COLOR OF SEED ALBUMIN, AND THE POSITION OF THE FLOWERS.

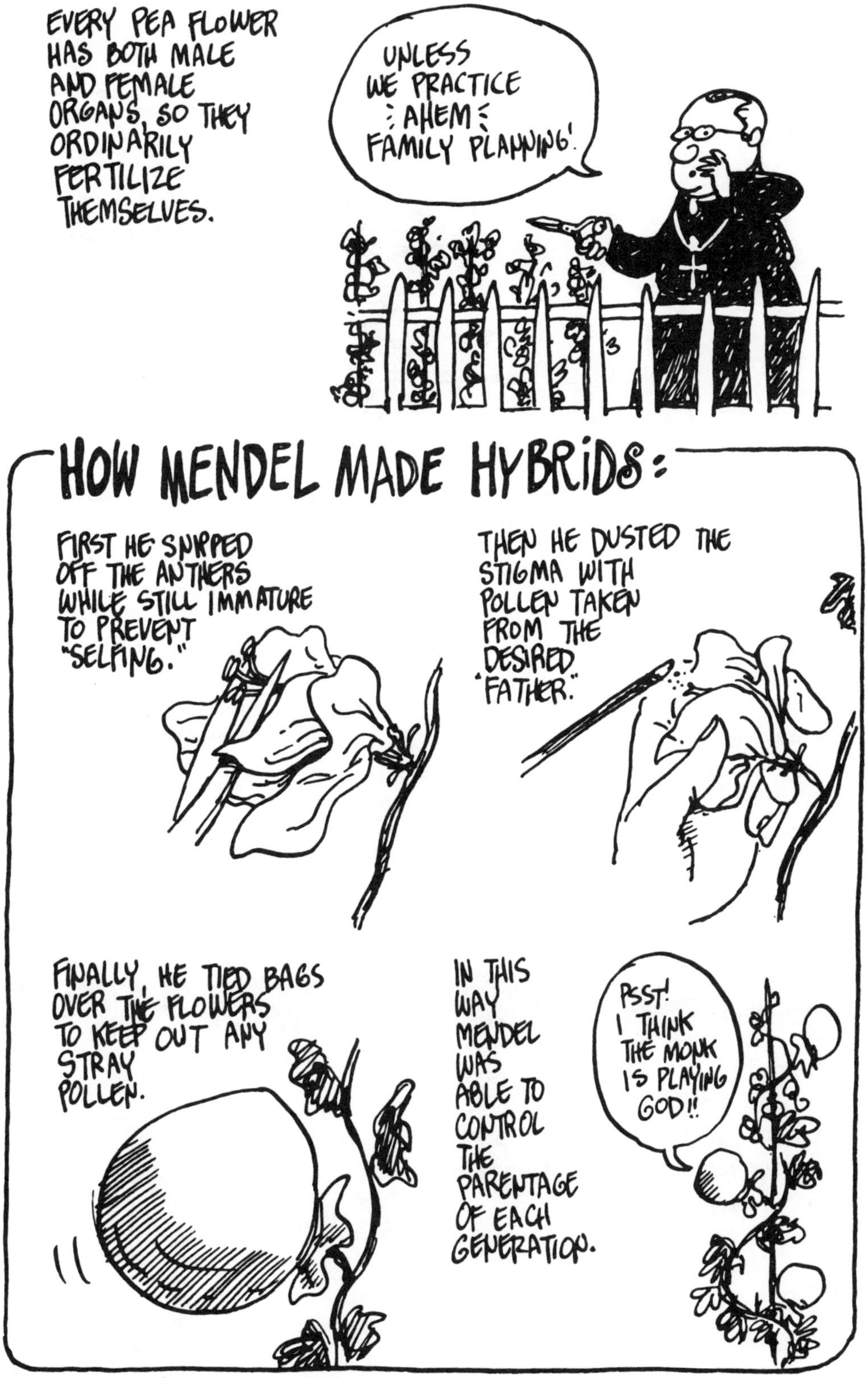

EVERY PEA FLOWER HAS BOTH MALE AND FEMALE ORGANS, SO THEY ORDINARILY FERTILIZE THEMSELVES.

HOW MENDEL MADE HYBRIDS:

FIRST HE SNIPPED OFF THE ANTHERS WHILE STILL IMMATURE TO PREVENT "SELFING."

THEN HE DUSTED THE STIGMA WITH POLLEN TAKEN FROM THE DESIRED "FATHER."

FINALLY, HE TIED BAGS OVER THE FLOWERS TO KEEP OUT ANY STRAY POLLEN.

IN THIS WAY MENDEL WAS ABLE TO CONTROL THE PARENTAGE OF EACH GENERATION.

PSST! I THINK THE MONK IS PLAYING GOD!!

MENDEL'S FIRST MAJOR RESULT WAS THE DISCOVERY OF DOMINANCE. WHAT HAPPENED WHEN A TALL PLANT WAS CROSSED WITH A SHORT? ONE MIGHT EXPECT MEDIUM-SIZED PLANTS, BUT
X
IN FACT, ALL THE HYBRIDS WERE TALL !!
MENDEL EXPRESSED THIS BY SAYING THAT TALLNESS WAS DOMINANT OVER SHORTNESS (IN PEAS!). THE TRAIT OF SHORTNESS IS THEN CALLED RECESSIVE. IN EVERY CASE, ONE TRAIT WAS FOUND TO BE DOMINANT.
ROUND SEEDS ARE DOMINANT OVER WRINKLED; PLUMP PODS OVER PINCHED; GREY SEED-COATS OVER WHITE SEED-COATS, ETC ETC ETC....
IT DIDN'T MATTER WHICH PARENT CONTRIBUTED THE POLLEN AND WHICH THE EGG. A TALL-SHORT HYBRID WAS ALWAYS TALL.
THE FUN BEGINS WHEN YOU START BREEDING THE HYBRIDS—
X
?

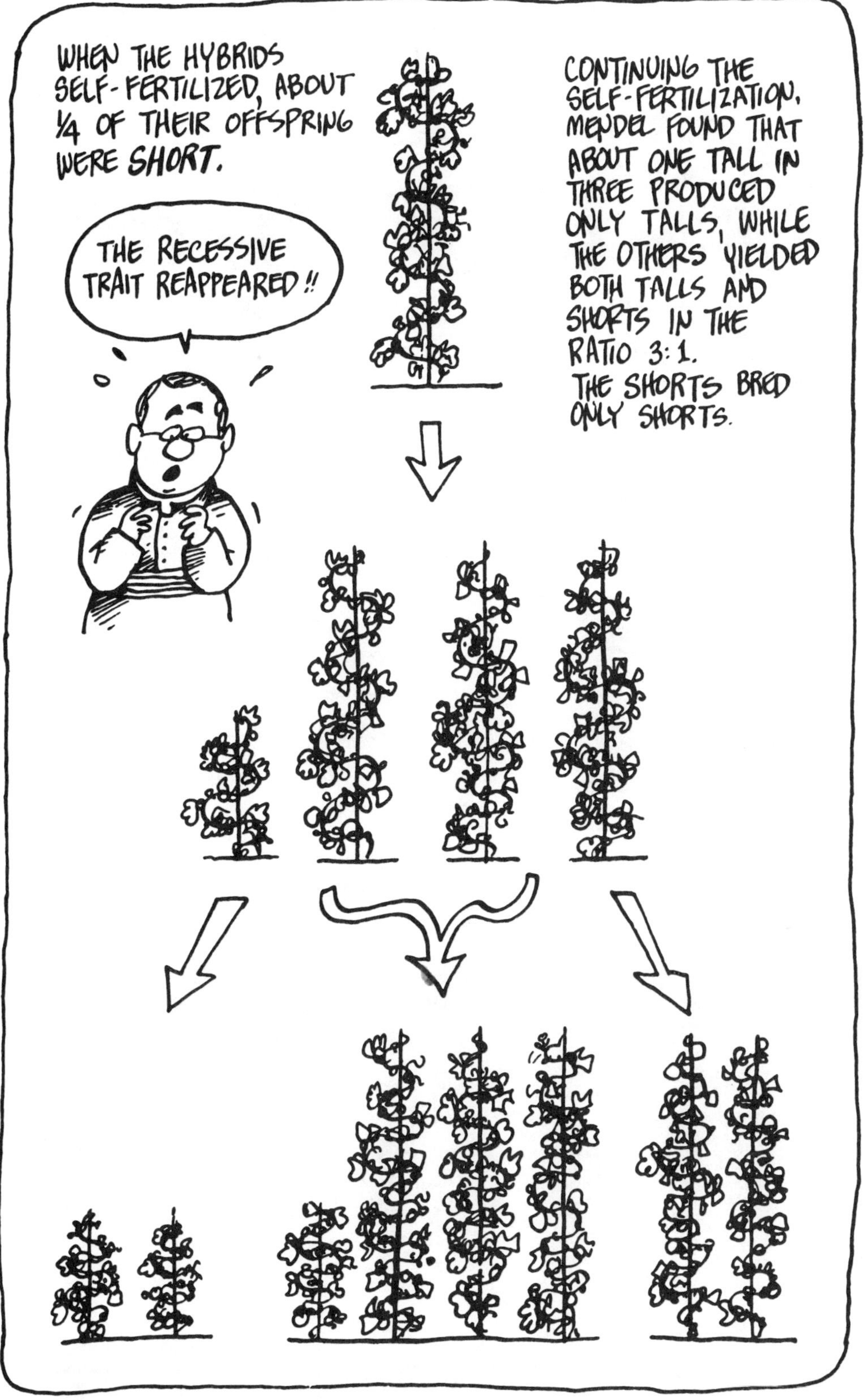
WHEN THE HYBRIDS SELF-FERTILIZED, ABOUT 1/4 OF THEIR OFFSPRING WERE **SHORT**.
THE RECESSIVE TRAIT REAPPEARED!!
CONTINUING THE SELF-FERTILIZATION, MENDEL FOUND THAT ABOUT ONE TALL IN THREE PRODUCED ONLY TALLS, WHILE THE OTHERS YIELDED BOTH TALLS AND SHORTS IN THE RATIO 3:1.
THE SHORTS BRED ONLY SHORTS.

IT'S MATHEMATICAL!

THERE IS SOMETHING IN POLLEN AND EGG WHICH DETERMINES THE HEIGHT OF PEA PLANTS. THIS "SOMETHING" WE CALL A

GENE.

EACH POLLEN GRAIN AND EGG HAS ONE HEIGHT GENE, SO THE PLANT FORMED BY THEIR UNION HAS **TWO.**

THE GENE MAY BE ONE OF TWO DISTINCT TYPES, OR

ALLELES.

ONE ALLELE, *A*, IS FOR *TALLNESS*; THE OTHER ONE, *a*, IS FOR *SHORTNESS.*

A

a

A PLANT MAY HAVE THE SAME OR DIFFERENT ALLELES.

AA

aa

Aa

THE ALLELE *A* IS *DOMINANT* OVER *a*. THAT IS, THE PLANT WITH THE COMBINATION *Aa* IS TALL. THE ALLELES DO NOT "BLEND."

WHAT HAPPENS WHEN AA BREEDS WITH AA? POLLEN AND EGG EACH GET ONE COPY OF THE GENE... IN THIS CASE, THE ALLELES ARE THE SAME—A—SO THE OFFSPRING WILL AGAIN BE AA, OR TALL. LIKEWISE, aa CAN YIELD ONLY aa. THESE ARE THE STABLE SHORT & TALL VARIETIES.

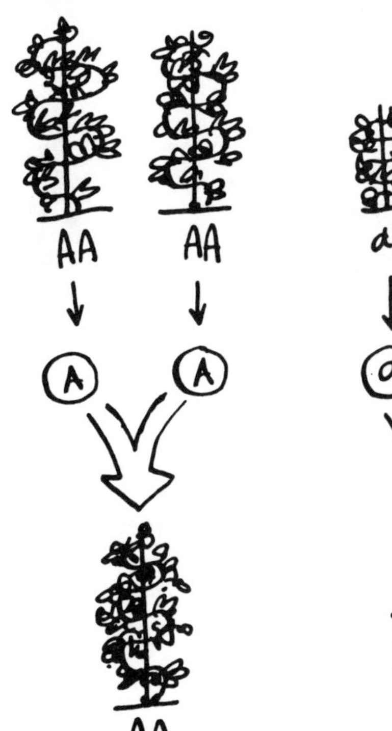

MENDEL'S FIRST HYBRID WAS A CROSS BETWEEN AA AND aa: THE POLLEN (OR EGG) FROM AA CONTAINS ONLY A, WHILE THE EGG (OR POLLEN) FROM aa CONTAINS ONLY a.

RESULT: Aa, WHICH IS TALL.

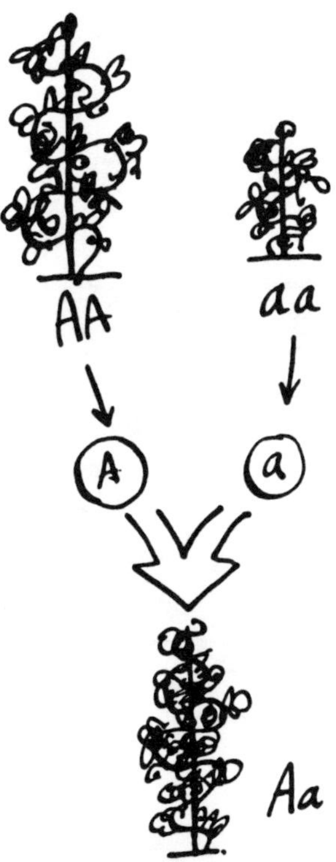

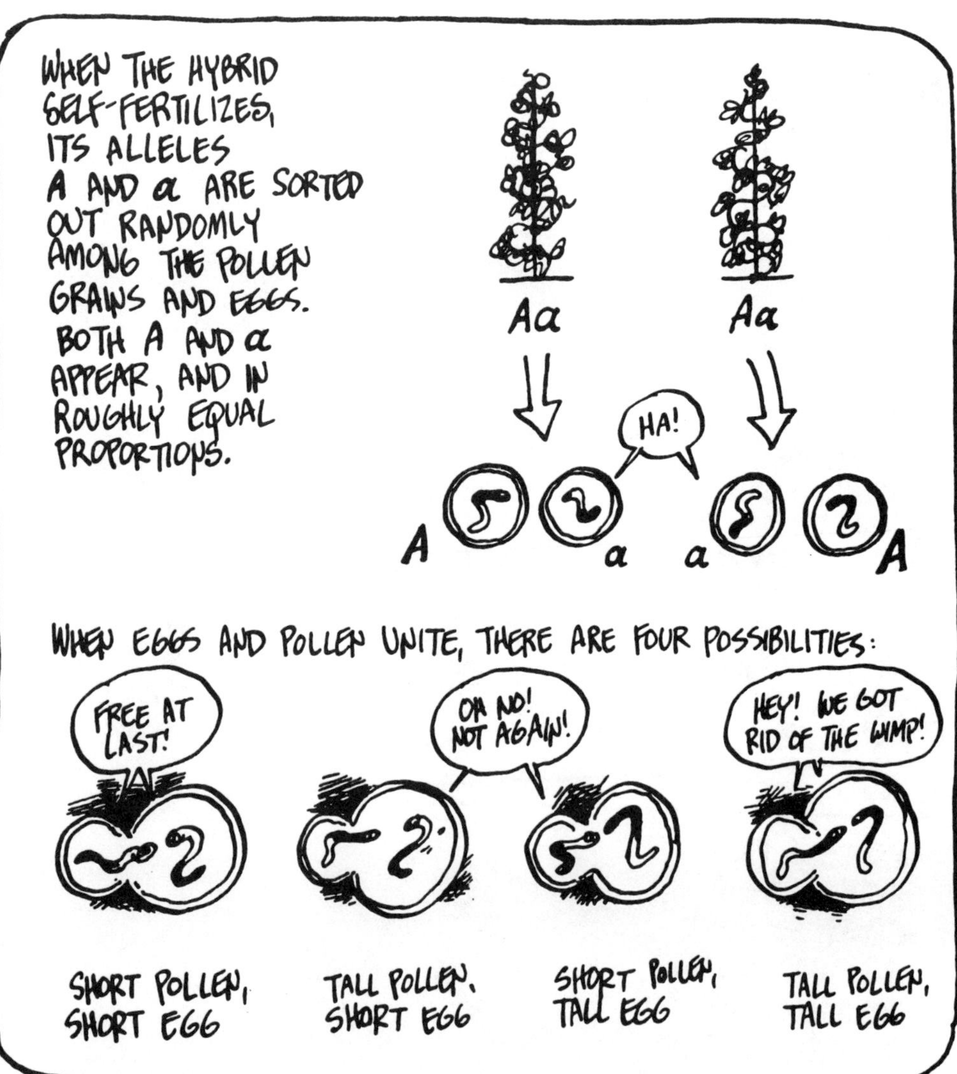
WHEN THE HYBRID SELF-FERTILIZES, ITS ALLELES A AND a ARE SORTED OUT RANDOMLY AMONG THE POLLEN GRAINS AND EGGS. BOTH A AND a APPEAR, AND IN ROUGHLY EQUAL PROPORTIONS.
Aa
Aa
HA!
A
a
a
A
WHEN EGGS AND POLLEN UNITE, THERE ARE FOUR POSSIBILITIES:
FREE AT LAST!
OH NO! NOT AGAIN!
HEY! WE GOT RID OF THE WIMP!
SHORT POLLEN, SHORT EGG
TALL POLLEN, SHORT EGG
SHORT POLLEN, TALL EGG
TALL POLLEN, TALL EGG

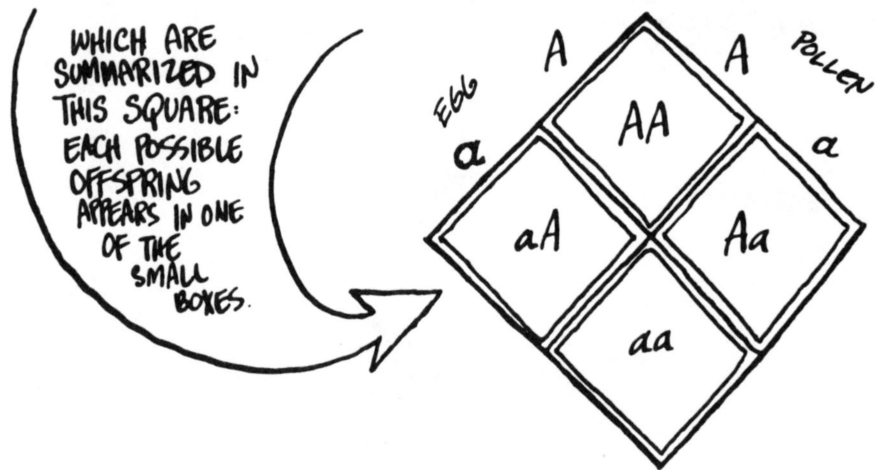
WHICH ARE SUMMARIZED IN THIS SQUARE: EACH POSSIBLE OFFSPRING APPEARS IN ONE OF THE SMALL BOXES.
EGG
A
A
POLLEN
a
a
AA
aA
Aa
aa

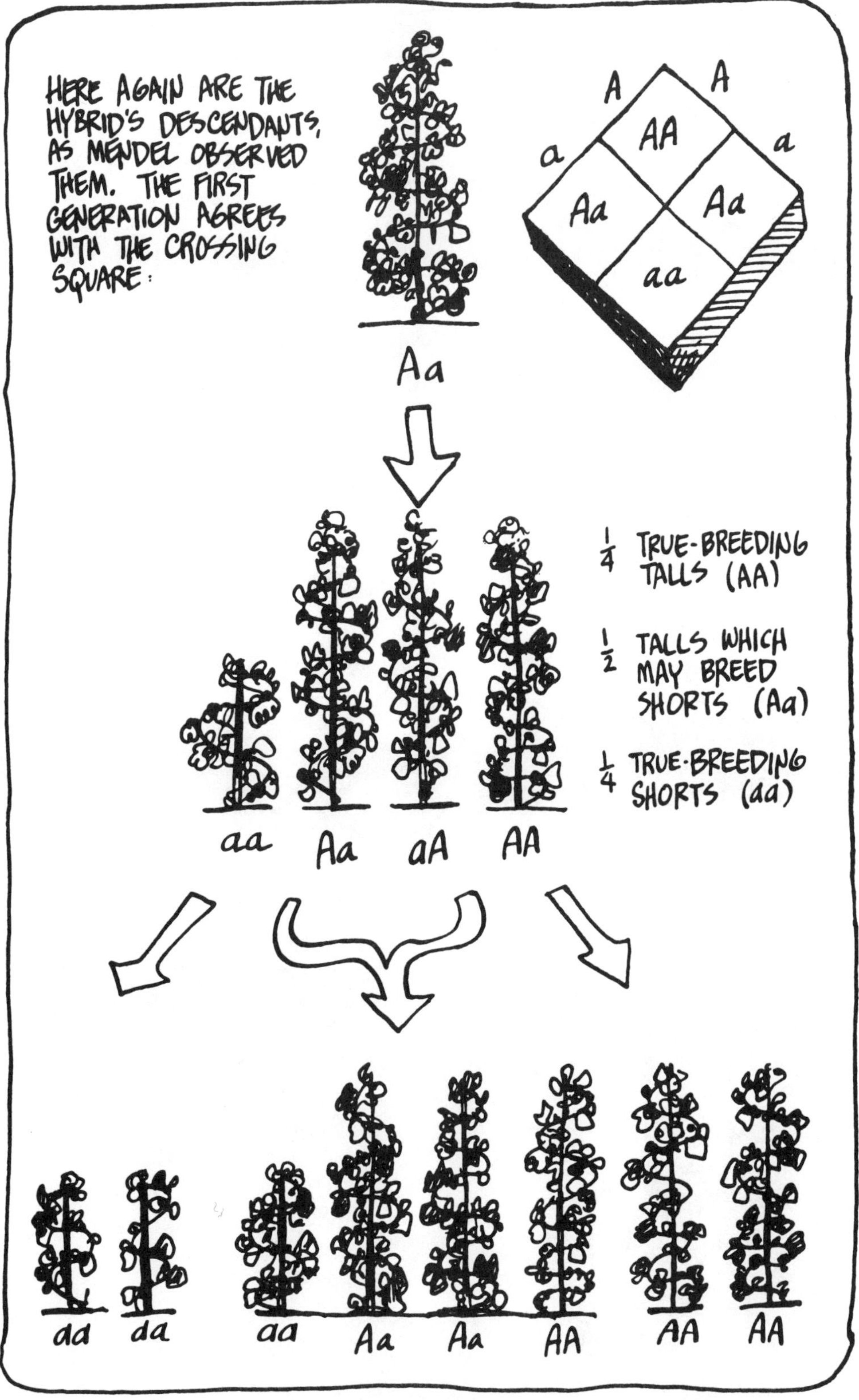
HERE AGAIN ARE THE HYBRID'S DESCENDANTS, AS MENDEL OBSERVED THEM. THE FIRST GENERATION AGREES WITH THE CROSSING SQUARE:
A
A
a
a
AA
Aa
Aa
aa
Aa
1/4 TRUE-BREEDING TALLS (AA)
1/2 TALLS WHICH MAY BREED SHORTS (Aa)
1/4 TRUE-BREEDING SHORTS (aa)
aa
Aa
aA
AA
aa
aa
aa
Aa
Aa
AA
AA
AA

MENDEL ALSO CROSSED SMOOTH-PEA PLANTS WITH WRINKLED, PURPLE FLOWERS WITH WHITE, ETC ETC ETC. IN EVERY CASE, HE FOUND THE CHARACTERISTIC TO BE CONTROLLED BY A SINGLE GENE WITH TWO DIFFERENT ALLELES, ONE OF WHICH WAS DOMINANT OVER THE OTHER.

SO IT SEEMED THAT POLLEN AND EGG WERE BOTH FULL OF THESE LITTLE "SOMETHINGS," ONE FOR EVERY HEREDITARY TRAIT OF THE ORGANISM. PRETTY CROWDED!

WITHOUT EVER SEEING A GENE, MENDEL CONCLUDED THAT HEREDITY IS CONTROLLED BY THESE "ATOMS OF INHERITANCE," WHICH NEVER BREAK OR BLEND, MAINTAINING THEIR CHARACTER FROM GENERATION TO GENERATION.

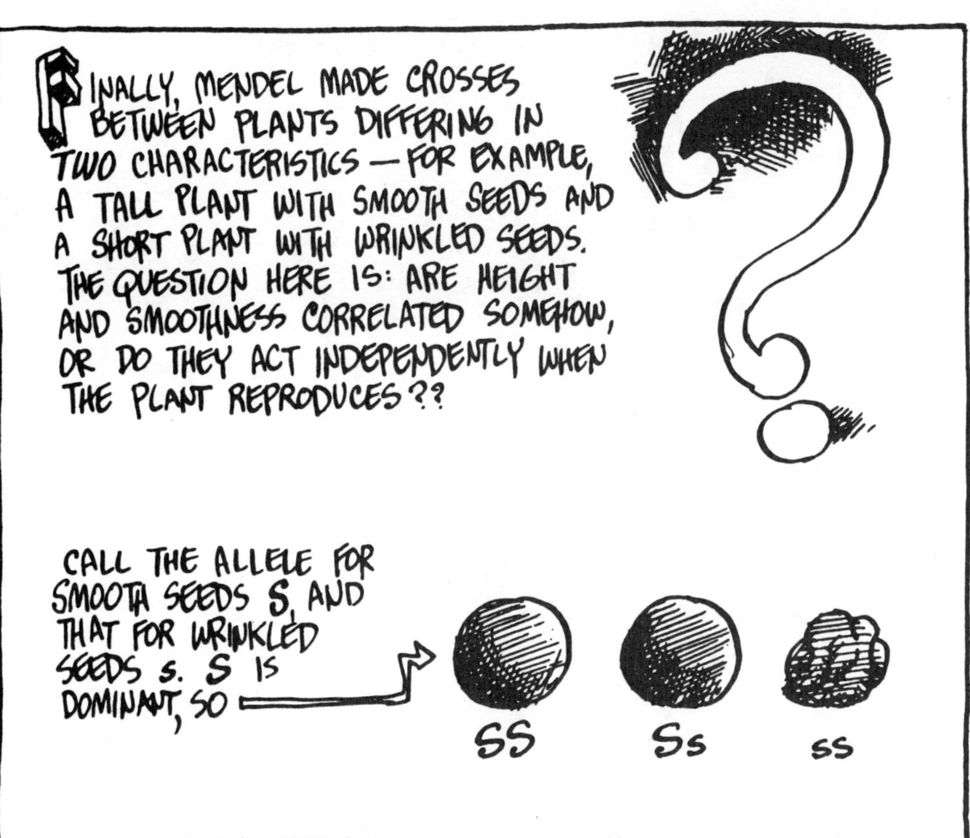

THE CROSS IS BETWEEN AASS AND aass.

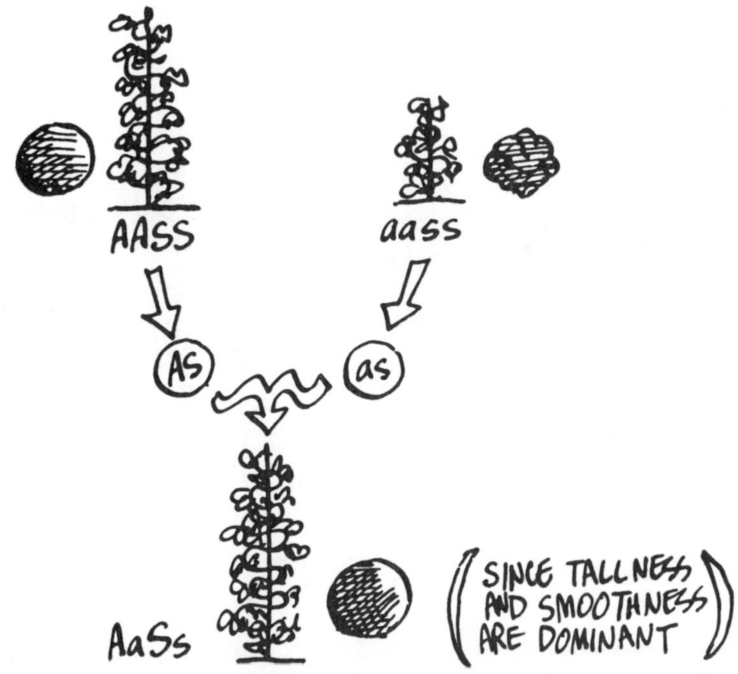

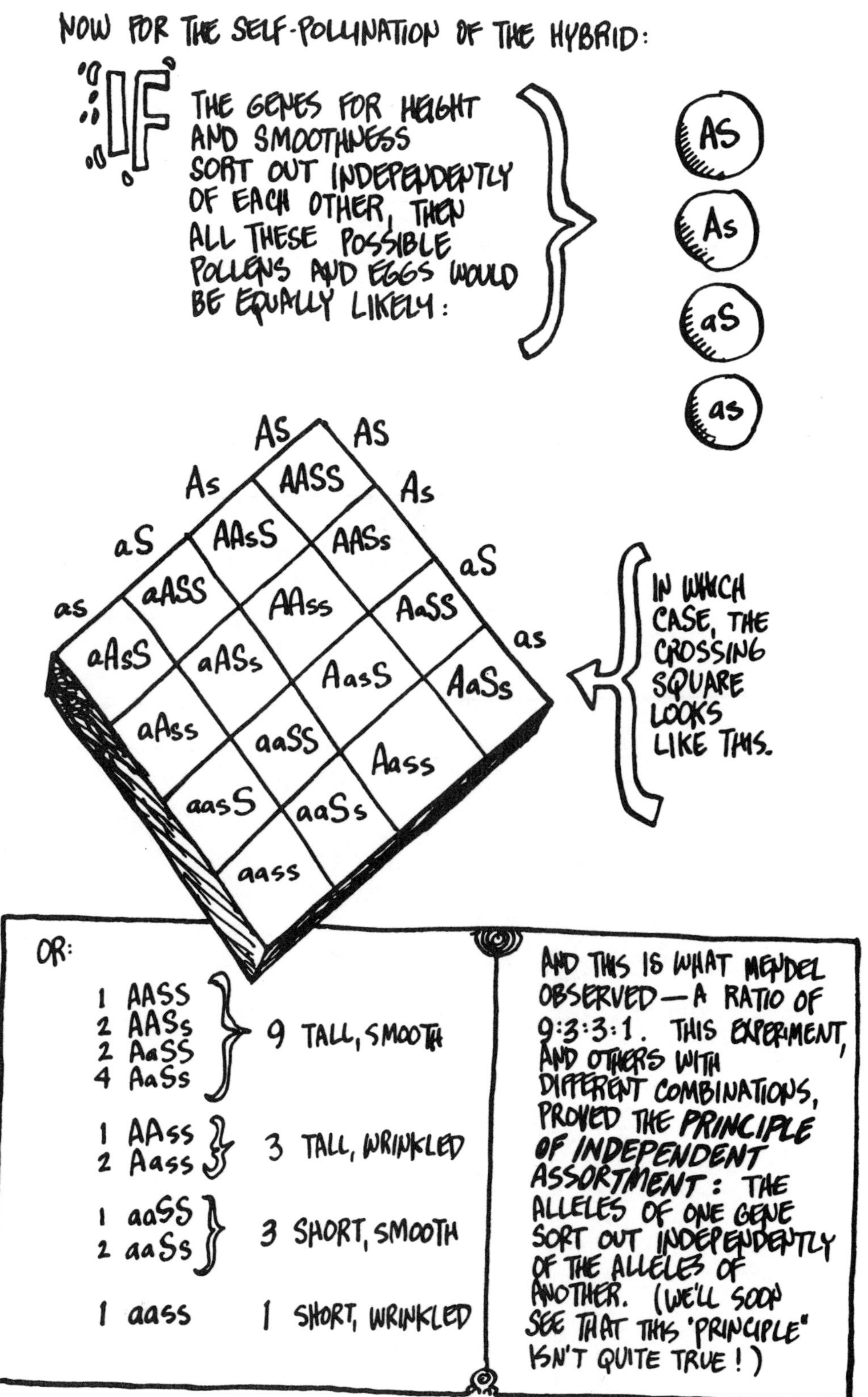
NOW FOR THE SELF-POLLINATION OF THE HYBRID:
IF
THE GENES FOR HEIGHT AND SMOOTHNESS SORT OUT INDEPENDENTLY OF EACH OTHER, THEN ALL THESE POSSIBLE POLLENS AND EGGS WOULD BE EQUALLY LIKELY:
AS
As
aS
as
AS
As
aS
as
AS
As
aS
as
AASS
AAsS
AASs
aASS
AAss
AaSS
aAsS
aASs
AasS
AaSs
aAss
aaSS
Aass
aasS
aaSs
aass
IN WHICH CASE, THE CROSSING SQUARE LOOKS LIKE THIS.
OR:
1 AASS
2 AASs
2 AaSS
4 AaSs
9 TALL, SMOOTH
1 AAss
2 Aass
3 TALL, WRINKLED
1 aaSS
2 aaSs
3 SHORT, SMOOTH
1 aass
1 SHORT, WRINKLED
AND THIS IS WHAT MENDEL OBSERVED—A RATIO OF 9:3:3:1. THIS EXPERIMENT, AND OTHERS WITH DIFFERENT COMBINATIONS, PROVED THE PRINCIPLE OF INDEPENDENT ASSORTMENT: THE ALLELES OF ONE GENE SORT OUT INDEPENDENTLY OF THE ALLELES OF ANOTHER. (WE'LL SOON SEE THAT THIS "PRINCIPLE" ISN'T QUITE TRUE!)

NOW THAT WE'VE SEEN HOW GENES WORK, HERE'S A BIT OF GENETICS JARGON, IN CASE YOU SHOULD EVER WANT TO EAVESDROP ON A MODERN GENETICIST...

WELL... NOT ***THAT*** KIND OF JARGON...

GENETICISTS DISTINGUISH BETWEEN AN ORGANISM'S ***PHENOTYPE*** —WHAT IT LOOKS LIKE— AND ITS ***GENOTYPE*** —WHAT ALLELES IT HAS.

AN ORGANISM IS ***HOMOZYGOUS*** WITH RESPECT TO A GIVEN GENE IF ITS TWO ALLELES ARE THE ***SAME***, AND ***HETEROZYGOUS*** IF THEY'RE DIFFERENT.

SO NOW YOU KNOW WHAT A GENETICIST MEANS BY "PHENOTYPICALLY SMOOTH, GENOTYPICALLY HETEROZYGOUS."

THE ALLELE FOR A BLACK COAT, CALL IT *B*, WAS DOMINANT. THERE WAS ALSO A **RECESSIVE** ALLELE, ω, FOR WHITE SPECKLES. MANY OF LABAN'S PHENOTYPICALLY BLACK ANIMALS SECRETLY HARBORED THIS ω, SO THEIR KIDS WERE SOMETIMES SPECKLED.*

Bω × Bω

BB Bω Bω ωω

* ACTUALLY, THE GENETICS OF COAT COLOR ARE MORE COMPLEX, BUT THE PRINCIPLE IS THE SAME: RECESSIVE ALLELES.

IF YOU SEE A DOMINANT PHENOTYPE, HOW CAN YOU TELL IF IT'S A HETEROZYGOTE?

FOR INSTANCE, IN HUMANS BROWN EYES ARE DOMINANT OVER BLUE. CALL THE GENES *B* AND *b*, RESPECTIVELY.

HOW CAN WE TELL IF THIS BROWN-EYED PERSON IS BB OR Bb?

ONE WAY IS TO CROSS HIM WITH A RECESSIVE HOMOZYGOTE—I.E., A BLUE-EYED PERSON, bb.

O.K... WE'LL USE SOMEBODY ELSE...

IF ANY OF THE LITTLE HYBRIDS HAS BLUE EYES, THE BROWN-EYED PARENT MUST HAVE BEEN A ***HETEROZYGOTE***, Bb. IF HE HAD BEEN BB, ALL THE CHILDREN WOULD HAVE BEEN Bb, WITH BROWN EYES.

MY SECOND WIFE HAS BLUE EYES LIKE ME. IF OUR CHILD HAD ***BROWN*** EYES, WHAT WOULD WE MAKE OF THAT? BETTER ASK THE MILKMAN!!

SOME EXAMPLES OF DOMINANT AND RECESSIVE GENES IN HUMANS:

- BROWN EYES ARE DOMINANT OVER BLUE EYES.
- COLOR VISION IS DOMINANT OVER COLOR BLINDNESS.
- HAIRY HEADS ARE DOMINANT OVER BALD ONES.
- THE ABILITY TO CURL THE TONGUE IS DOMINANT OVER THE INABILITY TO CURL THE TONGUE.
- EXTRA FINGERS ARE DOMINANT OVER FIVE FINGERS (ODD BUT TRUE!).

A DOUBLE DOSE OF RECESSIVES ALSO CAUSE SUCH RARE DISEASES AS HEMOPHILIA, SICKLE-CELL ANEMIA, TAY-SACHS SYNDROME, THALASSEMIA, DWARFISM...

1. HEREDITARY TRAITS ARE GOVERNED BY GENES WHICH RETAIN THEIR IDENTITY IN HYBRIDS. GENES ARE NEVER BLENDED TOGETHER.

2. ONE FORM ("ALLELE") OF A GENE MAY BE **DOMINANT** OVER ANOTHER. BUT RECESSIVE GENES WILL POP UP LATER!!

3. EACH ADULT ORGANISM HAS TWO COPIES OF EACH GENE—ONE FROM EACH PARENT. WHEN POLLEN OR SPERM AND EGGS ARE PRODUCED, THEY EACH GET ONE COPY.

4. DIFFERENT ALLELES ARE SORTED OUT TO SPERM AND EGG RANDOMLY AND INDEPENDENTLY. ALL COMBINATIONS OF ALLELES ARE EQUALLY LIKELY:

AABBCCDDEEFFGGHH
AaBBCCDDEEFFGGHH
aABBCCDDEEFFGGHH
aaBBCCDDEE
AAbBCCDDE GHH
AABbCCDD GGHH
AaBbCC GHH
aABbC GHH

ETC!

WE'LL SEE SHORTLY THAT NOT ALL THESE POINTS ARE EXACTLY CORRECT... DOMINANCE IS SOMETIMES ONLY PARTIAL... THERE ARE ORGANISMS WITH ONLY A SINGLE SET OF GENES... AND SOME WITH FOUR SETS... AND DEVIATIONS FROM INDEPENDENT ASSORTMENT TURN OUT TO BE VERY IMPORTANT...

MENDEL PRESENTED HIS THEORY IN 1865 TO THE BRÜNN NATURAL SCIENCE SOCIETY... IT PUT THEM TO SLEEP.

UNFORTUNATELY, NOBODY CARED ABOUT THE PROBLEM ANY MORE... IT HAD GONE OUT OF FASHION... AND, BESIDES, SINCE 1859, BIOLOGISTS HAD BEEN DISTRACTED BY THE NEW THEORY OF *EVOLUTION*, AND COULDN'T BE BOTHERED WITH MENDEL'S EQUATIONS.

BY THE TIME MENDEL DIED, THE SCIENTIFIC COMMUNITY HAD TOTALLY FORGOTTEN HIS WORK. "MY TIME WILL COME," HE SAID, NOT LONG BEFORE HIS DEATH IN 1884...

GARDENING IS OUT OF FASHION THESE DAYS..

SOME FIELDS NEVER GO OUT OF FASHION...

■ 2.10 Exercises: Genetic Equations

In garden peas, tall (T) is dominant over short (t) and round seeds (R) are dominant over wrinkled (r). Make the following crosses and give the phenotype and genotype ratios in the next generation.

Tt x Tt

Tt x tt

TtRr x TtRr

TTrr x TTRr

■ 2.10 Exercises: Genetic Equations

1. In chickens, feathered legs (F) are dominant to clean legs (f).

   A. Cross a homozygous feather-legged hen with a heterozygous feather-legged rooster and offer the ratios of phenotype and genotype for the next generation.

   B. Cross a homozygous feather-legged hen with a clean-legged rooster.

   C. Cross a heterozygous feather-legged hen with a clean-legged rooster.

2. In foxes, the occurrence of red coloring (R) is dominant over silver-black coat color (r).

   A. Cross a heterozygous red fox with a silver-black and offer the ratios of phenotype and genotype for the next generation.

   B. Cross two hybrids.

2.10 Exercises: Genetic Equations

Test your understanding of genetic principles by performing the following operations on yourself and interpreting the results. How can you explain dominant and recessive traits?

PTC (Phenylthiocarbamide) is a harmless compound that tastes bitter to those individuals who possess the dominant phenotype (T). Those with the recessive trait (t) do not taste the bitter compound. (Be aware that although this is a synthetic compound, PTC is related to the naturally occurring compounds found in many vegetables.)

Cerumen (Ear Wax) occurs in two forms. The dominant type (C) is sticky and yellow to brown in color. The recessive type (c) is dry, flaky and gray in color. Which best describes your findings? (Be sure never to stick anything smaller than your elbow in your ear.)

Tongue rolling, the ability to roll the tongue into a longitudinal tube (U-shape), is inherited as a dominant (R) trait. People who are recessive (r) for this trait will not be able to roll their tongue even with years of practice. (Does this mean that practice does not always make perfect?)

Interlocking fingers and thumbs demonstrates a dominant position (I) if the left thumb is over the right thumb. If the right thumb is over the left, this demonstrates the recessive trait (i).

Hitchhiker's thumb, where the thumb is bent backward at an angle of 50 degrees or less, is dominant (HT). The ability to flex one's thumb greater than 50 degrees, known as distal hyperextensibility, is a recessive trait (ht).

Mid-digital hair refers to the presence or absence of hair in the middle region of your fingers. The presence of hair is dominant (H) while the absence of hair is a recessive phenotype (h).

■ 2.10 Exercises: Genetic Equations

Complete the following equations:

1. What are the possible genotypes for the following phenotypes?

   A. A person who can taste PTC (which is inherited as a dominant condition) who also has attached earlobes (inherited as a recessive trait.)

   B. A person who has sticky earwax, which is inherited as a dominant condition, who also possesses a Darwin's Tubercle (meaning a small projection of cartilage in the helix of the ear which is also a dominant trait.)

   C. A person who is heterozygous for both PTC tasting and tongue rolling (which is a dominant trait).

2. If a child and his mother have attached earlobes (a recessive condition) and the father has free-hanging earlobes, what is the genotype of the father for this trait?

2.10 Exercises: Genetic Equations

Complete the following based upon the equations given:

If a male who demonstrates recessive phenotypes for both Darwin's Tubercle and for PTC tasting mates with a female who is heterozygous for both Darwin's Tubercle and PTC tasting:

A. What is the frequency of offspring who will demonstrate Darwin's Tubercle? Give the frequency as the number of offspring who demonstrate this trait over the total number of offspring.

B. What is the frequency of offspring who will be able to taste PTC and who will have a Darwin's Tubercle?

■ 2.10 Exercises: Genetic Equations

C. What is the frequency of offspring who will not be able to taste PTC and who will not have a Darwin's Tubercle?

D. What is the frequency of offspring who will not be able to taste PTC but who will have a Darwin's Tubercle?

2.10 Exercises: Genetic Equations

You can continue to practice your understanding of Punnett Squares on-line. Complete the activities at the following two university web sites. Be sure to print out and to keep a copy of your results.

Virtual Fly Lab:
http://vcourseware4.calstatela.edu/cgi-bin/Mate

Blue People of the Appalachian Mountains:
http://wsrv.clas.virginia.edu/~rjh9u/slidlist.html

2.11 Introduction to Non-Random Mate Selection

Evolutionary psychologists have stated that we look for certain physical characteristics (sexual selection) when choosing a potential mate. From an evolutionary perspective, males often choose a female who appears to be young and capable of nurturing the offspring. Females look for males to protect and provide for her and their offspring. While this is an oversimplified explanation for non-random mate selection, think about how it applies to our own description of the "perfect mate." Read the following articles and answer the corresponding questions.

2.12 *The Eggs Files*

Celia Farber

When Ron Harris put models' eggs for sale over the internet, it sparked a national outcry. But Harris wasn't doing anything that hadn't been done before. He was just being more honest about it.

In the middle of the night, shortly after *The New York Times* broke the story of the web site that was auctioning off models' eggs to the highest bidder, satellite trucks were making their way up the winding road that led to the Malibu home of Ron Harris, perhaps the most controversial American since Jack Kevorkian.

"At one o'clock in the morning, ABC was running their cables into the house," recalls Harris' shell-shocked publicist, who didn't want to be named.

By 9 AM on the morning the story broke, October 23, the publicist had received 600 emails, both answering machines were filled to capacity, and the phones were ringing nonstop. The story rocketed around the world. "It was huge," said the publicist. "Huge." Within 24 hours the web site had one million hits. Within days it had five million.

Inside the house, the 66-year-old Harris was calmly preparing breakfast. In an illustrious photographic career he has won 450 awards and been personal photographer to Johnny Carson. He taught Steve McQueen how to ride a motorcycle, and counted among his lovers Gloria Steinem. He also spent years breeding Arabian horses and fomenting his own ideas about beauty, genetics, and body shapes.

Now a cavalry of reporters were waiting for him to explain, defend, refract the fury his web site had ignited. It was a fury that never really coalesced, but a fury nonetheless. There was something inchoate about it, yet it struck every major American nerve: beauty, money, genetics, the internet. It was as though Ron Harris held up a mirror to America and said: this is who you are—and America hated it.

The site, *ronsangels.com*, featured eight seductive models (though four of them never intended to participate in the site after it was ready) with vaguely utopian promises floating over their lovely heads: "Come up to beauty. Come up to Ron's Angels. Starting bids $15,000–$150,000 in $1,000 increments." When Harris tried to fend off the controversy by peppering his comments with references to Darwin, it only made things worse. The site seemed influenced more by Aaron Spelling than Darwin. It was crass, perhaps, but certainly not ominous. We're talking, at press time, of precisely four donor models and one serious bidder. You could hardly argue that Harris was out to repopulate the planet with perfect-looking people.

Fertility experts, lawyers, clergymen, and professional feminists were ushered into the nation's talk show seats to express their disgust. On *Rivera Live* a former model who wrote a book, *Ageless Beauty: A Woman's Guide to Lifelong Beauty and Well-Being*, condemned the site, with no trace of irony, saying, "There's much more to one's life than one's physical attributes."

On the same show, Jerry Falwell said that Harris was "trafficking in God's work" and vulgarizing procreation. A reproductive medicine doctor said it represented "the worst of society," and that "no tissue or organ should be a commodity." A medical ethicist called it "the first step in creating designer babies." A female "former prosecutor" flatly compared Harris to Hitler and declared that this was eugenics, while Rivera devoted himself to making scrambled egg jokes. "I've got an egg," he joked, "I've got such an egg. Oh I've got a hot egg here. Let me flip this egg, let me flip this sale. Whoa, baby. Dr. Brothers?"

"You're going to waste your money," Dr. Joyce Brothers weighed in. "I'm going to scramble my egg," said Geraldo. (And he wonders why NBC won't let him anchor the news?)

Center stage was given to the directors of the nation's most prominent fertility clinics, who fumed piously about "commodifying human eggs" while plugging their very own clinics, which they'd have you believe were charity organizations, rather than some of the most lucrative businesses in the country.

"It's hilarious. It's almost like a Woody Allen scenario," says Dr. Glenn McGee, a professor at the University of Pennsylvania Center for Bioethics, and author of *The Perfect Baby: A Pragmatic Approach to Genetics*. "The models-eggs-on-the-internet thing highlights the fact that the fertility industry is totally unregulated. The circus animal training industry is better regulated. You have this model web site going on, and yes, it's absurd. But it's even more hilarious that the people who sell eggs for a living are saying it's bad. Talk about glass houses."

Shelley Smith, a former Ford model, and director of the Egg Donor Program in Los Angeles, calls the Harris web site "atrocious" echoing the sentiments of virtually the entire fertility profession. "Ron Harris is exploiting the hopes of desperate people," she told me. "I think it's appalling to place such an emphasis on beauty. At my clinic we have a protocol in place that screens the parents, that asks them all kinds of questions, and the donors as well. I don't think he has any idea where these eggs may be going."

Still, in the next breath she concedes that her customers "all want somebody who is beautiful and bright."

"I always said I wish we could get more models," she says, pointedly adding that Harris' models aren't really that beautiful. "When he gets Claudia Schiffer's eggs, give me a call."

McGee was in St. Louis for a conference when the story broke, and didn't get swept up in the media frenzy. "Among bio-ethicists it was what we call a second-tier story. What it seemed like above all, to me, was a field day for the directors of the fertility clinics. They really got to look like the good guys in this, and boy, they didn't miss that chance."

In fact, McGee points out that the fertility industry itself, with its "swipe and go philosophy," has created a culture of deception, exploitation, and quick consumerism. "The reason this got so much attention has everything to do with the way we talk about infertility in this country," says McGee. "The whole dialogue is sort of like insecurity on stilts. The notion that you could 'camera-match' somebody, as we call it, based on superficial physical traits, is bad genetics. It's crazy. Yet the infertility clinics operate on this premise every day."

Genetic inheritance is infinitely more complex than the new consumerism would suggest. From each parent, a child inherits 23 chromosomes, and at least three billion nucleotides, which mix together to create something that is entirely unpredictable, random, complex and unique: a human. "You can't inherit beauty," medical ethicist Arthur Caplan, also from the University of Pennsylvania Center for Bioethics, explained. "It's not that simple. Beauty is a matter of millimeters. It doesn't take much, genetically, to move a beautiful face to a plain one."

McGee pegs Harris not as a new eugenicist but as a snake oil salesman. "There is no way in the world this project could ever have produced anything like what he was promising. But it's no crazier than the couple in Boston who promised $50,000 for the eggs of a woman with a SAT score of 1400."

Bottom line? "The only relative of a model who is guaranteed to look beautiful is an identical twin," says McGee. In fact, Harris himself admitted as much on a TV show, when he commented that a golden egg buyer could well "wind up with dumb and ugly."

The media searchlight fell, it would seem, on the wrong infertility scandal. If you turn to the back of any college newspaper, you'll see ads from fertility clinics enticing female students to make some quick cash by selling their eggs, for around $1,500 to $3,000. The better the college, the higher the sums offered.

As Caplan commented, "One could probably ditch college rankings of the sort that *U.S. News and World Report* provides each year and replace them with a price list of the schools at which women are able to charge the most for their eggs." A woman from Princeton sold her eggs for $25,000, according to Caplan, and at least two women have died from the egg donation process—one from the anaesthesia and one from a ruptured ovary.

The relatively low price that has been the informal industry standard is ostensibly a measure not of the egg's worth, but mere reimbursement for the woman's time. "It's always considered to be normal compensation for the risks and the shots and the amount of time involved and the side effects," says Shelley Smith. "The fees for donors haven't varied much in 10 years." Caplan is skeptical. "At least one clinic jumped the price from about $4,200 to $7,500. And when you're recruiting Ivy League eggs, it's clearly recruiting for more than just their time, it's for who they are."

Caplan does not think that what Harris is doing is intrinsically different from what's been going on for a long time. "They're clearly running an egg auction," he says, referring to fertility clinics who advertise in college papers. "Since they continue to use the word 'donation' and not 'purchase', I assume they think there's something unacceptable about it too. They are not donors, they're sellers, so this language of 'donation' is completely inappropriate." Smith, for her part, says she doesn't distinguish between donors when it comes to price. But when I ask her about the morality of advertising in college newspapers to attract young students, she at first denies that she does, but when pressed admits "we advertise a bit in colleges" and talks about her own prize donors. "I've got a girl with an IQ of 165 who's got three masters degrees, and I've got another girl who's drop dead gorgeous, who's got a Stanford scholarship."

According to the Pacific Connection Fertility Services, there is a small risk of death, and a higher risk of infection and intense pain to the donor. In other countries it is strictly forbidden to compensate a person for their genetic tissue, be it eggs or sperm. Many infertile women from around the world travel here to purchase American eggs, sold through fertility clinics. "I am on the side of the women," says Harris. "I think it is very exploitative that they should go through such a risky procedure and risk their future children for only $3,000."

Harris comes across as a warm, friendly person. He believes that most of the anger over his web site is coming from people within the fertility industry, whose business he is threatening. But he is undeterred, working feverishly to expand his site to include "20 or 30" women of all ethnic origins.

"I'm not doing eugenics, society is doing eugenics," Harris insists. "Society is trying to shape the way we are. Just look at any magazine. Look at *Gear*, look at *Vogue*."

Eugenics is a loaded word that is used to invoke Hitler but goes much farther back in history. It was Darwin's cousin, Francis Galton, who first argued for the "science of improving human stock," in his book *Hereditary Genius*, which laid the groundwork for the many thousands of forced sterilizations that took place in America and England in the early part of the 20th century.

Eugenics had little to do with beauty, but focused instead on purging mental retardation from the gene pool. Hitler based his ideas about eugenics on American sterilization laws. But judging from the reaction in the media, you'd think Harris had recommended mass extermination of ugly people.

In actual fact, Harris' web site is not really new at all, but a continuation on trends already in full swing. Most fertility clinics advertise on the internet, and many list the attributes of both the sperm and egg donors. Sperm donation began half a century ago, and egg donation has been in practice since the 1980s, but has proliferated in the last 10 years.

Last June, *60 Minutes* ran a program about people finding egg donors on the internet. Karen Synesiou, who runs a program called Egg Donation Inc., admitted that she discourages unattractive donors from participating.

What if she gets donors who are not attractive? "Then I'm gonna phone her and tell her."

"That she's not pretty enough?"

"Tell her I don't think a couple's gonna choose her."

It was during a photo shoot with model Nicole Newman that Harris mentioned the Boston newspaper ad he'd seen, in which a couple offered up to $50,000 for the eggs of a beautiful, intelligent, athletic woman who "must be at least 5ft. 10in., 1,400-plus on college boards, with no major family medical issues."

Newman recalls her innocuous comment that triggered an avalanche in the landscape of American bio-ethics. "I said, 'I'd do that. For that kind of money? I would definitely do that.'

"Ron said, 'I'm gonna do an egg auction,' and I said 'great.' I didn't expect all this. I didn't think it was that big of a deal."

When I ask Harris what kind of models these "angels" are exactly, he answers somewhat evasively that they are "models, actresses and comedians."

One lives in Romania, and wants the money so she can move to this country. Another was a Playmate in January of 1996, and, yes, she has had breast implants. But people are paying for the genetic imprint, I point out. "Absolutely right," he says. "And I post all such information on the web site."

Shrugging off accusations that he is simply trying to make a quick buck, Harris says, "I'm negative cash flow on this. This site is not a money maker at this time. It will be because I know something about beauty that very few people know. I know how the symmetry works and how it all goes together.

"I intend to create a web site where you have other genetic choices than you would have had. It's not elitism or eugenics or supremacy of any kind. I'm just mirroring society's interests and the way society works."

No eggs have been sold yet, but that's because the bids don't close until several months from now.

"It is not a hoax," model Misty McFern told me, in response to media skepticism that the story had no foundation. "I know because I am doing it."

Asked what her concerns were, if any, model Nicole Newman says, "I would like to know that the egg is going to someone that doesn't have a substance abuse problem."

"I think this is very good for society," Harris says cheerfully. "It's no different from what they're all doing, which is selling eggs and sperm, except that they're not doing it right.

"As long as everybody else is doing it, and making millions of dollars, I have no problem with it. But, hey, if everybody else stops, I'll stop."

Caplan doubts anyone is about to stop, envisaging a future of designer babies on demand. He recalls a case of one woman who was fertile yet chose another woman to carry her baby to avoid interrupting her career, and of another of a couple who sued a sperm bank when their children turned out ugly.

"Right now you can't breed for beauty," says Caplan. "But in 10 years you might be able to weed out genetic diseases, and you might be able to look for certain traits that people want, like musical ability.

"At that point people might choose to have babies using genetic screening and infertility-type treatments—people who are fertile but want a particular kind of baby."

I ask Caplan why Harris' web site triggered the reaction that it has.

"Because beauty is seen as more shallow than brains," he answered.

2.12 Study Questions: The Eggs Files — Celia Farber

1. If you and your partner were to purchase the egg or sperm of a Yale graduate, successful in the business world, does that guarantee the same life for your potential offspring? Why or why not?

2. What types of risks exist for women donating eggs?

3. Do you feel genetic choices should appear on the internet and why?

4. What is eugenics?

5. What do you feel is valued in our society, brain, beauty or both?

2.13 *The Biology of Beauty*

Geoffrey Cowley

Looking good is a universal human obsession. How do we perceive physical beauty, and why do we place so much stock in it? Scientists are now taking those questions seriously, and gaining suprising insights.

When it comes to choosing a mate, a female penguin knows better than to fall for the first creep who pulls up and honks. She holds out for the fittest suitor available—which in Antarctica means one chubby enough to spend several weeks sitting on newly hatched eggs without starving to death. The Asian jungle bird *Gallus gallus* is just as choosy. Males in that species sport gaily colored head combs and feathers, which lose their luster if the bird is invaded by parasites. By favoring males with bright ornaments, a hen improves her odds of securing a mate (and bearing offspring) with strong resistance to disease. For female scorpion flies, beauty is less about size or color than about symmetry. Females favor suitors who have well-matched wings—and with good reason. Studies show they're the most adept at killing prey and at defending their catch from competitors. There's no reason to think that any of these creatures understands its motivations, but there's a clear pattern to their preferences. "Throughout the animal world," says University of New Mexico ecologist Randy Thornhill, "attractiveness certifies biological quality."

Is our corner of the animal world different? That looks count in human affairs is beyond dispute. Studies have shown that people considered attractive fare better with parents and teachers, make more friends and more money, and have better sex with more (and more beautiful) partners. Every year, 400,000 Americans, including 48,000 men, flock to cosmetic surgeons. In other lands, people bedeck themselves with scars, lip plugs or bright feathers. "Every culture is a 'beauty culture'," says Nancy Etcoff, a neuroscientist who is studying human attraction at the MIT Media Lab and writing a book on the subject. "I defy anyone to point to a society, any time in history or any place in the world, that wasn't preoccupied with beauty." The high-minded may dismiss our preening and ogling as distractions from things that matter, but the stakes can be enormous. "Judging beauty involves looking at another person," says University of Texas psychologist Devendra Singh, "and figuring out whether you want your children to carry that person's genes."

It's widely assumed that ideals of beauty vary from era to era and from culture to culture. But a harvest of new research is confounding that idea. Studies have established that people everywhere—regardless of race, class or age—share a sense of what's attractive. And though no one knows just how our minds translate the sight of a face or a body into rapture, new studies suggest that we judge each other by rules we're not even aware of. We may consciously admire Kate Moss's legs or Arnold's biceps, but we're also viscerally attuned to small variations in the size and symmetry of facial bones and the placement of weight on the body.

This isn't to say that our preferences are purely innate—or that beauty is all that matters in life. Most of us manage to find jobs, attract mates and bear offspring despite our physical imperfections. Nor should anyone assume that the new beauty research justifies the biases it illuminates. Our beautylust is often better suited to the Stone Age than to the Information Age; the qualities we find alluring may be powerful emblems of health, fertility and resistance to disease, but they say nothing about people's moral worth. The human weakness for what Thornhill calls "biological quality" causes no end of pain and injustice. Unfortunately, that doesn't make it any less real.

No one suggests that points of attraction never vary. Rolls of fat can signal high status in a poor society or low status in a rich one, and lip plugs go over better in the Kalahari than they do in Kansas.

But local fashions seem to rest on a bedrock of shared preferences. You don't have to be Italian to find Michelangelo's David better looking than, say, Alfonse D'Amato. When British researchers asked women from England, China and India to rate pictures of Greek men, the women responded as if working from the same crib sheet. And when researchers at the University of Louisville showed a diverse collection of faces to whites, Asians and Latinos from 13 countries, the subjects' ethnic background scarcely affected their preferences.

To a skeptic, those findings suggest only that Western movies and magazines have overrun the world. But scientists have found at least one group that hasn't been exposed to this bias. In a series of groundbreaking experiments, psychologist Judith Langlois of the University of Texas, Austin, has shown that even infants share a sense of what's attractive. In the late '80s, Langlois started placing 3- and 6-month-old babies in front of a screen and showing them pairs of facial photographs. Each pair included one considered attractive by adult judges and one considered unattractive. In the first study, she found that the infants gazed significantly longer at "attractive" white female faces than at "unattractive" ones. Since then, she has repeated the drill using white male faces, black female faces, even the faces of other babies, and the same pattern always emerges. "These kids don't read Vogue or watch TV," Langlois says. "They haven't been touched by the media. Yet they make the same judgments as adults."

What, then, is beauty made of? What are the innate rules we follow in sizing each other up? We're obviously wired to find robust health a prettier sight than infirmity. "All animals are attracted to other animals that are healthy, that are clean by their standards and that show signs of competence," says Rutgers University anthropologist Helen Fisher. As far as anyone knows, there isn't a village on earth where skin lesions, head lice and rotting teeth count as beauty aids. But the rules get subtler than that. Like scorpion flies, we love symmetry. And though we generally favor average features over unusual ones, the people we find extremely beautiful share certain exceptional qualities.

When Randy Thornhill started measuring the wings of Japanese scorpion flies six years ago, he wasn't much concerned with the orgasms and infidelities of college students. But sometimes one thing leads to another. Biologists have long used bilateral symmetry—the extent to which a creature's right and left sides match—to gauge what's known

Balancing Act

One key to physical attractiveness is symmetry; humans, like other species, show a strong preference for individuals whose right and left sides are well matched. The face below is almost completely symmetrical.

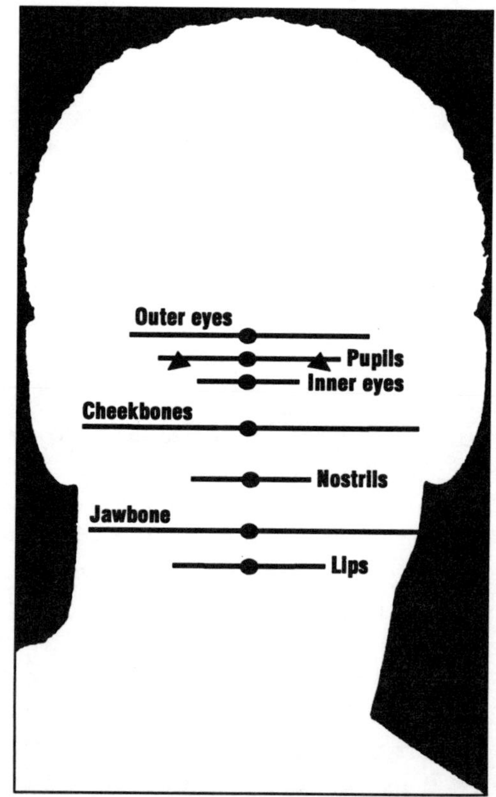

Golden mean: By drawing lines between paired features and marking the midpoints, researchers get an index of asymmetry.

as developmental stability. Given ideal growing conditions, paired features such as wings, ears, eyes and feet would come out matching perfectly. But pollution, disease and other hazards can disrupt development. As a result, the least resilient individuals tend to be the most lopsided. In chronicling the scorpion flies' daily struggles, Thornhill found that the bugs with the most symmetrical wings fared best in the competition for food and mates. To his amazement, females preferred symmetrical males even when they were hidden from view; evidently, their smells are more attractive. And when researchers started noting similar trends in other species, Thornhill turned his attention to our own.

Working with psychologist Steven Gangestad, he set about measuring the body symmetry of hundreds of college-age men and women. By adding up right-left disparities in seven measurements—the breadth of the feet, ankles, hands, wrists and elbows, as well as the breadth and length of the ears—the

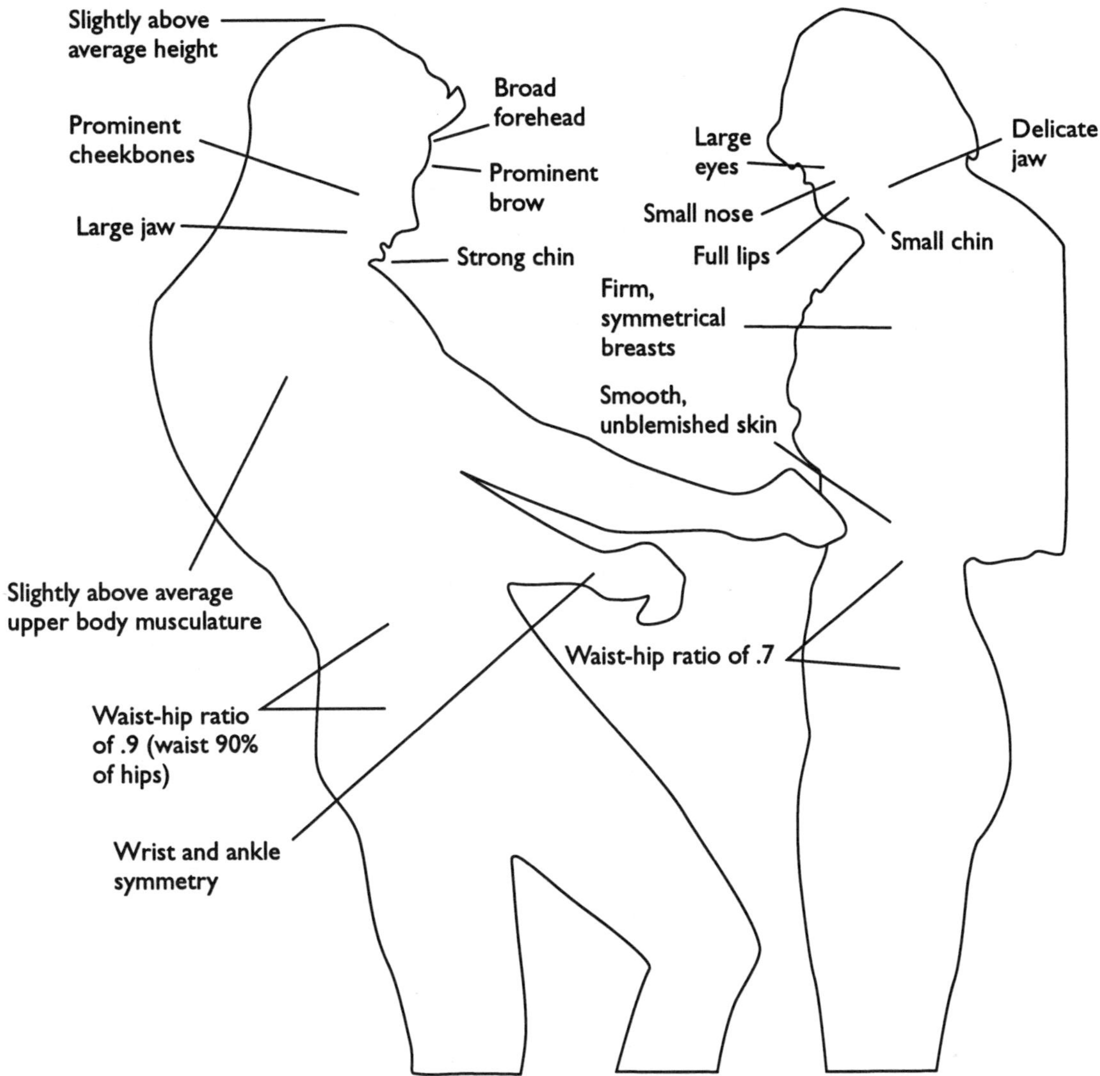

What goes into sex appeal?
Studies suggest that male attractiveness hinges on outward signs of maturity, robust health and, above all, dominance. Most of the features associated with feminine beauty signal youthfulness and an abundance of female reproductive hormones.

researchers scored each subject's overall body asymmetry. Then they had the person fill out a confidential questionnaire covering everything from temperament to sexual behavior, and set about looking for connections. They weren't disappointed. In a 1994 study, they found that the most symmetrical males had started having sex three to four years earlier than their most lopsided brethren. For both men and women, greater symmetry predicted a larger number of past sex partners.

That was just the beginning. From what they knew about other species, Thornhill and Gangestad predicted that women would be more sexually responsive to symmetrical men, and that men would exploit that advantage. To date, their findings support both suspicions. Last year they surveyed 86 couples and found that women with highly symmetrical partners were more than twice as likely to climax during intercourse (an event that may foster conception by ushering sperm into the uterus) than those with low-symmetry partners. And in separate surveys, Gangestad and Thornhill have found that, compared with regular Joes, extremely symmetrical men are less attentive to their partners and more likely to cheat on them. Women showed no such tendency.

It's hard to imagine that we even notice the differences between people's elbows, let alone stake our love lives on them. No one carries calipers into a singles bar. So why do these measurements predict so much? Because, says Thornhill, people with symmetrical elbows tend to have "a whole suite of attractive features." His findings suggest that besides having attractive (and symmetrical) faces, men with symmetrical bodies are typically larger, more muscular and more athletic than their peers, and more dominant in personality. In a forthcoming study, researchers at the University of Michigan find evidence that facial symmetry is also associated with health. In analyzing diaries kept by 100 students over a two-month period, they found that the least symmetrical had the most physical complaints, from insomnia to nasal congestion, and reported more anger, jealousy and withdrawal. In light of all Thornhill and Gangestad's findings, you can hardly blame them.

If we did go courting with calipers, symmetry isn't all we would measure. As we study each other in the street, the office or the gym, our beauty radars pick up a range of signals. Oddly enough, one of the qualities shared by attractive people is their averageness. Researchers discovered more than a century ago that if they superimposed photographs of several faces, the resulting composite was usually better looking than any of the images that went into it. Scientists can now average faces digitally, and it's still one of the surest ways to make them more attractive. From an evolutionary perspective, a preference for extreme normality makes sense. As Langlois has written, "Individuals with average population characteristics should be less likely to carry harmful genetic mutations."

So far, so good. But here's the catch: while we may find average faces attractive, the faces we find most beautiful are not average. As New Mexico State University psychologist Victor Johnston has shown, they're extreme. To track people's preferences, Johnston uses a computer program called FacePrints. Turn it on, and it generates 30 facial images, all male or all female, which you rate on a 1–9 beauty scale. The program then "breeds" the top-rated face with one of the others to create two digital offspring, which replace the lowest-rated faces in the pool. By rating round after round of new faces, you create an ever more beautiful population. The game ends when you award some visage a perfect 10. (If you have access to the World Wide Web, you can take part in a collective face-breeding experiment by visiting http://www-psych.nmsu.edu/ vic/faceprints/.)

For Johnston, the real fun starts after the judging is finished. By collecting people's ideal faces and comparing them to average faces, he can measure the distance between fantasy and reality. As a rule, he finds that an ideal female has a higher forehead than an average one, as well as fuller lips, a shorter jaw and a smaller chin and nose. Indeed, the ideal 25-year-old woman, as configured by participants in a 1993 study, had a 14-year-old's abundant lips and an 11-year-old's delicate jaw. Because her lower face was so small, she also had relatively prominent eyes and cheekbones.

The participants in that study were all college kids from New Mexico, but researchers have since shown that British and Japanese students express the same bias. And if there are lingering doubts about the depth of that bias, Johnston's latest findings should dispel them. In a forthcoming study, he reports that male volunteers not only consciously prefer women with small lower faces but show marked rises in brain activity when looking at pictures of them. And though Johnston has yet to publish specs on the ideal male, his unpublished findings suggest that a big jaw, a strong chin and an imposing brow are as prized in a man's face as their opposites are in a woman's.

Few of us ever develop the heart-melting proportions of a FacePrints fantasy. And if it's any consolation, beauty is not an all-or-nothing proposition. Madonna became a sex symbol despite her strong nose, and Melanie Griffith's strong jaw hasn't kept her out of the movies. Still, special things have a way of happening to people who approximate the ideal. We pay them huge fees to stand on windblown bluffs and stare into the distance. And past studies have found that square-jawed males not only start having sex earlier than their peers but attain higher rank in the military.

None of this surprises evolutionary psychologists. They note that the facial features we obsess over are precisely the ones that diverge in males and females during puberty, as floods of sex hormones wash us into adulthood. And they reason that hormonal abundance would have been a good clue to mate value in the hunter-gatherer world where our preferences evolved. The tiny jaw that men favor in women is essentially a monument to estrogen—and, obliquely, to fertility. No one claims that jaws reveal a woman's odds of getting pregnant. But like breasts, they imply that she could.

Likewise, the heavy lower face that women favor in men is a visible record of the surge in androgens (testosterone and other male sex hormones) that turns small boys into 200-pound spear-throwers. An oversized jaw is biologically expensive, for the androgens required to produce it tend to compromise the immune system. But from a female's perspective, that should make jaw size all the more revealing.

Evolutionists think of androgen-based features as "honest advertisements" of disease resistance. If a male can afford them without falling sick, the thinking goes, he must have a superior immune system in the first place.

No one has tracked the immune responses of men with different jawlines to see if these predictions bear out (Thornhill has proposed a study that would involve comparing volunteers' responses to a vaccine). Nor is it clear whether penis size figures into these equations. Despite what everyone thinks he knows on the subject, scientists haven't determined that women have consistent preferences one way or the other.

Our faces are our signatures, but when it comes to raw sex appeal, a nice chin is no match for a perfectly sculpted torso—especially from a man's perspective. Studies from around the world have found that while both sexes value appearance, men place more stock in it than women. And if there are social reasons for that imbalance, there are also biological ones. Just about any male over 14 can produce sperm, but a woman's ability to bear children depends on her age and hormone levels. Female fertility declines by two thirds between the ages of 20 and 44, and it's spent by 54. So while both sexes may eyeball potential partners, says Donald Symons, an anthropologist at the University of California in Santa Barbara, "a larger proportion of a woman's mate value can be detected from visual cues." Mounting evidence suggests there is no better cue than the relative contours of her waist and hips.

Before puberty and after menopause, females have essentially the same waistlines as males. But during puberty, while boys are amassing the bone and muscle of paleolithic hunters, a typical girl gains nearly 35 pounds of so-called reproductive fat around the hips and thighs. Those pounds contain roughly the 80,000 calories needed to sustain a pregnancy, and the curves they create provide a gauge of reproductive potential. "You have to get very close to see the details of a woman's face," says Devendra Singh, the University of Texas psychologist. "But you can see the shape of her body from 500 feet, and it says more about mate value."

Almost anything that interferes with fertility—obesity, malnutrition, pregnancy, menopause—changes a woman's shape. Healthy, fertile women typically have waist-hip ratios of .6 to .8, meaning their waists are 60 to 80 percent the size of their hips, whatever their actual weight. To take one familiar example, a 36-25-36 figure would have a WHR of .7.

Body Language

When men are asked to rank figures with various weights and waist-hip ratios (0.7 to 1.0), they favor a pronounced hourglass shape. The highest-ranked figures are N7, N8 and U7 (in that order). The lowest ranked is O10.

Underweight

U7 U8 U9 U10

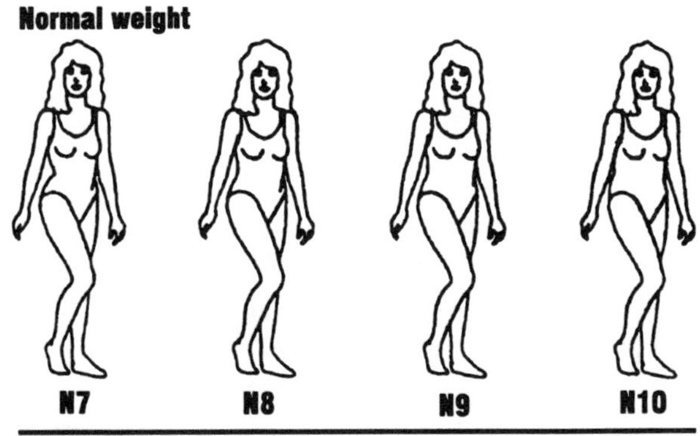

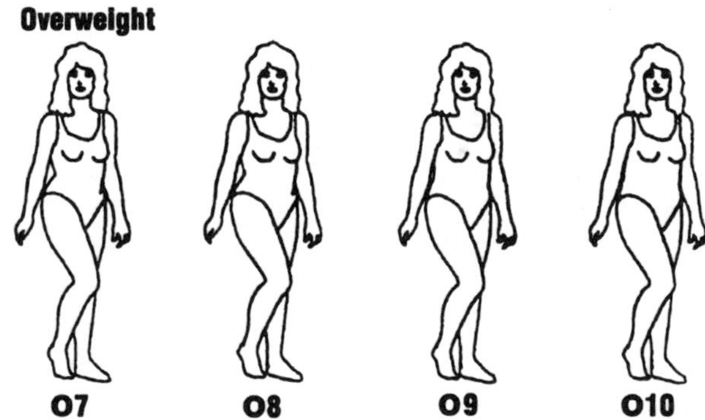

The order chosen: (1) N7, (2) N8, (3) U7, (4) U8, (5) N9, (6) N10, (7) O7, (8) U9, (9) O8, (10) U10, (11) O9, (12) O10. Source: Devendra Singh, University of Texas at Austin.

Many women outside this range are healthy and capable of having children, of course. But as researchers in the Netherlands discovered in a 1993 study, even a slight increase in waist size relative to hip size can signal reproductive problems. Among 500 women who were attempting in vitro fertilization, the odds of conceiving during any given cycle declined by 30 percent with every 10 percent increase in WHR. In other words, a woman with a WHR of .9 was nearly a third less likely to get pregnant than one with a WHR of .8, regardless of her age or weight. From an evolutionary perspective, it's hard to imagine men not responding to such a revealing signal. And as Singh has shown repeatedly, they do.

Defining a universal standard of body beauty once seemed a fool's dream; common sense said that if spindly Twiggy and Rubens's girthy Three Graces could all excite admiration, then nearly anyone could. But if our ideals of size change from one time and place to the next, our taste in shapes is amazingly stable. A low waist-hip ratio is one of the few features that a long, lean Barbie doll shares with a plump, primitive fertility icon. And Singh's findings suggest the fashion won't change any time soon. In one study, he compiled the measurements of Playboy centerfolds and Miss America winners from 1923 to 1990. Their bodies got measurably leaner over the decades, yet their waist-hip ratios stayed within the narrow range of .68 to .72. (Even Twiggy was no tube; at the peak of her fame in the 1960s, the British model had a WHR of .73.)

The same pattern holds when Singh generates line drawings of different female figures and asks male volunteers to rank them for attractiveness, sexiness, health and fertility. He has surveyed men of various backgrounds, nationalities and ages. And whether the judges are 8-year-olds or 85-year-olds, their runaway favorite is a figure of average weight with a .7 WHR. Small wonder that when women were liberated from corsets and bustles, they took up girdles, wide belts and other waist-reducing contraptions. Last year alone, American women's outlays for shape-enhancing garments topped a half-billion dollars.

To some critics, the search for a biology of beauty looks like a thinly veiled political program. "It's the fantasy life of American men being translated into genetics," says poet and social critic Katha Pollitt. "You can look at any feature of modern life and make up a story about why it's genetic." In truth, says Northwestern University anthropologist Micaela di Leonardo, attraction is a complicated social phenomenon, not just a hard-wired response. If attraction were governed by the dictates of baby-making, she says, the men of ancient Greece wouldn't have found young boys so alluring, and gay couples wouldn't crowd modern sidewalks. "People make decisions about sexual and marital partners inside complex networks of friends and relatives," she says. "Human beings cannot be reduced to DNA packets."

Homosexuality is hard to explain as a biological adaptation. So is stamp collecting. But no one claims that human beings are mindless automatons, blindly striving to replicate our genes. We pursue countless passions that have no direct bearing on survival. If we're sometimes attracted to people who can't help us reproduce, that doesn't mean human preferences lack any coherent design. A radio used as a doorstop is still a radio. The beauty mavens' mission—and that of evolutionary psychology in general—is not to explain everything people do but to unmask our biases and make sense of them. "Our minds have evolved to generate pleasurable experiences in response to some things while ignoring other things," says Johnston. "That's why sugar tastes sweet, and that's why we find some people more attractive than others."

The new beauty research does have troubling implications. First, it suggests that we're designed to care about looks, even though looks aren't earned and reveal nothing about character. As writer Ken Siman observes in his new book, "The Beauty Trip," "the kind [of beauty] that inspires awe, lust, and increased jeans sales cannot be evenly distributed. In a society where everything is supposed to be within reach, this is painful to face." From acne to birth defects, we wear our imperfections as thorns, for we know the world sees them and takes note.

A second implication is that sexual stereotypes are not strictly artificial. At some level, it seems, women are designed to favor dominant males over meek ones and men are designed to value women for youthful qualities that time quickly steals. Given the slow pace of evolutionary change, our innate preferences aren't likely to fade in the foreseeable future. And if they exist for what were once good biologic reasons, that doesn't make them any less nettlesome. "Men often forgo their health, their safety, their spare time and their family life in order to get rank," says Helen Fisher, the Rutgers anthropologist, "because unconsciously, they know that rank wins women." And all too often, those who can trade cynically on their rank do.

But do we have to indulge every appetite that natural selection has preserved in us? Of course not. "I don't know any scientist who seriously thinks you can look to nature for moral guidance," says Thornhill. Even the fashion magazines would provide a better compass.

2.13 Study Questions: The Biology of Beauty — Geoffrey Cowley

1. What does attractiveness seem to certify throughout the animal world?

2. What evidence is there that looks count in human affairs?

3. In what sense is every culture a "beauty culture?" What is involved in "judging beauty?"

4. Although ideals of beauty may vary, in what respects do cultures share a sense of what is attractive?

5. Is the author saying that our preferences are purely innate? That beauty is all that matters? That the new beauty research justifies the biases it illuminates? Explain the author's positions.

6. In what respects may points of attraction vary? What evidence is there that preferences are shared across cultures?

7. Are the shared preferences simply reflective of the fact that Western movies and magazines have overrun the world? Explain.

8. What is beauty made of, according to Helen Fisher? In what sense do "the rules get subtler?" How did Thornhill's study of Japanese scorpion flies support this view?

9. Be aware of the results of the study of symmetry among college-age men and women.

10. What is the significance of the "averageness" of attractive people? Are the most attractive people also average in appearance?

11. Which facial features are considered most attractive in males and females? How do evolutionary psychologists explain this?

12. Why do men place more stock in physical appearance than do women?

13. Why is it important to distinguish between a woman's size vs. shape with respect to standards of beauty?

14. Why do some critics say this kind of research represents a "thinly veiled political program?"

15. Why is homosexuality difficult to explain in terms of the "biology of beauty?" How does the author respond to this criticism?

16. What are the "troubling implications" of beauty research?

17. Should we look solely to our "natural appetites" for moral guidance? Explain.

2.14 *Eyes of the Beholders*

A sharp exchange on the meaning of beauty

Is beauty a source of female power or an instrument of oppression? Is our preoccupation with good looks innate? Or are scientists inventing biological explanations for acquired habits of mind? And if beautylust is indeed part of our nature, can we hope to rise above it? NEWSWEEK correspondent Karen Springen moderated a forum in which scientists, social critics and people in the beauty business debated the issues raised by this week's cover story. Some excerpts:

Naomi Wolf, author of "The Beauty Myth" The questions science asks are often dictated by cultural ideology. It's notable that the inquiry is one-sided, looking at men's perceptions of women and not women's perceptions of men nearly as much. Do we want to take this one quality and assign the primary worth of a person on that basis? Would men in America want to be judged in the workplace on the basis of their height, if that were found to be a preference for a majority of women? All of human society isn't ordered around fertility selection. If you reduce people to one aspect of their identities, you get a very distorted and ill-functioning society.

Nancy Etcoff, neuroscientist at Massachusetts General Hospital, author of a forthcoming book on evolution and beauty These feminist critiques are only the most recent in a long line of searing attacks on beauty and its handmaiden, fashion. Until the age of capitalism, every civilized country enacted laws attempting to control sumptuous dress. For centuries the church has railed against the deceit and vanity of fashion, and the medical doctors have expressed horror at the risks and dangers people incur in the name of beauty. None of it has made a dent. There is now deep cultural dissatisfaction with the focus on beauty. But the beauty business shows no signs of abating. A pursuit so ardent, so passionate, so risk-filled, so unquenchable reflects the workings of a basic instinct. To tell people not to take pleasure in beauty is like telling them to stop enjoying food or sex or love. Rather than denigrate one source of women's power, feminists should embrace all sources of women's power. Why is being beautiful and being prized for it a social evil? The idea that beauty is unimportant or a cultural construct is the real beauty myth.

Katha Pollitt, poet and essayist Part of [evolutionary psychologists'] argument is that the most beautiful woman gets together with the most powerful man, and their children have the best chance of survival. That's not necessarily true. In a lot of small, primitive societies, resources are shared and there's a lot of collective caring for children. As to these being innate preferences, I don't think so. All over the world, one fifth of the people are watching "Baywatch." No society is immune from pop culture. So, increasingly, what is regarded as beautiful on a television set in America is regarded as beautiful in Peru and Africa and Korea. What these researchers are really describing is our social world, in which men have money power and women defined by their looks and sexuality. What they deny is that there could be other social worlds, in which different qualities would matter. If the sexes were equal, would women still swoon for Henry Kissinger? Would Susan Sarandon be "too old" for sexy roles? I don't think so!

Helen Fisher, Rutgers University anthropologist, author of "Anatomy of Love" The feminists raise good questions that have scientific answers. But will they listen? I have come to think the human animal is more deeply wired for politics than for truth.

Why do some scientists and laymen continue to fight investigations into our human nature? They seem unable to embrace the simple concept that biology and culture go hand in hand. We are not packets of DNA or social creatures acting in complex networks of friends and relatives. We are both. I hope the 21st century sees an end to the nature-nurture argument. What a waste of ink and paper. We need to move forward and investigate how nature and culture interact.

Jane Mansbridge, Northwestern University political scientist, author of "Why We Lost the E.R.A." Should you worry about having small breasts or a high waist-hip ratio? No. What does this new evidence tell a woman who looks like that? It tells her to look for a thinking mate. That move will improve her life and her children's lives more than the best waist-hip ratio on the planet. Our hunter-gatherer days, when these beauty-oriented aspects of our psyches formed, are over. Humans came to dominate the world by brain, learning to master the natural urgings that were bad for us. In no culture do human beings defecate spontaneously, a natural outcome of our primate heritage. We should ask: is today's focus on female beauty good for us? If not, we should change it.

Marcia Ann Gillespie, editor, Ms. magazine In a world where women bear the brunt of the beauty hype and hundreds of millions of dollars are spent in pursuit of this ideal, reports like this give me the willies because I can't forget the high price we've paid. Women have had ribs removed, their feet bound, their thighs suctioned, their breasts siliconed. Women get lifted and tucked and snipped and tightened, and have their faces totally recast. Girls and women binge and purge and starve themselves until their bodies fail. Beyond reinforcing the hype, what does it matter that scientists can now "prove" that there are universal standards?

Camille Paglia, author, "Sexual Personae" I am delighted by the recent resurgence in evolutionary biology, which is forcing science back onto the feminist agenda, where it has been disgracefully absent. We are half-animal beings, driven by instinctual forces that we can only dimly know. Science is our best hope of understanding the strange alchemy of lust that so disrupts our social lives. Supreme moments in the history of civilization, as in ancient Egypt, classical Athens or Renaissance Florence, were always accompanied by the worship of beauty. Feminism is shot through with puritanical Judeo-Christian assumptions, which exalt the soul over the body and moralistically devalue the physical realm. Today the human hunger for beauty is satisfied by the much maligned fashion magazines, which are glorious art for the masses.

Linda Wells, editor, Allure magazine Readers continually bemoan the absence of real women in magazines, including Allure. They say they want to see themselves. If that means the average American woman, then they'd want their models to be asymmetrical, 5 feet 4 and 143 pounds. OK. But whenever Allure runs pictures of women with asymmetrical features, we get letters of vehement objection. We ran a story in the March issue about obese women, complete with pictures. Readers wrote us in disgust. One said, "How could you waste your time writing about these marginal, abnormal creatures?"

Melvin Konner, Emory University anthropologist, author of "The Tangled Wing" Supporters and critics are mostly talking past each other. This is not junk science, but it is baby-step science; those who pursue it had better use caution. Critics, whose remarks here show little understanding, should study the research before judging it. Social psychologists have known for decades that the more attractive are more likely to be favored by teachers, to be successful at work, even to be acquitted by a jury. The effect is clear to everyone who watches the news and wonders why people have to be so good-looking to explain the budget crisis. The answer: more of us believe them. But bias toward beauty is bias against those who lack it. As with other kinds of prejudice, change can come only after we recognize it for what it is.

Arthur Danto, art critic Evolution could no more leave differential attractiveness to culture than it could metabolism or respiration. Beauty is beauty across all cultural divisions. This leaves the question of why, randomness aside, we are not all symmetrically beautiful, the way robins are uniformly red-breasted, or tigers striped. The answer is that most animals must make do with second best. An asymmetrical male primate who happens to be a good hunter has his choice among well-favored carnivorous females. And among humans, cleverness, power, wealth, wit, fame and family fill the beds of the aesthetically lopsided.

2.14 Study Questions: Eyes of the Beholders

How many different points of view are expressed here? Synthesize the various opinions expressed into as few—or as many—consistent perspectives as you can.

■ 2.15 Exercise: Non-Random Mate Selections

Take a picture of yourself or clip an image from a magazine and test for symmetry as shown in the article. Attach the photograph to this page and report your findings in terms of physical attractiveness.

■ 2.16 Web Sites

Darwin and General Evolution

Charles Darwin Foundation

The Charles Darwin Foundation is dedicated to the conservation of the Galapagos ecosystem. Its operative arm, the Charles Darwin Research Station, conducts and facilitates research in the Galapagos Islands and the Galapagos Marine Reserve.
http://www.darwinfoundation.org/

Talk of Origins

Evolution is a fact and a theory.
http://www.talkorigins.org/faqs/evolution-fact.html

Evolution Revolution

Welcome to the Evolution Revolution, a page designed to educate users on evolution theory.
http://library.thinkquest.org/19926/java/tour/index.htm

Darwin and Evolution Overview

An overview of Victorian science.
http://landow.stg.brown.edu/victorian/darwin/darwinov.html

Biological Evolution

The big ideas here are that living things are related through common ancestry, and that living things have changed since they shared that common ancestry.
http://landow.stg.brown.edu/victorian/darwin/darwinov.html

Human Genome Project Information

An information resource at Oak Ridge National Laboratory.
http://www.ornl.gov/TechResources/Human-Genome/home.html

3 Non-Human Primates

3.1 Introduction to Classifications

We, as humans, are constantly categorizing events into smaller units. We do so to make sense of the world around us. For instance, when looking at a cup of water, do you describe it as half full or half empty? These categories are not rigid, but rather are flexible and can change with the introduction of additional information.

Carolus Linnaeus, a Swedish naturalist, introduced a system of biological classification known as "**systema naturae**." While this was not the first classification system for living matter, it was the first to include *all living organisms,* including humans. This system is based upon natural relationships and it is still in use today.

"Systema naturae," meaning the natural system, assigns each species a unique classification. This system involves binomial nomenclature, in which each animal species is designated two names, the genus and species. Humans are known as *Homo sapiens,* or the "wise man." Please be sure to capitalize the first letter of the genus and the species always begins with a lower case letter. In addition, the entire name is underlined or *italicized.* The biological classification of humans is as follows:

Kingdom:	Animalia
Phylum:	Chordata
Class:	Mammalia
Order:	Primates
Family:	Hominidae
Genus:	*Homo*
Species:	*sapiens*
Scientific Name:	*Homo sapiens*

The diagram above is known as a taxonomic hierarchy, or a ranking system. It is made up of categories, each considered to be sufficiently distinct from others and treated as separate units or **taxa**.

This system starts off very broad; as it continues, the categories narrow based upon natural relationships. Ultimately, we are left with the genus and species for a particular species. This is often referred to as the scientific name.

There are two basic taxonomies used for primates. The first is the more traditional taxonomy; the second is a newer version, based primarily on genetic evidence, and not yet firmly established in the scientific community.

Taxonomy 1:

Order	Suborder	Infraorder	Superfamily	Family	Common Name
Primates	Prosimii				Lemurs, Lorises, Tarsiers
	Anthropoidea	Platyrrhini			New World Monkeys
		Catarrhini	Cercopithecoidea		Old World Monkeys
			Hominoidea	Hylobatidae	Gibbons, Siamangs
				Pongidae	Orangutans, Chimpanzees, Bonobos, Gorillas
				Hominidae	Humans

Taxonomy 2:

Order	Suborder	Infra-order	Super-family	Family	Subfamily	Tribe	Common Name
Primates	Prosimii						Lemurs, Lorises, Tarsiers
	Anthro-poidea	Platyrrhini					New World Monkeys
		Catarrhini	Cerco-pithecoidea				Old World Monkeys
			Hominoidea	Hylobatidae			Gibbons, Siamangs
				Hominidae	Ponginae		Orangutans
					Homininae	Panini	Gorillas, Chimps, Bonobo
						Hominini	Humans

It may be difficult to visualize the similarities between certain species, yet the categories are not constructed by phenotypes, but rather, based upon evolutionary relationships. For instance, in the second taxonomy shown above, the genus *Homo* is represented by one living species. Yet, the genus for chimpanzees includes two closely related species, *Pan troglodytes* (common chimpanzees) and *Pan paniscus* (bonobo.) All three of these species, as well as the gorilla, are classified into the same sub-family, Homininae. Thus, this system of classification indicates the fact that humans and the African great apes may look differently (phenotype) but that evolutionary relationships are based upon shared genetic (genotype) material.

While most of the rules of biological classification are well established, there are still unresolved issues amongst **taxonomists** (researchers that describe, name and classify organisms) relating to the classification of species. In short, the complex nature of the hominid fossil record can lead to various interpretations. While most scientists agree that species are made up of groups of interbreeding natural populations that are reproductively isolated from other groups, the degree to which interbreeding takes place may differ. A horse and a donkey can mate, producing a mule. Yet, the product of the interbreeding results in a sterile offspring. Should the offspring, a result of two distinct organisms, be classified as a unique (but sterile) species?

In short, it may be difficult to determine the degree of interbreeding between unique species. We must then ask ourselves, how does this impact our classification of fossilized remains?

3.2 Study Guide: Key Terms

Define the following terms:

alpha male: (social ranking system)

anthropomorphism:

bipedal:

cladistics:

communication: (verbal and non-verbal)

culture:

dentition:

diurnal:

DNA hybridization:

evolutionary classification:

higher primates:

homiotherm:

K-selection:

locomotion:

lower primates:

mammal:

nature versus nurture debate:

nocturnal:

opposable thumb:

primitive:

r-selection:

sexual dichromatism:

sexual dimorphism:

taxonomy:

tool use:

vertebrae:

zoomorphism:

■ 3.3 Introduction to Cladistics and Evolutionary Classification

As already stated, most biologists accept that the classification of organisms is determined by evolutionary relationships which, in turn, established links between current species and their common ancestors. This is known as **phylogenetic relationships**. The phylogenetic approach to classification is divided into two approaches: cladistics and evolutionary classification.

Cladistics is based upon genealogy, meaning that a genus should include a group of species which all descended from a common ancestor. Organisms are grouped together based upon shared derived characteristics. Derived (sometimes called advanced) physical characteristics have evolved from the more primitive traits demonstrated in ancient ancestors. For example, a derived characteristic of anthropoids is that they have nails on all of their digits. Prosimians demonstrate the more primitive characteristic in that they retain grooming claws. The presence of the grooming claws in prosimians demonstrates a primitive physical characteristic or a trait relating to an ancestral form. Monkeys, apes and humans have nails on all of their digits which exemplifies a shared derived characteristic among anthropoids. Organisms that share derived characteristics are grouped into a **clade** or a group of related organisms. Yet, organisms may evolve through the process of parallel or convergent evolution. This suggests that it is difficult to exclusively illustrate relationships in terms of cladistics.

While **evolutionary classification** is based upon common relationships, it also takes into account different rates of evolution within different lineages. Although the two systems of classification are based upon similar principles, the final result may differ significantly.

■ 3.4 Exercise: Evolutionary Relationships

Review the diagram on the following page. How are relationships being established and depicted in this illustration? List the general physical characteristics associated with each species. Are these traits derived or primitive?

■ 3.5 Diagram: Evolutionary Relationships

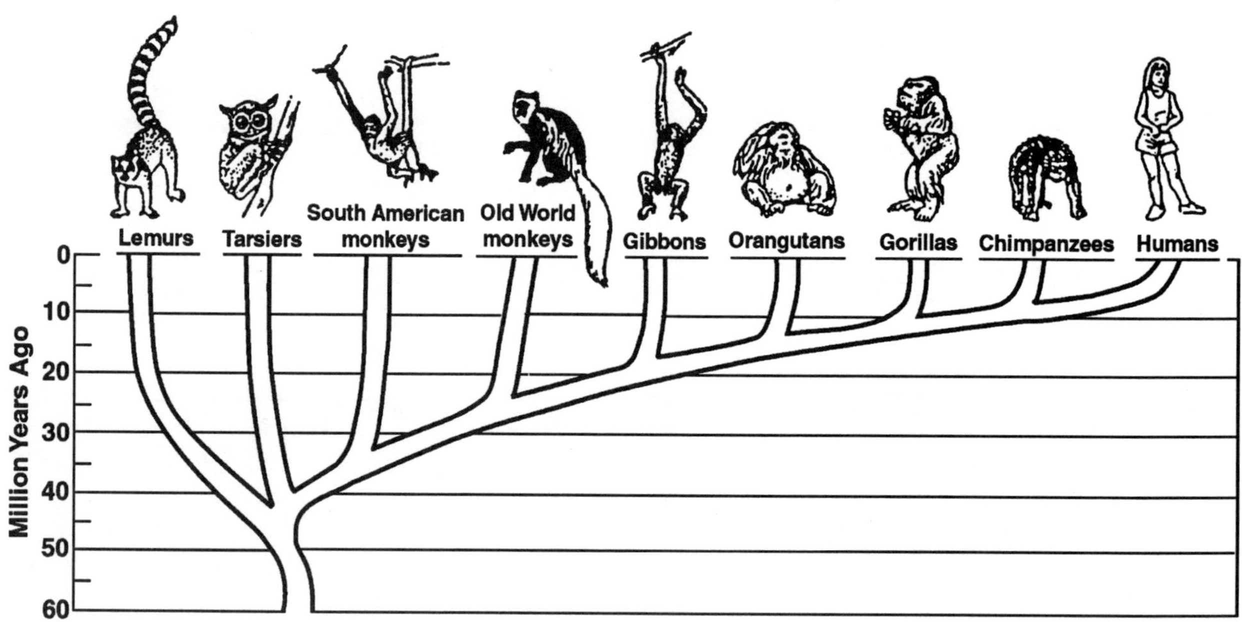

3.6 Study Hints

■ Transition: From Insectivore to Primate

A. Insectivore

TREE SHREWS

Location: Tropical forests of Southeast Asia. (India, Burma, Malay Peninsula, Sumatra, Java, Borneo.)

Evolutionary Position: Insectivore order. Fossil forms are believed to be the ancestral prototype for the primate order.

Appearance: Small, squirrel-sized. With relatively long body and tails and short legs, compared to primates.

Eyes—Large, compared to other insectivores. (Visual area of brain large.) They stand at right angles to each other, with little overlap. A bony ridge protects the eyes.

Ears—Large and mobile.

Nose—Wet; large compared to primates, small for an insectivore. (Olfactory center of the brain is reduced compared to other insectivores.)

Tactile whiskers.

Frenum—A thin membrane connecting the upper lip to jaw, resulting in lack of facial expression.

Dental comb—Lower incisors protrude forward for grooming.

Dental formula—$\frac{2133}{3133}$ (primitive mammalian formula-$\frac{3143}{3143}$)

Jaw—V-shaped.

Digits—Considerable range of movement of "fingers" and "toes," especially those which are equivalent to the big toe and thumb, though these latter are not opposable.

Claws on all digits. (Though an Oligocene tree shrew had nails on all hind digits, with claws on forepaws.)

Habits: Diurnal (active in daylight); high metabolic rate; omnivorous

B. Primates

LEMURS

Location: Madagascar forests.

Appearance: Size of a house cat.

Eyes—Large, stereoscopic vision somewhat advanced.

Ears—Large and mobile.

Nose—Somewhat large; wet; good sense of smell.

Tactile whiskers, frenum, and dental comb present.

Dental formula—$\frac{2133}{2133}$

Jaw—V-shaped

Digits—Claws on 2nd and 3rd fingers and toes, nails on others.

Habits: Some diurnal, some nocturnal; almost all arboreal; some insectivorous, some vegetarian, some omnivorous; most are quadrupedal, some move by "modified quadrupedalism" (leap and cling) with prehensile hands and feet.

TARSIERS

Location: Borneo, Philippines, Celebes Islands.

Appearance: Small, size of a two-week old kitten.

Eyes—Huge, almost fully stereoscopic.

Ears—Large and mobile.

Nose—Small and dry.

Tactile whiskers present. Frenum and dental comb absent.

Jaw—V-shaped.

Dental Formula: $\frac{2133}{1133}$

Digits—Claws on 2nd and 3rd toes.

Tarsal bones—Elongated for the leap and cling locomotion.

Habits: Nocturnal; arboreal; modified quadrupedalism; mainly insectivorous.

Primate Comparative Anatomy

Prosimians

Lemurs and tarsiers

Monkeys (with armoset somewhat exceptional)

Quadrupedal gait—forelimbs and hindlimbs about equal.
Tails (for balancing)
Nails on all digits.
Eyes forward for stereoscopic vision.
Opposable thumb (though thumb is absent in Spider monkey—a brachiator occupying niche of the gibbon—and it is absent in the colobus monkeys, an Old World primate).
Increased brain size over prosimians.
Color vision.

New World Monkeys	*Old World Monkeys*
Wide septum	Narrow septum
Dental formula: $\frac{2.1.3.3}{2.1.3.3}$	Dental formula: $\frac{2.1.2.3}{2.1.2.3}$
	(same as apes & humans)
Prehensile tails among some	Ischial Callosities

(Marmoset: A New World monkey with $\frac{2.1.3.2}{2.1.3.2}$, claws on all digits except thumb and big toe, tactile whiskers, eyes a little to the side and a single sheet of immovable muscle in the face.)

Apes differ from monkeys in generally

1. being *larger* (except the gibbon/siamang group)
2. *not having tails*
3. having relatively *long arms* and *short legs*, having to do with their *brachiating* ability. They are *knuckle-walkers* as a result.

Three patterns among non-human primates:

1. Short arms and long legs—(Vertical Clingers)
2. Arms and legs subequal—(Quadrupeds)
3. Long arms and short legs—(Brachiators)

*Lesser apes include the gibbons and siamangs. Great apes include the orangutan (of Borneo and Sumatra) and the gorilla, chimp, and bonobo (of Africa).

Humans: Represent a fourth pattern—*bipedalism*

Comparative Anatomy: Apes and Humans

Teeth	*Hominidae*	*Pongidae*
1. *Dental Arcade*	Elliptical or parabolic	U-Shaped, with cheek teeth in parallel rows.
2. *Diastema* (a conspicuous gap separating upper canine from the lateral incisor)	Generally absent (We will see exceptions)	Present. Accommodate lower canine in occlusion, when it moves upward.

3. *Canines*	Small, spatulate (spoon-shaped) & bluntly pointed.	Large, conical & sharply pointed.
	Wear down from the tip only.	Wear down on sides as well—partly because the canines interlock in occlusion.
	No pronounced sexual dimorphism (marked difference in the male & female of a species)	Male canines are much longer, sharper & more daggerlike.
4. *Anterior lower premolar*	Bicuspid, non-sectorial (non-cutting) (cusp: a pointed projection formed by converging curves)	Unicuspid, with a cutting edge which shears against upper canine.

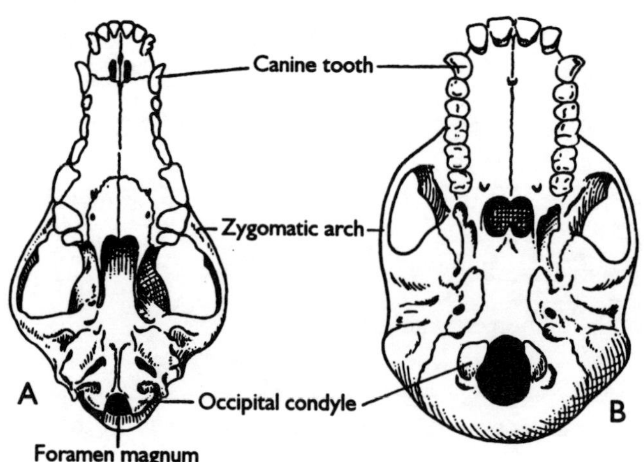

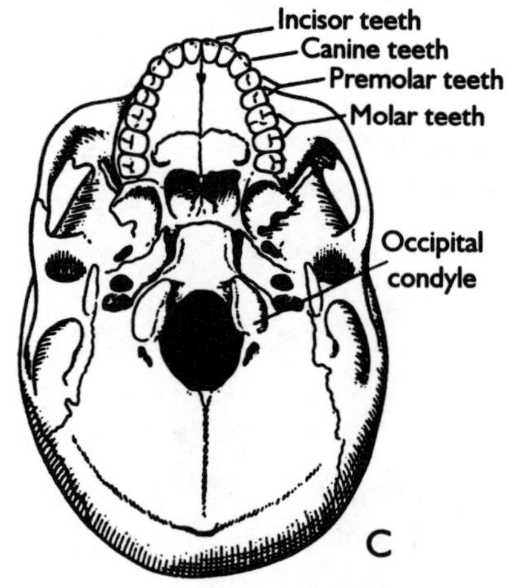

The basal aspect of the skull of a dog (A), chimpanzee (B), and human (C), with the lower jaw removed. The foramen magnum, which is placed at the back end of the skull in the dog, is situated relatively further forward in the chimpanzee, and much more so in humans. Note also that the relative length of the palate diminishes in this series.

W. E. LeGros Clark, *History of the Primates*, 5th ed. University of Chicago Press.

■ Comparative Anatomy: Apes and Humans

This assists anthropologists to identify evolutionary relationships in the fossil record.

The Skull

The differences between apes and humans in relation to the skull have to do with three primate evolutionary trends:

I. The adoption to varying degrees of an **upright position** of the trunk.

Foramen magnum: A large opening through which the spinal column meets the brain.

In four-legged animals, the foramen magnum is at the back of the skull.

In bipedal humans, the foramen magnum is directly underneath.

In apes, it is in an intermediate position, reflecting semi-erectness.

II. A progressive enlargement of the brain.

A. One direct effect is an enlargement of the cranium or *cranial capacity*.

B. A less obvious effect has to do with the fact that the skull serves for the attachment of some powerful muscles.

The *sagittal crest* is a sharp bony ridge at the top of the skull in animals which do a lot of chewing.

The sagittal crest serves for the attachment of the *temporal muscle* at one end. This muscle attaches to the *mandible* (lower jaw) at the other. (In the area of the *ascending ramus*.)

This feature is generally found among the largest of the living great apes, notably male orangutans and gorillas. (Although it will also be seen in some fossil hominids.)

This feature appears in species which possess small crania.

With an expanded brain case in humans, there is sufficient surface area for the attachment of this muscle without the need for a sagittal crest.

Moreover, humans are more likely to be using their hands and tools in food-getting and food-processing. (Trend #3)

C. Increased protection over the eyes reduces the need for a *supraorbital torus* (brow ridge). A reduction in chewing (Trend #3) also reduces the need for this "shock-absorber."

III. Replacement of the grasping functions of the teeth by the forelimb.

This trend not only plays a role in explaining the sagittal crest, but also helps to understand the reduction of the *zygomatic arch*, which serves as surface attachment for the *masseter muscle*, another chewing muscle which operates the jaw.

The less chewing, the smaller the masseter muscle and the more narrow the zygomatic arch.

3.7 Study Sheet: Primates

Define the following terms. Be sure to differentiate between each based upon evolutionary relationships.

prosimian:

anthropoid:

hominoid:

hominid:

3.8 Summary of Evolutionary Trends in Higher and Lower Primates

Physical anthropologists often distinguish between lower primates, those possessing primitive physical characteristics, and higher primates. The following is a list of evolutionary trends associated with higher primates:

1. Increase in brain size in relation to body size
2. Variation in locomotion patterns
3. Retention of five digits on hands and feet
4. Nails on all digits (rather than claws)
5. Opposable thumbs for grasping
6. Generally 32 teeth
7. Loss of dental comb
8. Tactile (touch sensitive) pads on the hands and feet
9. Eyes are fully encased in a ring of bone and are placed close together toward the front of the face allowing for depth perception and binocular vision
10. Many species possess color vision
11. Smaller snouts
12. Loss of rhinarium and tapetum
13. Generally only one infant born at a time. Twins are rare except in the case of New World monkey families (tamarins and marmosets) where twins are the norm.
14. Great variation in habitat and diet
15. An increase in the amount of time spent caring for the dependent offspring (K-selection)
16. Complex social behaviors
17. Cultural components (learned behaviors passed down through the generations)

A list of physical characteristics of lower primates includes:

1. Generally smaller in brain size relative to body size
2. Claws on at least one digit
3. 36 teeth, including a dental comb
4. Longer snouts due to reliance on sense of smell
5. Rhinarium to enhance sense of smell
6. Eyes are not fully encased in bone
7. Tapetum for night vision (nocturnal)
8. The term 'prosimian' means "before apes"

■ 3.9 Diagram: Pelvis and Leg Anatomy

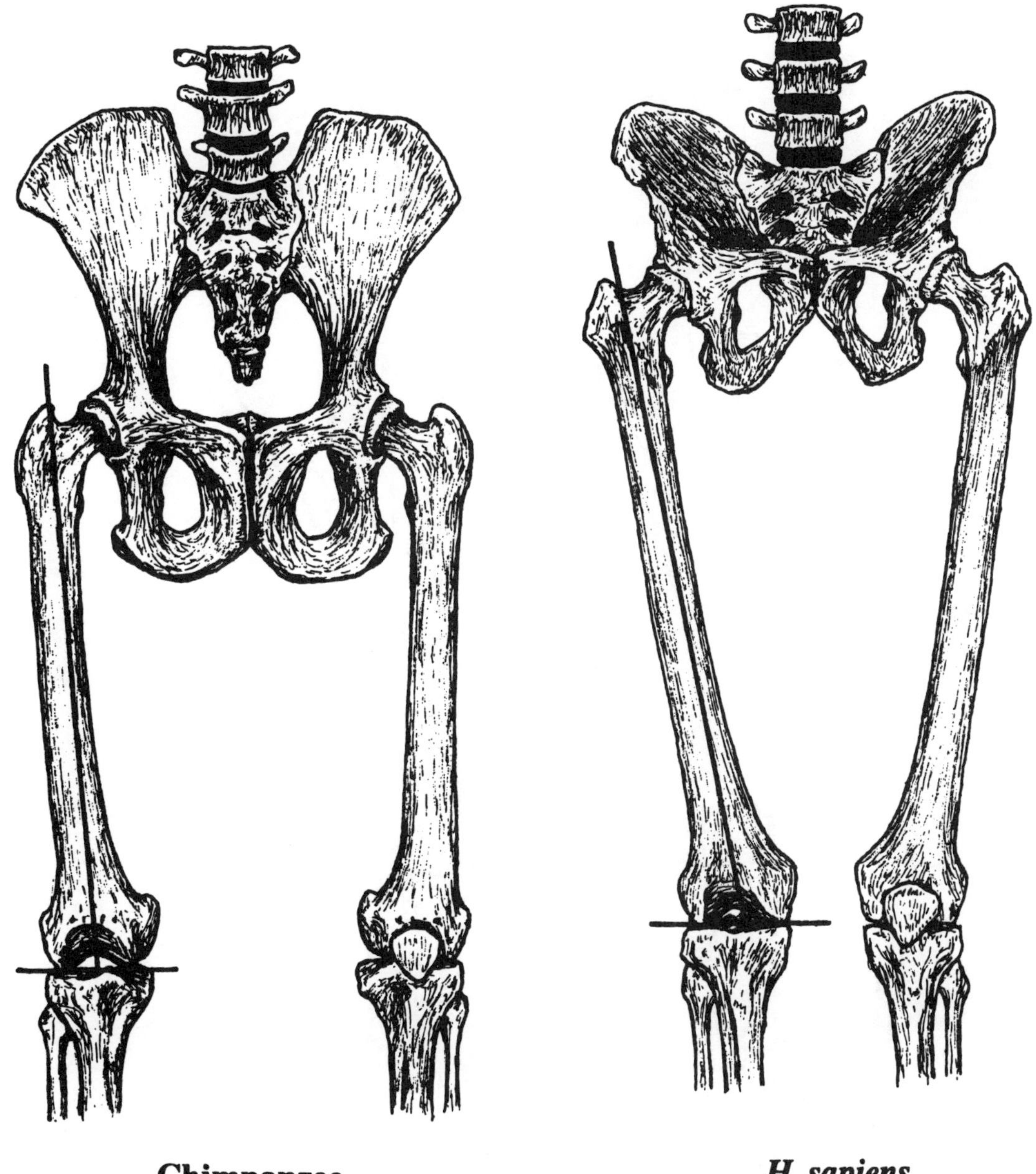

■ 3.10 Diagram: Hands of Living Primates

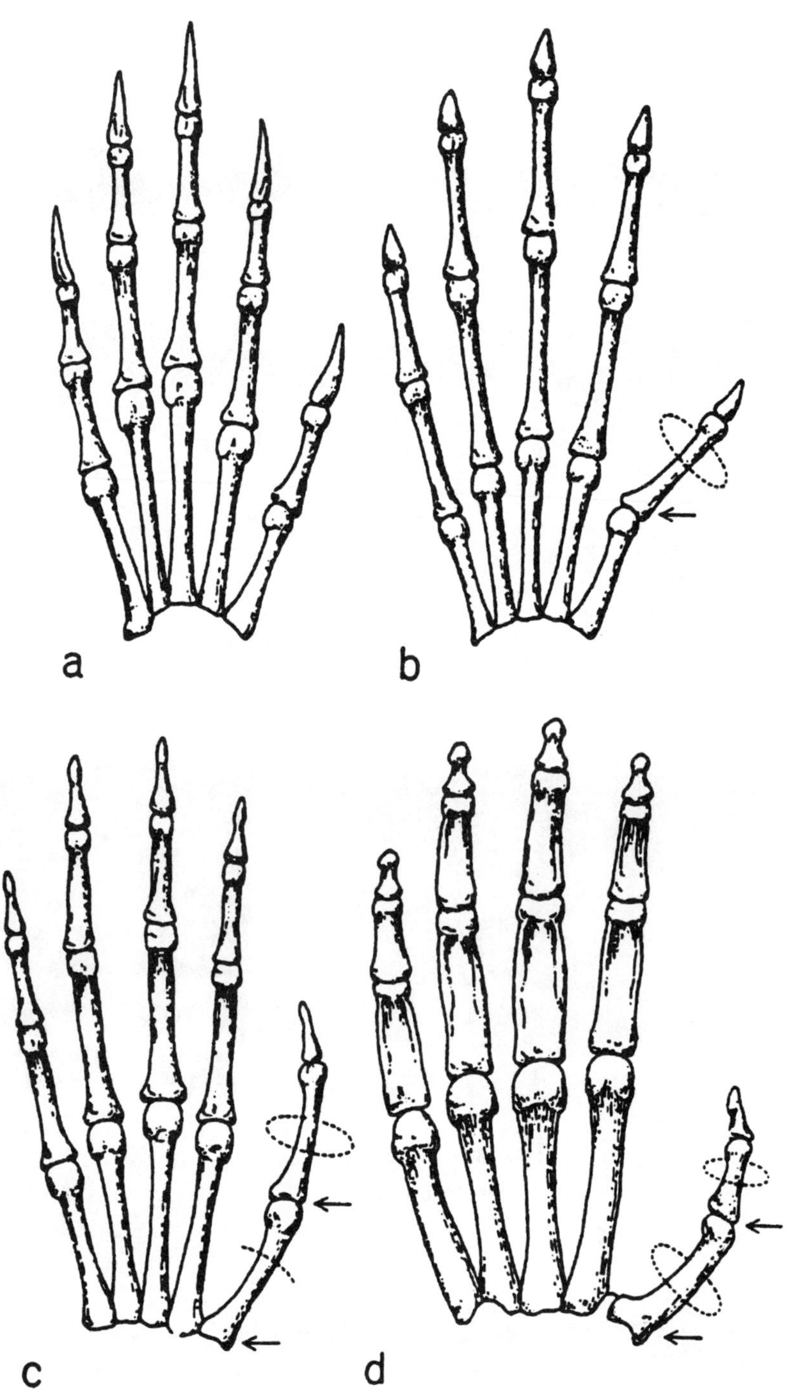

Hands of living primates, all drawn same size, show evolutionary changes in structure related to increasing manual dexterity. Tree shrew (a transitional species that is no longer accepted as a primate species) (a) shows beginnings of unique primate possession, specialized thumb (digit at right). In tarsier (b) thumb is distinct and can rotate around joint between digit and palm. In capuchin monkey (c), a typical New World species, angle between thumb and finger is wider and movement can be initiated at joint at base of palm. Gorilla (d), like other Old World species, has saddle joint at base of palm. This allows full rotation of thumb, which is set at a wide angle. Only palm and hand bones are shown here.

■ 3.11 Introduction to the Study of Animal Behavior

Primatologists study the behavioral patterns of primates both in the wild and in captive settings. It is true that we cannot generally ask the animals how they are feeling or what motivates their behavior, but through detailed observation, we can note long-term interactions between members of a given community. While patterns of behavior cannot always be conclusively drawn from observations alone, this method of data collection is extremely valuable and improves our understanding of primate life ways.

Ethology is the study of animal behavior. This field sheds light on behavioral patterns and improves our understanding of physiological adaptations in non-human primates. Many researchers have investigated the behavioral patterns of primates in the wild and in captivity. Most notably recognized are three women first contracted by Louis Leakey because of their knowledge and enthusiasm to investigate the behaviors of great apes in the wild. Jane Goodall has been studying chimps at Gombe National Reserve for almost 40 years. Birute Galdikas continues her investigation of the orangutan populations in Borneo and Sumatra. Dian Fossey began the research project on the mountain gorillas which still is in existence today despite her untimely death at the hands of poachers.

Currently, there are researchers stationed around the globe observing primate behavior. It is important to understand that most primatologists are studying the lives of either threatened or endangered animals. What has happened to non-human primate populations? What can we do to help? Please be sure to review (and to contact) the list of organizations posted in the back of this workbook for more information.

Why are these data so important to the investigation of physical anthropology?

3.12 Introduction to Sampling Techniques

There are many sampling techniques used to record primate behavior. Possible methods include the following:

Scan sampling is when the researcher records the behavior, generally of a group of animals, at regular time intervals, such as every five minutes. When conducting this strategy with a group of animals, the number of individuals must not be too large and all members of the group should be visible. This technique can be very effective when conducting observations within a captive setting.

Focal animal sampling concentrates on recording behaviors displayed by one animal for a specific period of time. Checklists of animal behaviors are often used in conjunction with this sampling technique.

Ad-lib sampling is when the researcher records certain behaviors which seem important and which are displayed at any given time. While this may appear to be a less scientific approach, it allows the researcher to collect data essential to their area of investigation. It has also led to some fascinating discoveries. For instance, this technique led to the discovery of wild chimps making and using tools! It was once believed that tool use was only a skill possessed by "man the thinker."

Sequence sampling focuses on behaviors rather than animals. Data collection is initiated at the beginning of a sequence of behaviors (such as mating) and stops when the behavioral sequence ends.

Please be aware that it is difficult at best to determine emotional responses and motivations for behaviors based upon observations alone. For instance, when conducting your observations, you may witness a chimpanzee turn up its front lip to another animal, which may appear to us as the act of smiling. Yet, what may be occurring is a display of canines in order to demonstrate a threatening posture.

Long periods of time dedicated to recording observational data (over numerous years) allow us to better interpret what we see; yet in most cases, we cannot ask the animals about their desires and drives. In other words, primatologists may be drawing inferences based upon recurring behavioral patterns.

The following exercises require a visit to the zoo. You will be asked to differentiate the morphology of specific primate species. Next, you will be asked to collect observational data utilizing the scan sampling technique.

■ 3.13 Exercise: Classification, Morphology and Locomotion

Welcome to the zoo! Today you have the opportunity to witness differences in primate morphology, locomotion patterns and social behaviors. Complete the following exercise and compare the physical characteristics of a prosimian to that of a monkey, ape, and human. You may wish to visit the library or to search the internet for additional information on the species chosen for review. When documenting your human, please ask permission first!

	Prosimian	Monkey
Common name:		
Order:		
Family:		
Scientific name: (Genus and Species)		
Countries of origin:		
Social grouping in captivity:		
Social grouping in the wild:		
Prehensile tail:		
Nails or claws on digits:		
Opposable thumb: (joint type)		
Relative length of forelimbs to hind limbs:		
Locomotion pattern(s):		

	Prosimian	Monkey
Indications of sexual dimorphism:		
Indications of sexual dichromatism:		
Dentition:		
Status in the wild: (threatened or endangered)		
Additional observations:		

Exercise: Classification, Morphology and Locomotion

	Ape	Human
Common name:		
Order:		
Family:		
Scientific name: (Genus and Species)		
Countries of origin:		
Social grouping in captivity:		
Social grouping in the wild:		
Prehensile tail:		
Nails or claws on digits:		
Opposable thumb: (joint type)		
Relative length of forelimbs to hind limbs:		
Locomotion pattern(s):		
Indications of sexual dimorphism:		

	Ape	Human
Indications of sexual dichromatism:		
Dentition:		
Status in the wild: (threatened or endangered)		
Additional observations:		

■ 3.14 Exercise: Observation of Non-Human Primates

Choose a primate species in which you are interested in observing. Observe the behaviors of *one* animal (the focal animal) utilizing the scan sampling technique. You will be recording the actions of *one animal and documenting behaviors that are displayed every five minutes*. Total observation time should be a minimum of two hours.

Date:

Beginning time:

Ending time:

Weather conditions:

Special events:

Scientific name: Common name:

Description of focal animal:

Age group: (adult, juvenile, infant)

Sex :

Summary of findings:

■ 3.15 Exercise: Check-List of Primate Behaviors

Raw data collected from focal animal sampling. Each number represents a 5 minute interval of time—for a total of 2 hours of observation time.

	Number of occurrences during time interval																							
	1	2	3	4	5	6	7	8	9	10	11	12	13	14	15	16	17	18	19	20	21	22	23	24
Walking																								
Sitting																								
Standing																								
Eating																								
Scratching																								
Vocalizing																								
Sleeping																								
Grooming/Groomed																								
Displayed																								
Threat/Threatened																								
Chase/Chased																								
Attack/Attacked																								
Inspecting																								
Playing																								
Courtship/Courted																								
Mount/Mounted																								

Construct an **ethogram** which illustrates the behavior of the chosen focal animal in terms of a bar chart or pie chart.

■ 3.16 Exercise: Study Questions

1. Why is the study of primatology so important to our understanding of hominid evolution?

2. Name three derived physical characteristics of humans and identify if these traits are present in a prosimian, monkey, or ape.

3. Do you feel that the African great apes should be classified in the same subfamily as humans and why?

4. What have you learned about evolutionary relationships from your visit to the zoo?

3.17 Web Sites

Primate Anatomy and Behavior

PRIMATE GALLERY

To provide a central source for collecting, digitizing, and distributing primate images.
http://www.selu.com/bio/PrimateGallery/

PRIMATE INFO NET

The Wisconsin Regional Primate Research Center University of Wisconsin-Madison.
http://www.primate.wisc.edu/pin/

ORDER PRIMATES

Primate characteristics from the University of Michigan Museum of Zoology.
http://animaldiversity.ummz.umich.edu/chordata/mammalia/primates.html

AFRICAN PRIMATES AT HOME

See and hear several species of African monkeys and apes.
http://www.indiana.edu/~primate/primates.html

LANGUAGE RESEARCH CENTER

Primate research center studying language acquisition through work with bonobos and chimpanzees.
http://www.gsu.edu/~wwwlrc/

PRIMATE CONSERVATION, INC.

(PCI) is an all volunteer not for profit foundation dedicated to studying, preserving, and maintaining the habitats of the least known and most endangered primates in the world.
http://www.primate.org/

INTERNATIONAL PRIMATE PROTECTION LEAGUE

Working to protect all living primates.
http://www.ippl.org/

4 Fossils and Adaptations

4.1 Introduction to Adaptations

As you already know, there are numerous factors which impact evolution. To begin, the genetic make-up of a species is constantly changing, altering the phenotypes upon which selection acts. Mutation provides new genetic variation by producing new alleles. Gene flow and genetic drift contribute to variation and are continuously supplying new combinations of genetic variables. An additional evolutionary factor is **adaptation,** the process of adjustment to better suit environmental conditions.

The process of evolutionary modification (biologically, developmentally or behaviorally) which results in the enhancement of the survival and reproductive success of an organism is referred to as an adaptation. A species is forever in an adaptive relationship with its environment. Phenotypes are naturally selected for reproductive success as a species adapts to its environment. The following chart illustrates the processes associated with evolution. Take special note of the importance of adaptive relationships.

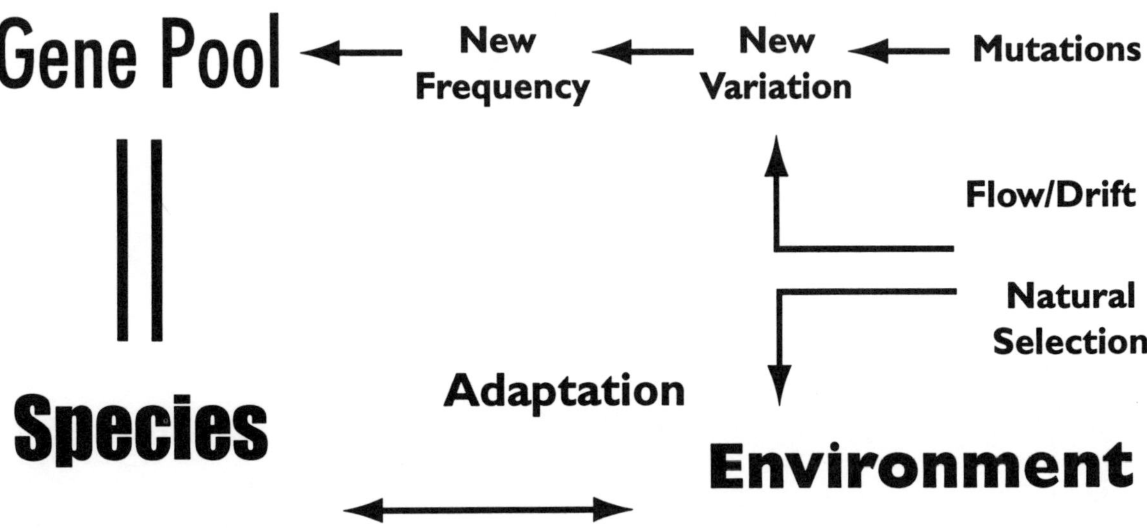

4.2 Study Guide: Key Terms

Define the following terms:

absolute dating techniques:

potassium-argon (K/Ar):

carbon 14 (C-14):

dendrochronology:

argon/argon (Ar/Ar):

fission track dating:

electron spin:

Aegyptopithecus:

analogies:

bioculturalism:

chronometric:

Dryopithecus:

Fayum:

fossil:

half-life:

homologies:

lumpers/splitters:

mosaic evolution:

phylogeny:

Purgatorius:

Piltdown hoax:

Proconsul:

Ramapithecus:

relative dating techniques:

stratigraphy:

faunal analysis: (index markers)

flourine analysis:

nitrogen analysis:

Sivapithecus:

triangulation:

4.3 Introduction to Excavation Techniques

Physical anthropologists rely upon a variety of techniques to effectively uncover fossil evidence. With the odds of locating hominid remains estimated to be approximately 1:10 million, researchers often use both survey and excavation techniques, and hope for a bit of luck.

The Leakey family's discoveries exemplify the importance of **surveying** a site. Each year, research crews are sent to walk across the large expanse of Olduvai Gorge. The goal is to look for clues as to where fossil evidence may be buried or where it is actually being exposed by erosion. Changes in soil color, dirt mounds, or erosion (from rains) cue researchers to a particular location. Surveying may also be accomplished on horseback or in the air, from a plane, satellite or space craft.

Surveying is non-invasive. There is no destruction to the physical environment since the researchers are only looking for clues upon the surface of the earth.

The practice of **excavation** involves breaking ground and digging deep within the strata of the earth. This technique is complemented by the use of scientific methodologies for data collection. Test pits are often utilized to determine the depth and placement of the fossil in space. Large scale excavation often necessitates a large crew, as well as experts from a variety of scientific disciplines. To date, this strategy has been shown to maximize the amount of data collected as well as enhance our ability to interpret such data.

■ 4.4 Exercise: Excavation Techniques

Practice your hand at excavation techniques. Log on to the following site and complete the corresponding exercises:

http://www.mc.maricopa.edu/academic/cult_sci/anthro/Archy/index.html

Attach your results below.

4.5 Chemistry in Action

How Can We Tell that a Mummy is 3,000 Years Old?

We often hear that artifacts found in archeological excavations are estimated to be so many thousands of years old. How can scholars determine the age of an object? If someone tried to sell you a manuscript that supposedly dates back to 1000 B.C., how could you be certain of its authenticity? Is a mummy found buried beneath an Egyptian pyramid *really* three thousand years old (Figure 1)? The answers to these questions can usually be obtained by applying chemical kinetics, using the *radiocarbon dating technique.*

The earth's atmosphere is constantly bombarded by cosmic rays. These rays are radiation of extremely high penetrating power that originate in outer space and consist of electrons, neutrons, and atomic nuclei. One of the important reactions between the atmosphere and cosmic rays is the capture of neutrons by atmospheric nitrogen to produce carbon and hydrogen.

$$^{14}_{7}N + ^{1}_{0}n \rightarrow ^{14}_{6}C + ^{1}_{1}H$$

The unstable carbon atoms are eventually converted into $^{14}CO_2$, which mixes with the ordinary carbon dioxide ($^{12}CO_2$) in the air. The carbon-14 isotope is radioactive and decays according to the equation

$$^{14}_{6}C \rightarrow ^{14}_{7}N + ^{0}_{-1}e$$

The rate of decay (measured by the number of electrons produced per second) obeys first-order kinetics, that is

$$\text{rate} = kN$$

where k is the first-order rate constant and N the number of ^{14}C nuclei present. If we measure the rate of radioactive decay at a given time ($t = 0$) and then at time interval t later, we have

$$k = \frac{2.303}{t} \log \frac{(\text{rate of decay at } t = 0)}{(\text{rate of decay at } t = t)}$$

$$= \frac{2.303}{t} \log \frac{N_0}{N_t}$$

where N_0 and N_t are the number of carbon-14 nuclei present at $t = 0$ and $t = t$. Knowing the first-order rate constant k (1.21×10^{-4}/year), we can calculate the half-life of the reaction as follows:

Figure 1. An Egyptian mummy. The age of mummies is usually determined by the carbon-dating technique.

$$t_{1/2} = \frac{0.693}{1.21 \times 10\text{-}/\text{yr}} = 5730 \text{ yr}$$

This means that given any amount of ^{14}C isotope, one-half of it will disappear by decay over a period of 5730 years.

The carbon-14 isotopes enter all living organisms via plant photosynthesis, as well as through air and water that are taken in. Plants are eaten by animals, who exhale carbon-14 as CO_2. Eventually, these isotopes participate in many aspects of the carbon cycle. The carbon lost by decay is constantly replenished by the production of new isotopes in the atmosphere, and a dynamic equilibrium is established, whereby the ratio of $^{14}C/^{12}C$ remains a constant in living matter. When a plant or an animal dies, the carbon-14 isotope is no longer replenished, so that the ratio decreases as ^{14}C decays. We find this happening when carbon atoms are trapped in coal, petroleum, or wood preserved underground and, of course, in Egyptian mummies. After a number of years, a given number of carbon atoms would be less radioactive than the same number from fresh plants or animals.

In 1955, Willard F. Libby[†] suggested that this fact can be used to estimate the length of time the carbon-14 isotope of a particular specimen has been decaying without replenishment. The equation

$$t = \frac{2.303}{k} \log \frac{\text{decay rate of fresh sample}}{\text{decay rate of old sample}}$$

gives us *t*, or the age of the sample. This ingenious technique is based on a remarkably simple idea; its success depends on how accurately we can measure the rate of decay. In fresh samples, the ratio of $^{14}C/^{12}C$ is about $1/10^{12}$, and very sensitive equipment is needed to monitor the radioactive decay. The situation is even more difficult for older samples because there are even fewer carbon-14 nuclei present. Care must be taken to discriminate between radiation from the sample and that produced by sources outside of the sample, called *background radiation*. Despite the experimental difficulties, radiocarbon dating has become an extremely valuable tool for estimating the age of archeological objects, paintings, and other objects ranging in age from 1000 to 50,000 years.

† Willard Frank Libby (1908–1980). American chemist. Libby received the Nobel prize in chemistry in 1960 for his work on radiocarbon dating.

■ 4.6 Exercises: Mosaic Evolution

Mosaic evolution states that major evolutionary changes tend to take place in stages, not all at once. Hominid evolution displays a mosaic pattern in that bipedal locomotion, small canine teeth and large brains did not evolve all at once. Answer the following questions pertaining to hominid evolution. Discuss the various hypotheses attempting to answer the following questions. Based upon your current knowledge of the subject, which hypothesis makes the most sense to you and why?

1. Why did our hominid ancestors change from quadrupedal locomotion to bipedal locomotion? What do you think may have attributed to that change? Do you think it was primarily an anatomical, cultural or environmental adaptation? Why?

2. What is the difference between a "family tree" and an "evolutionary bush?" Why is this distinction important?

3. Think about the evolution of the human brain. Are humans "smarter" than other primates? Does a bigger brain equate with higher intelligence? Why?

■ 4.7 Diagram: Time-Line

Era	Time in Millions of Years	Period	Beginning of Period (million of years ago)	Biological Features
Cenozoic		Holocene	0.01	Hominid use of technology, agriculture, and industry
	0	Pleistocene	1.8	Migration of *Homo* lineage
		Pliocene	5	The genus *Homo* evolved toward end of period
		Miocene	22	First hominoids, radiation of early apes
	50	Oligocene	38	First anthropoids
		Eocene	55	Physical characteristics of evolutionarily advanced primates
		Paleocene	65	Early prosimians at beginning of period
Mesozoic	100	Cretaceous	146	First placental mammals
	150, 200	Jurassic	208	First flowering plants First mammals and birds
		Triassic	245	
Paleozoic	250	Permian	290	
	300, 350	Carboniferous	363	First coniferous trees First reptiles and insects
	400	Devonian	409	First amphibians and land plants First bony fish
		Silurian	439	First fish with jaws
	450, 500	Ordovician	510	First vertebrates; armored fish without jaws
	550	Cambrian	570	Invertebrate fossils, molluscs, crustaceans, Echinodermata
Proterozoic	600, 4600	Precambrian		First fossilized animals and plants; protozoa, sponges, corals and algae First fossil bacteria

■ 4.8 Exercises: Labeling Epochs

Describe the major events associated with each epoch within the Cenozoic Era. Include major geological changes, shifts in climate and the approximate time period associated with each.

Paleocene:

Eocene:

Oligocene:

Miocene:

Pliocene:

Pleistocene:

Holocene:

■ 4.9 Diagram: Skeleton of an Old World Monkey

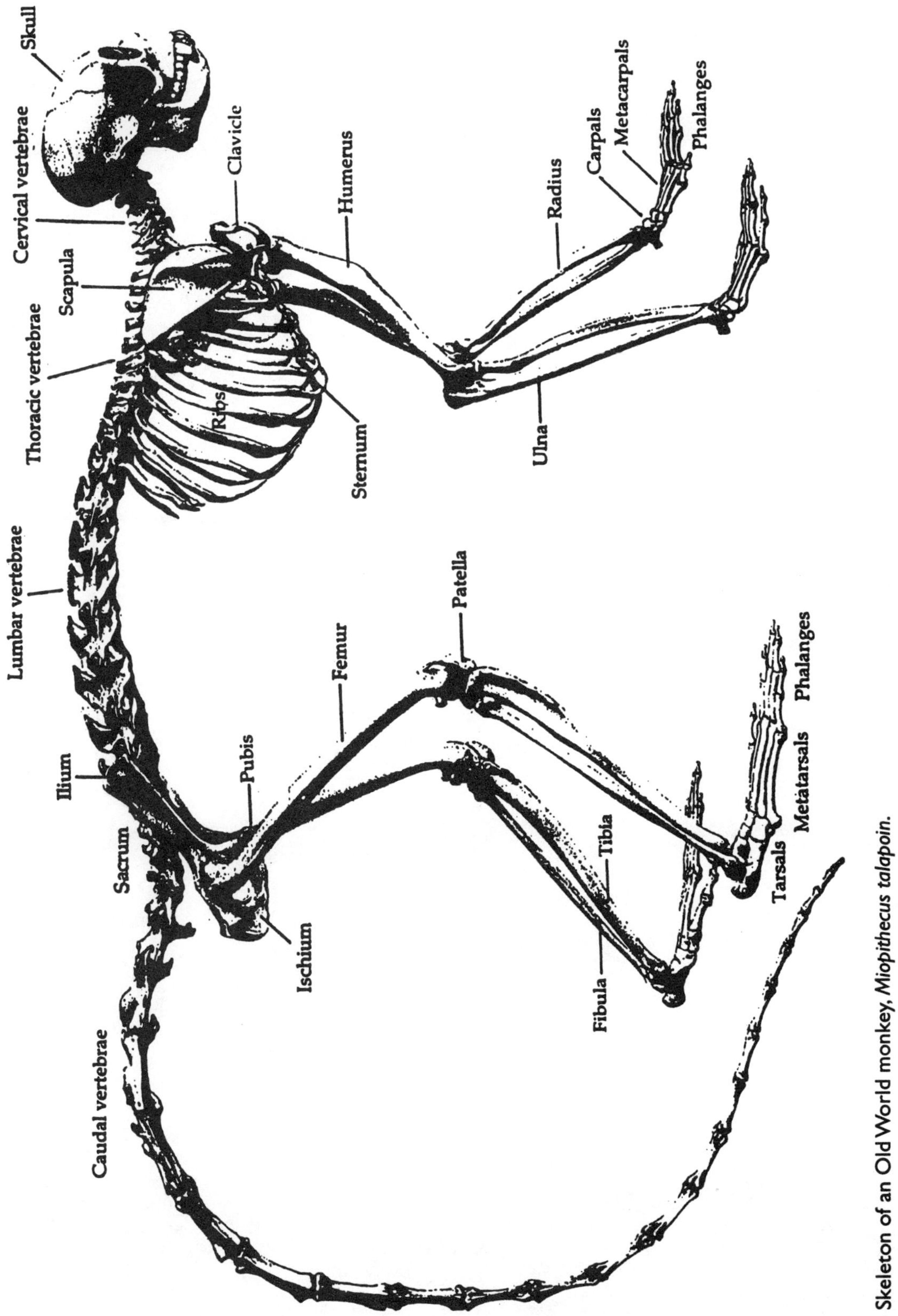

Skeleton of an Old World monkey, *Miopithecus talapoin*.

■ 4.10 Exercise: Labeling the Anatomy of Modern Humans

The following diagram represents a modern human skeleton from a frontal view. Label each of the designated body parts.

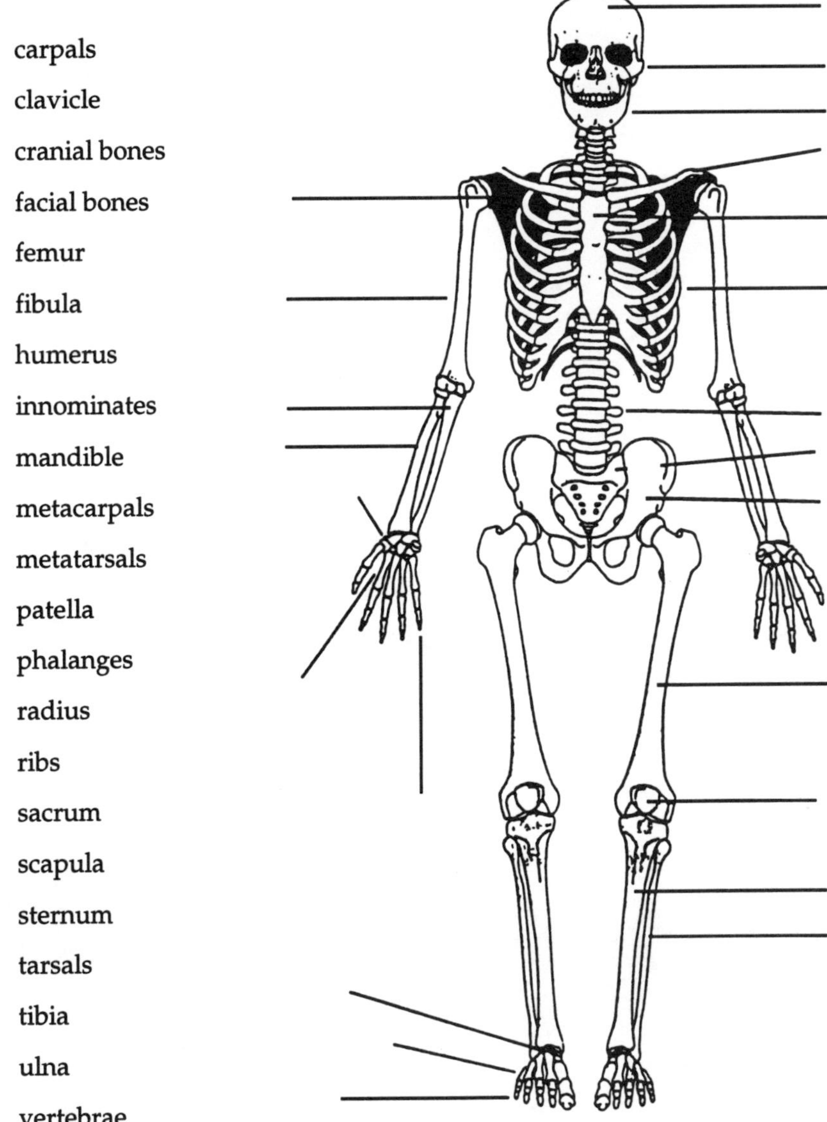

4.11 Introduction to Emotions as Evolutionary Strategies for Survival

Research has confirmed a hypothesis stated by Darwin in his book *The Expression of Emotions in Man and Animals* (1872) that humans possess innate, genetically 'hardwired' templates for emotional expression and recognition. These emotions, refined in humans but nevertheless (according to Darwin) existing in all primate species, seem to trigger off responses that impact bodily functions. In short, our brains seem to be programmed to size up the emotional importance of external stimuli.

Researchers, such as Paul Ekman, Robert Levenson and Wallace Friesen, have demonstrated how a particular emotional expression, such as a grimace of disgust, can produce changes in the automatic nervous system, including change in heart rate and rising skin temperature. Similar responses were also triggered when a respondent was asked to relive the memory of a particular emotional experience.

4.12 Study Guide: Evolution of Emotions

In trying to understand why a specific emotion evolved, consider the following:

1. Most emotions make us feel either "good" or "bad."
2. We generally experience emotions under particular experiences.
3. Most emotions either lead us to behave in a particular, predictable way or inspire (influence) others to respond in a particular and predictable way.
4. If an emotion makes us feel positively, we will oftentimes behave in ways that will produce that same emotion.
5. If an emotion makes us feel badly, we will generally behave in ways that will reduce or stop that feeling.
6. Ultimately, the six basic emotions that have evolved in all humans can be explained as resulting in behaviors that will:

   a) lead to increased chances of survival (natural selection)

   b) lead to increased chances of sex (sexual selection)

   In turn, this leads to increased **reproductive success** or what Darwin refers to as 'fitness.'
7. Other concepts that can help to explain the evolution of a particular emotion include:

   a) **Inclusive fitness**: this means that the emotion may not lead to your own personal reproductive success, but it may contribute to the survival of your genes in people who are genetically related to you. For example, a grandmother caring for and assuring the survival of her child's offspring, who share 50% of the same genetic material.

   b) **Stimulus generalization**: we have a tendency to generalize from one stimulus to another. For example, it is adaptive to find babies "cute." It keeps us from harming them (infanticide.) Yet, we can transfer this feeling to other living beings. We can also find puppies cute. This is because we have generalized the stimulus of small bodies, large eyes, and a small face to any creature displaying similar features.
8. There are six basic emotions. It has been stated that these emotions have existed throughout hominid evolution. Therefore, these basic emotions exist in all human cultures across the globe. These emotions are: **fear, anger, sadness, disgust, happiness** and **surprise**. Current researchers also include an additional emotion, **embarrassment**.

   A variety of studies have been conducted in order to test whether emotions are truly cross-cultural responses. Data conclude, as Darwin indicated, that the six basic emotions are felt and understood in all human cultures.

   Darwin stated that emotions are an adaptive strategy that exists in all primate species.

Reprinted with permission from Geri-Ann Galanti, Ph.D.

4.13 *Face It!*

Deborah Blum

How we make and read the fleeting split-second expressions that slip across our countenances thousands of times each day is crucial to our emotional health as individuals and to our survival as a species.

Who hasn't waited for an old friend at an airport and scanned faces impatiently as passengers come hurrying through the gate? You can recognize instantly the travelers with no one to meet them, their gaze unfocused, their expressions carefully neutral; the people expecting to be met, their eyes narrowed, their lips poised on the edge of a smile; the children returning home to their parents, their small laughing faces turned up in greeting. Finally, your own friend appears, face lighting up as you come into view. If a mirror suddenly dropped down before you, there'd be that same goofy smile on your face, the same look of uncomplicated pleasure.

Poets may celebrate its mystery and artists its beauty, but they miss the essential truth of the human countenance. As scientists now are discovering, the power of the face resides in the fleeting split-second expressions that slip across it thousands of times each day. They guide our lives, governing the way we relate to each other as individuals and the way we connect together as a society. Indeed, scientists assert, the ability to make faces—and read them—is vital both to our personal health and to our survival as a species.

Growing out of resurging interest in the emotions, psychologists have been poring over the human visage with the intensity of cryptographers scrutinizing a hidden code. In fact, the pursuits are strikingly similar. The face is the most extraordinary communicator, capable of accurately signaling emotion in a bare blink of a second, capable of concealing emotion equally well. "In a sense, the face is equipped to lie the most and leak the most, and thus can be a very confusing source of information," observes Paul Ekman, Ph.D., professor of psychology at the University of California in San Francisco and a pioneer in studying the human countenance.

"The face is both ultimate truth and fata morgana," declares Daniel McNeill, author of the new book *The Face* (Little Brown & Company), a vivid survey of face-related lore from the history of the nose to the merits of plastic surgery. "It is a magnificent surface, and in the last 20 years, we've learned more about it than in the previous 20 millennia."

Today, scientists are starting to comprehend the face's contradiction, to decipher the importance of both the lie and leak, and to puzzle out a basic mystery. Why would an intensely social species like ours, reliant on communication, be apparently designed to give mixed messages? By connecting expression to brain activity with extraordinary precision, researchers are now literally going beyond "skin deep" in understanding how the face connects us, when it pulls us apart. "The face is a probe, a way of helping us see what's behind people's interactions," explains psychology professor Dacher Keltner, Ph.D., of the University of California-Berkeley. Among the new findings:

- With just 44 muscles, nerves, and blood vessels threaded through a scaffolding of bone and cartilage, all layered over by supple skin, the face can twist and pull into 5,000 expressions, all the way from an outright grin to the faintest sneer.
- There's a distinct anatomical difference between real and feigned expressions—and in the biological effect they produce in the creators of those expressions.
- We send and read signals with lightning-like speed and over great distances. A browflash—the lift of the eyebrow common when greeting a friend—lasts only a sixth of a second. We can tell in a blink of a second if

a stranger's face is registering surprise or pleasure—even if he or she is 150 feet away.

- Smiles are such an important part of communication that we see them far more clearly than any other expression. We can pick up a smile at 300 feet—the length of a football field.
- Facial expressions are largely universal, products of biological imperatives. We are programmed to make and read faces. "The abilities to express and recognize emotion are inborn, genetic, evolutionary," declares George Rotter, Ph.D., professor of psychology at Montclair University in New Jersey.
- Culture, parenting, and experience can temper our ability to display and interpret emotions. Abused children may be prone to trouble because they cannot correctly gauge the meaning and intent of others' facial expressions.

Making Faces

Deciphering facial expressions first entails understanding how they are created. Since the 1980s, Ekman and Wallace Friesen, Ph.D., of the University of California in San Francisco, have been painstakingly inventorying the muscle movements that pull our features into frowns, smiles, and glares. Under their Facial Action Coding System (FACS), a wink is Action Unit 46, involving a twitch of a single muscle, the *obicularis oculi*, which wraps around the eye. Wrinkle your nose (Action Unit 09), that's a production of two muscles, the *levator labii superioris* and the *alaeque nasi*.

The smile, the most recognizable signal in the world, is a much more complex endeavor. Ekman and colleagues have so far identified 19 versions, each engaging slightly different combinations of muscles. Consider two: the beam shared by lovers reunited after a long absence and the smile given by a teller passing back the deposit slip to a bank patron.

The old phrase "smiling eyes" is exactly on target. When we are genuinely happy, as in the two lovers' reunion, we produce what Ekman and Richard Davidson of the University of Wisconsin-Madison call a "felt" smile. The *zygomatic major* muscles, which run from cheekbone to the corner of the mouth, pull the lips upward, while the *obicularis oculi* crinkle the outer corner of the eyes. In contrast, the polite smile offered by the bank teller (or by someone hearing a traveling salesman joke for the hundredth time) pulls up the lips but, literally, doesn't reach the eyes.

It doesn't reach the brain either. Felt smiles, it seems, trigger a sort of pleasurable little hum, a scientifically measurable activity in their creators' left frontal cortex, the region of the brain where happiness is registered. Agreeable smiles simply don't produce that buzz.

Are we taught to smile and behave nicely in social situations? Well, certainly someone instructs us to say, "Have a nice day." But we seem to be born with the ability to offer both felt and social smiles. According to studies by Davidson and Nathan Fox of the University of Maryland, ten-month-old infants will curve their lips in response to the coo of friendly strangers, but they produce happy, felt smiles only at the approach of their mother. The babies' brains light with a smile, it appears, only for those they love.

Evolution's Imperative

Why are we keyed in so early to making faces? Charles Darwin argued in his 1872 book, *The Expression of the Emotions in Man and Animals*, that the ability to signal feelings, needs, and desires is critical to human survival and thus evolutionarily based. What if infants could not screw up their faces to communicate distress or hunger? Or if foes couldn't bare their teeth in angry snarls as a warning and threat? And what if we couldn't grasp the meaning of those signals in an instant but had to wait minutes for them to be decoded?

"Everything known about early hominid life suggests that it was a highly social existence," observes Ekman, who has edited a just-published new edition of Darwin's classic work. "We had to deal with prey and predators; we had a very long period of child rearing. All of that would mean that survival would depend on our being able to respond quickly to each other's emotional states."

Today, the need is just as great. As Ekman points out, "Imagine the trouble we'd be in, if when an aunt came to visit, she had to be taught what a newborn baby's expression meant—let alone if she was going to be a caretaker." Or if, in our world of non-stop far-flung travel, an expression of intense pain was understood in one society but not in another. "And yet," says Ekman, "we can move people from one culture to another and they just know."

Researchers have identified six basic or universal expressions that appear to be hardwired in our brains, both to make and to read: anger, fear, sadness, disgust, surprise, and happiness. Show photos of an infuriated New Yorker to a high-mountain Tibetan or of a miserable New Guinea tribeswoman to a Japanese worker, and there's no translation problem. Everyone makes the same face—and everyone gets the message.

One of the expressions that hasn't made the universal list but probably should is embarrassment. It reflects one of our least favorite emotions: who doesn't loathe that red-faced feeling of looking like a fool? Yet such displays are far less self-centered than has been assumed. Rather than marking a personal humiliation, contends Keltner, embarrassment seems designed to prompt social conciliation.

Think about it. If we accidentally spill a drink on a colleague, stumble into a stranger in the hall, what's the best way to defuse the tension and avoid an escalation into battle? Often, notes Keltner, even before offering a verbal apology, we appease the injured party by showing embarrassment.

When we're embarrassed, our hands tend to come up, partly covering the face. We rub the side of the nose. We cast our eyes downward. We also try to appear smaller, to shrink into ourselves. These behaviors aren't uniquely ours. In awkward social situations, chimpanzees and monkeys do the same thing—and accomplish the same end. The actions defuse hostility, offer a tacit apology, even elicit sympathy in viewers. (When Keltner first tentatively introduced his chosen topic at research meetings, even jaded scientists let out immediate empathetic "oohs" at the slides of people with red faces).

"There are physiological changes associated with this," notes Keltner. "If people see an angry face staring at them, they have a heightened autonomic response—rising stress hormones, speeding pulse—all the signs of fear. When they see an embarrassment response, fear is reduced."

A reddened face and downward glance typically start a rapid de-escalation of hostility among children involved in playground quarrels, says Keltner. Parents go easier on youngsters who show visible embarrassment after breaking a household rule, such as playing handball on the living room wall or chasing the dog up and downstairs throughout the house. Adults also go easier on adults. In one of Keltner's studies, jurors in a hypothetical trial meted out much lighter sentences when convicted drug dealers displayed the classic signs of embarrassment.

■ Cultural Rules

Expressions aren't dictated by biology alone, however; they are deeply influenced by cultural attitudes. De Paul University psychologist Linda Camras, Ph.D., has been exploring why European-American adults seem so much more willing than Asians to express emotion in public. In one experiment, she studied the reactions of European-American and Asian infants, age 11 months, to being restrained by having one arm lightly grasped by a researcher.

European-American and Japanese babies were remarkably similar in their visible dislike of being held still by a stranger's grip. (The scientists let go if the babies cried for seven seconds straight.) Since infants show no apparent inborn difference in the willingness to publicly express dismay, it stands to reason that they must eventually learn the "appropriate" way to express themselves from their families and the society in which they are reared.

Ekman's work clearly shows how culture teaches us to subdue our instinctive emotional reactions. In one set of studies, he asked American and Japanese college students to watch nature films of streams tumbling down mountainsides and trees rustling in the wind, and also graphic tapes of gory surgeries, including limb amputations. Everyone grimaced at the spurting blood at first. But when a note-taking scientist clad in a white coat—the ultimate authority figure—sat in on watching the films, the Japanese students' behavior altered radically. Instead of showing revulsion, they greeted the bloody films with smiles.

"No wonder that foreigners who visit or live among the Japanese think that their expressions are different from Americans," says Ekman. "They see the results of the cultural display rules, masking and modifying the underlying universal expressions of emotion."

■ Blank Looks

Mental or physical illness, too, can interfere with the ability to make faces—with profound consequences for relationships, researchers are learning. Neurophysiologist Jonathan Cole, of Poole Hospital at the University of Southampton, Great Britain, and author of the new book *About Face* (MIT Press), points out that people with Parkinson's disease are often perceived as boring or dull because their faces are rigid and immobile.

Consider also depression. As everyone knows, it shuts down communication. But that doesn't mean only that depressed people withdraw and talk less. The normal expressiveness of the face shuts down as well.

In one experiment, psychologist Jeffrey Cohn, Ph.D., of the University of Pittsburgh had healthy mothers mimic a depressed face while holding their infants. The women were told not to smile. Their babies responded with almost instant dismay. At first they tried desperately to recruit a response from their mother, smiling more, gurgling, reaching out. "The fact that the babies were trying to elicit their mother's response shows that at an early age, we do have the beginnings of a social skill for resolving interpersonal failures," Cohn notes.

But equally important, the infants simply could not continue to interact without receiving a response. They stopped their efforts. The experiment lasted only three minutes, but by that time, the babies were themselves withdrawn. "When mothers again resumed normal behavior, babies remained distant and distressed for up to a minute," says Cohn. "You can see that maternal depression, were it chronic, could have developmental consequences."

In fact, children of depressed parents tend to become very detached in their relationships with others. They often fail to connect with other people throughout their life and experience difficulties in romantic relationships and marriage, in large part, researchers suspect, because they have trouble producing and picking up on emotional signals. "We think that the lack of facial animation interferes with forming relationships," says Keltner.

■ Reading Faces

Displays of emotion are only half the equation, of course. How viewers interpret those signals is equally important. "We evolved a system to communicate and a capacity to interpret," observes Keltner. "But much less is known about the interpreting capacity."

What scientists do know for certain is that we are surprisingly bad at discerning the real emotions or intentions behind others' facial expressions. "One of the problems that people don't realize is how complicated face reading is," notes Pollak. "At first glance, it seems very straightforward. But if you break it down—think of all the information in the face, how quickly the brain has to comprehend and analyze it; memories come in, emotions, context, judgments—then you realize that we really can't do it all."

Or can't do it all well. What we seem to have done during our evolution is to learn shortcuts to face reading. In other words, we make snap judgments. "It's not actually a conscious decision," Pollak

Face Shape

Since ancient times, human beings have been making judgments about each other based not just on the expressions that cross the face but on its very structure. The practice of finding meaning in anatomy is enjoying a remarkable renaissance today.

A plethora of pop books ponder the significance of chins, eye slant, and eyebrows. One popular magazine has even started a new face-reading feature. First to be analyzed: President William Jefferson Clinton. His triangular face apparently indicates a dynamic and—big surprise—sexual personality. Among the theories now being trotted out: heavy eyelids denote jealousy, a rosebud mouth promises fidelity, and a hairy brow line ensures restlessness.

Scientists dismiss these readings as no more than facial astrology. "There is as yet no good data to support this practice," observes Lesley Zebrowitz, professor of psychology at Brandeis University.

While many may regard it as a sort of harmless parlor game, face reading does have a more pernicious effect. Charles Darwin noted that he was almost barred from voyaging on the H.M.S. Beagle because the captain thought his nose suggested a lazy nature. In the 1920s, Los Angeles judge Edward Jones insisted that he could, with over 90% accuracy, determine someone was a "born criminal" by his protruding lips and too-close-together eyes.

Though today no one would make such a blatant assessment of character based on anatomy, facial shape at least subconsciously does appear to figure into our judgments. In her book, *Reading Faces*, Zebrowitz meticulously documents her research showing that baby-faced adults, with big eyes and full cheeks and lips, bring out in the rest of us a nurturing protective response, the kind we give to children.

In one remarkable study, she tracked proceedings in Boston small claims court for more than 500 cases and found that, whatever the evidence, chubby-cheeked plaintiffs were more apt to prevail than claimants with more mature-looking faces. Says Zebrowitz: "Although our judicial system talks about 'blind justice,' it's impossible to control the extra-legal factor of stereotyping based on physical appearance." —*D.B.*

explains. "But decisions are being made in the brain—What am I going to pay attention to? What am I going to clue into?"

Most of us are pretty good at the strong signals—sobbing, a big grin—but we stumble on the subtleties. Some people are better than others. There's some evidence that women are more adept than men at picking up the weaker signals, especially in women's faces.

In an experiment conducted by University of Pennsylvania neuroscientists Ruben and Raquel Gur, men and women were shown photos of faces. Both genders did well at reading men's expressions. Men also were good at picking up happiness in female faces; they got it right about 90% of the time. But when it came to recognizing distress signals in women's faces, their accuracy fell to 70%.

"A woman's face had to be really sad for men to see it," says Ruben Gur. The explanation may lie in early human history. Charged with protecting their tribes, men had to be able to quickly read threats from other males, suggests Gur. Women, in contrast, entrusted with child-rearing, became more finely-tuned to interpreting emotions.

We may be biologically primed to grasp certain expressions, but our individual experiences and abilities also filter the meaning. Mental disorders, apparently, can swamp the biology of facial recognition. People with schizophrenia, for instance, are notoriously bad at face reading; when asked to look at photographs, they struggle to separate a happy face from a neutral one.

■ Mistaking Cues

Seth Pollak, Ph.D., a psychologist at the University of Wisconsin-Madison, has been exploring how children who have suffered extreme parental abuse—broken bones, burn scarring—read faces. In his studies, he asks these youngsters and those from normal homes to look at three photographs of faces which display classic expressions of fear, anger, and happiness. Meanwhile, electrodes attached to their heads measure their brain activity.

Battered children seem to sustain a damaging one-two punch, Pollak is finding. Overall, they have a subdued level of electrical activity in the brain. (So, in fact, do people suffering from schizophrenia or alcoholism. It seems to be a sign of trouble within.) However, when abused youngsters look at the photo of an angry face, they rapidly generate a rising wave of electrical energy, sharper and stronger than anything measured in children who live in less threatening homes.

When Pollak further analyzed the brain activity readings, he found that abused children generate that panicky reaction even when there's no reason to, misreading as angry some of the other pictured faces. They are so primed to see anger, so poised for it, that when making split-second judgments, they tilt toward detection of rage.

This falls in line with findings from DePaul's Camras and other psychologists, which show that abused children struggle significantly more in deciphering expression. "Overall, there's a relationship between the expressive behavior of the mother and the child's recognition ability," Camras says. "And it's an interesting kind of a difference."

Identifying negative expressions seems to be essential in human interaction; four of the six universal expressions are negative. In most homes, notes Camras, mothers use "mild negative expressions, little frowns, tightening of the mouth." Children from such families are very good at detecting early signs of anger. But youngsters from homes with raging furious moms have trouble recognizing anger. "If the mom gets really angry, it's so frightening, it's so disorganizing for children that it seems they can't learn anything from it."

■ The Best Defense

So, out of sheer self-protection, if the children from abusive homes are uncertain about what a face says—as they often are—they'll fall back on anger as the meaning and prepare to defend themselves. "They overdetect rage," says Pollak. Does this create problems in their relationships outside the home? It's a logical, if as yet unproven, conclusion.

"What Darwin tells us is that emotions are adaptations," Pollak explains. "If a child is physically abused, I'd put my money on an adaptation toward assuming hostile intent. Look at the cost for these kids of missing a threat. So what happens is, they do better in the short run—they're very acute at detecting anger and threat because unfortunately they have to be. But take them out of those maltreating families and put them with other people and their reactions don't fit."

One of Pollak's long-term goals is to find out if such harmful effects can be reversed, if abused children can regain or reconstruct the social skills—that is, reading faces—that are evidently so critical to our design.

The Face of the Future

Just five-and-a-half weeks after conception, the human face begins to form. Three nodes emerge on the surface of the fetus; the middle one grows outward to create the countenance. We grow muscle and nerves and eventually, unlike our more "primitive" cold-blooded cousins, we develop soft, supple skin, and thick hair, which helps protect our warm-blooded bodies from chilly temperatures. Because we chew our food instead of swallowing it whole like lowlier creatures, our mouths are more than crude openings; they are sensitive malleable structures.

Early mammals, covered in hair, had smell and touch as their dominant senses. But over eons, vision became vital. Eyes migrated frontally, the better to see prey; long and dense facial hair eroded, leaving muscles free to work other parts of the face. Finally, the face could see and be seen by the world—and react to it. Today, thanks to evolution, we have faces capable of exquisite expressions of emotion.

But evolution continues. The faces we enjoy today may not be the ones our descendants bear, say scientists. What will the face of the future look like? Probably more youthful, predict researchers, because it is more sexually desirable. Attracting a mate is a driving imperative in nature, after all. Moving in the direction of looking younger, our teeth are gradually getting smaller and our heads balder.

According to some scientists, even more radical changes are in store, albeit millions of years down the evolutionary road. As the amount of sensory information assaulting the body increases, our eyes and ears may increase in size to handle all the input. As our verbal abilities and needs become more complex, our palates, larynxes, and tongues will grow larger. Our noses will shrink, however, as scent becomes even less important (we already have a very weak sense of smell compared with other animals). Nose hair, once used to warm incoming air, will become entirely superfluous, thanks to controlled temperatures.

New scientific research and technology will likely add to the changes in our visage. The dawning of genetic engineering takes our faces at least partly out of evolution's control and puts it in our own hands. In the future, we may be able to pick our features from a pattern book and anti-aging drugs may keep us wrinkle-free. Explorations through the cosmos will affect our faces as well. As studies with astronauts show, zero gravity initially erases wrinkles by redistributing blood and fluid in the head. With time, however, this face-lift becomes a downfall: eyes soon become bloodshot and skin becomes puffy. In just a few days, the distended face loses the ability to produce distinct expressions. Such setbacks are manageable. "Body suction machines," or aluminum barrels pulling fluid back down in the body, will allow space travelers to save face.

One of the most intriguing questions that confronts us is how the proliferation of communications technologies that diminish face-to-face interaction will alter the human countenance. Fax machines, e-mail, phones—all increase the ease and frequency of communication, yet decrease the need to actually see and read partners' faces. Part of the wonder of the evolved face has been its nuanced response to the countenances around it. What will become of our features—our faces—if they can't react to those of others? —*Camille Chatterjee*

Failure to read signals accurately may also figure in juvenile delinquency. "There are studies that have found that juvenile delinquents who are prone to aggression have trouble deciphering certain expressions," says Keltner. "They're not as good as other kids at it. Is that because they're particularly bad at reading appeasement signals like embarrassment? That's something we'd really like to know."

■ Truth or Lies?

One area where *everyone* seems to have trouble in reading faces is in detecting deception. We average between 45 and 65% accuracy in picking up lies—pretty dismal when one considers that chance is 50%. Secret Service agents can notch that up a bit to about 64%; scientists suspect that improvement comes only after years of scanning crowds, looking for the faces of potential assassins.

Con artists, too, seem to be especially adept at reading expressions. The latter are also skilled at faking emotions, a trait they share with actors. Not surprising, since success in both careers depends on fooling people.

We seem to be duped particularly easily by a smile. In fact, we tend to implicitly trust a smiling face, just as we do a baby-faced one. In one experiment, Rotter cut out yearbook photos of college students and then asked people to rate the individuals pictured for trustworthiness. In almost every instance, people chose the students with smiling faces as the most honest. Women with the biggest grins scored the best; men needed only a slight curve of the lips to be considered truthful. "Smiles are an enormous controller of how people perceive you," says Rotter. "It's an extremely powerful communicator, much more so than the eyes."

Incidentally, we aren't suckered only by human faces. We can be equally and easily tricked by our fellow primates. In one classic story, a young lowland gorilla gently approached a keeper, stared affectionately into his face, gave him a hug—and stole his watch. Chimpanzees, too, are famous for their friendly-faced success in luring lab workers to approach, and then triumphantly spraying them with a mouthful of water.

There *are* clues to insincerity. We tend to hold a simulated expression longer than a real one. If we look carefully, a phony smile may have the slightly fixed expression that a child's face gets when setting a smile for a photograph. As we've discussed, we also use different muscles for felt and fake expressions. And we are apt to blink more when we're lying. But not always—and that's the problem. When Canadian researchers Susan Hyde, Kenneth Craig, and Chrisopher Patrick asked people to simulate an expression of pain, they found that the fakers used the same facial muscles—lowering their brows, tightening their lips—as did those in genuine pain. In fact, the only way to detect the fakers was that the expressions were slightly exaggerated and "blinking occurred less often, perhaps because of the cognitive demands to act as if they were in pain," the scientists explain.

We do a better job of finding a falsehood by listening to the tone of a voice or examining the stance of a body than by reading the face, maintains Ekman, who has served as a consultant for police departments, intelligence agencies, and antiterrorist groups. He's even been approached by a national television network—"I can't tell you which one"—eager to train its reporters to better recognize when sources are lying.

Which brings us to perhaps the most provocative mystery of the face: why are we so willing to trust in what the face tells us, to put our faith in a steady gaze, a smiling look? With so much apparently at stake in reading facial cues correctly, why are we so prone to mistakes?

■ Living Smoothly

"Most of us don't pick up lies and, actually, most of us don't care to," declares Ekman. "Part of the way politeness works is that we expect people to mislead us sometimes—say, on a bad hair day. What we care about is that the person goes through the proper role."

Modern existence, it seems, is predicated to some extent on ignoring the true meaning of faces: our lives run more smoothly if we don't know whether people really find our jokes funny. It runs more smoothly if we don't know when people are lying to us. And perhaps it runs more smoothly if men can't read women's expressions of distress.

Darwin himself told of sitting across from an elderly woman on a railway carriage and observing that her mouth was pulled down at the corners. A proper British Victorian, he assumed that no one would display grief while traveling on public transportation. He began musing on what else might cause her frown.

While he sat there, analyzing, the woman's eyes suddenly overflowed with tears. Then she blinked them away, and there was nothing but the quiet distance between two passengers. Darwin never knew what she was thinking. Hers was a private grief, not to be shared with a stranger.

There's a lesson in that still, for all of us airport face-watchers today. That we may always see only part of the story, that what the face keeps secret may be as valuable as what it shares.

4.13 Study Questions: Face It! — Deborah Blum

1. Be familiar with the new findings regarding the human face.

2. Why was the ability to signal feelings, needs, and desires critical to early hominid survival? Why is the need just as great today?

3. What are six basic or universal expressions?

4. What seems to be the purpose of "embarrassment?" What physiological change is associated with it? What different lines of evidence show a rapid de-escalation of hostility when there is embarrassment?

5. Does culture teach us to subdue our emotional reactions? Explain.

6. What evidence is there that the expression of depression or a lack of facial expression altogether interferes with forming relationships?

7. With regard to our ability to interpret facial expressions, what have scientists found?

8. What evidence is there that abused children struggle significantly more in deciphering facial expression?

9. How good are we at detecting deception? Who tends to be better at it and why?

10. Be aware of how easy it is to be duped by a smile.

11. What are the clues to insincerity?

12. In what ways do we do a better job in detecting a falsehood than by reading the face?

13. Why are we so prone to mistakes in reading facial cues?

4.14 Exercises: Study Questions

Keep a written record (2 weeks minimum) of your emotions and accompanying physiological reactions to feelings resulting from external stimuli. Include your reactions to such interactions as important phone conversations with friends, disagreements with parents and the pleasure of a perfect meal with fond company. Next, choose one particular incident from the journal for analysis. Describe a possible evolutionary justification for your response. Can you define the reaction in terms of genetic responses, learned responses to external factors, or a combination of the two? What may be an evolutionary justification for that particular emotional expression?

How would you construct a study to test whether this emotion is apparent in all human cultures?

5 Hominid Evolution

5.1 Introduction to Hominid Evolution

An understanding of evolution from the perspective of the ancient past is a complicated undertaking at all levels of study. At every paleontological site, there is information to be learned about the past, especially concerning the environment in which hominids and their predecessors lived. Survival techniques and general lifestyle can be discovered by the use of a complex array of disciplines (e.g., geology, paleontology, and archaeology) which all help to reconstruct a paleoecological context for hominid evolution. Much of the mystery of past populations is due in part to the fact that the fossilized and nonfossilized remains that are recovered by paleontologists and other scientists represent only a very small portion of the once living populations from which they are taken. Consequently, many of the discussions by anthropologists often center around the larger issue of what exactly it is that these fossils represent. That is, can we safely say that individual fossils are representative of past populations, and, if so, how? The study of natural processes—**taphonomy**—associated with the preservation or destruction of past life forms helps us to provide answers to this question by examining in greater detail the process of fossilization and events that take place following the death of hominids and other organisms.

References: Shipman, 1981; Behrensmeyer, 1984; Behrensmeyer and Hill, 1980; Weigelt, 1989.

Bone Chemistry and Fossilization

It is usually only the hard tissues—bones and teeth—that remain for anthropologists to study. The hardness of bones and teeth is due to the presence of inorganic minerals. In bone, in particular, the inorganic component accounts for about two-thirds the weight. This includes roughly 85% calcium phosphate and 10% calcium carbonate. The remaining one-third is the organic component, mostly formed by the protein collagen. Fossil bones and teeth are usually harder than more recent bones and teeth. For the most part, this hardness arises from the chemical replacement of the organic and inorganic components of bone by elements in the surrounding matrix in which the remains rest. In general, the older the fossil, the less of the original constituents remain present. The rate of replacement of the original hard tissues is dependent upon local conditions, including water content, minerals in the soil matrix, and a host of other factors. In some instances, very old bones and teeth show relatively little replacement, whereas materials of recent age are known to be well on the way to being fossilized.

References: McLean and Urist, 1968; Goldberg, 1982; Wolpoff, 1998.

The Skeleton

The skeleton is divided into two major groups of bones. The *axial* group consists of bones that form the body cavities and act to protect vital organs. They include the skull (cranium and mandible), hyoid (small bone in the neck region), vertebral column, ribs, and sternum. The *appendicular* group includes the limbs—

the bones of the shoulder (clavicle and scapula), arm (humerus, radius, and ulna), wrist and hand, pelvis (innominates), leg (femur, patella, fibula, tibia), ankle, and foot. In total, there are 206 bones in the human skeleton.

The human dentition is comprised of two age-successive generations of teeth, the earlier deciduous (or milk) dentition (20 teeth: 8 incisors, 4 canines, and 8 molars) and a later permanent (or adult) dentition (32 teeth: 8 incisors, 4 canines, 8 premolars, and 12 molars). Unlike the skeletal tissues, once the teeth are formed they do not change in morphology except by disease (e.g., decay) or wear. Teeth are perhaps the most studied of the hard tissues that are preserved in the fossil record. Given their compact size and durability, they have survived much better in the fossil record than bones, thereby providing a greater amount of information about phylogenetic relationships, evolutionary history, and dietary adaptations.

The original skeletal tissues from which fossils originate are from a system that in life serve a number of important functions, including protection of the soft and vital organs of the body (e.g., brain, heart, lungs, liver, kidneys); attachment areas for muscles, ligaments, and tendons; production of red blood cells; and storage of important salts and minerals for later use by the body. The skeleton also acts as a superstructure for the support of other tissues. Mechanically, bones are comprised of materials and are shaped so as not to deform appreciably under great pressure. Animals—including humans—engage themselves in a variety of physical behaviors that influence the degree and kind of mechanical loads to which they are subjected. By studying the materials and structure of bones, paleoanthropologists are able to reconstruct some of these behaviors in humans and our hominid ancestors, such as those associated with the acquisition and processing of food, locomotion, general level of activity and pattern of activity, and related behaviors.

References: McLean and Urist, 1968; Goldberg, 1982; Frankel and Nordin, 1980; Currey, 1984; Hildebrand, Bramble, Liem, and Wake, 1985; Shipman, Walker, and Bichell, 1985; Cartmill, Hylander, and Shafland, 1987; Steele and Bramblett, 1988; Fleagle, 1988; White, 1991; Bass, 1995; Schwartz, 1995; Hillson, 1996; Larsen, 1997.

5.2 Exercise: Hominid Phylogeny

The term **phylogeny** refers to the depiction of evolutionary relationships based upon common ancestry. The following represents a recent depiction of the hominid phylogeny. It is important to understand that not all paleoanthropologists agree with this depiction.

Be sure to note dates and tools corresponding with each species.

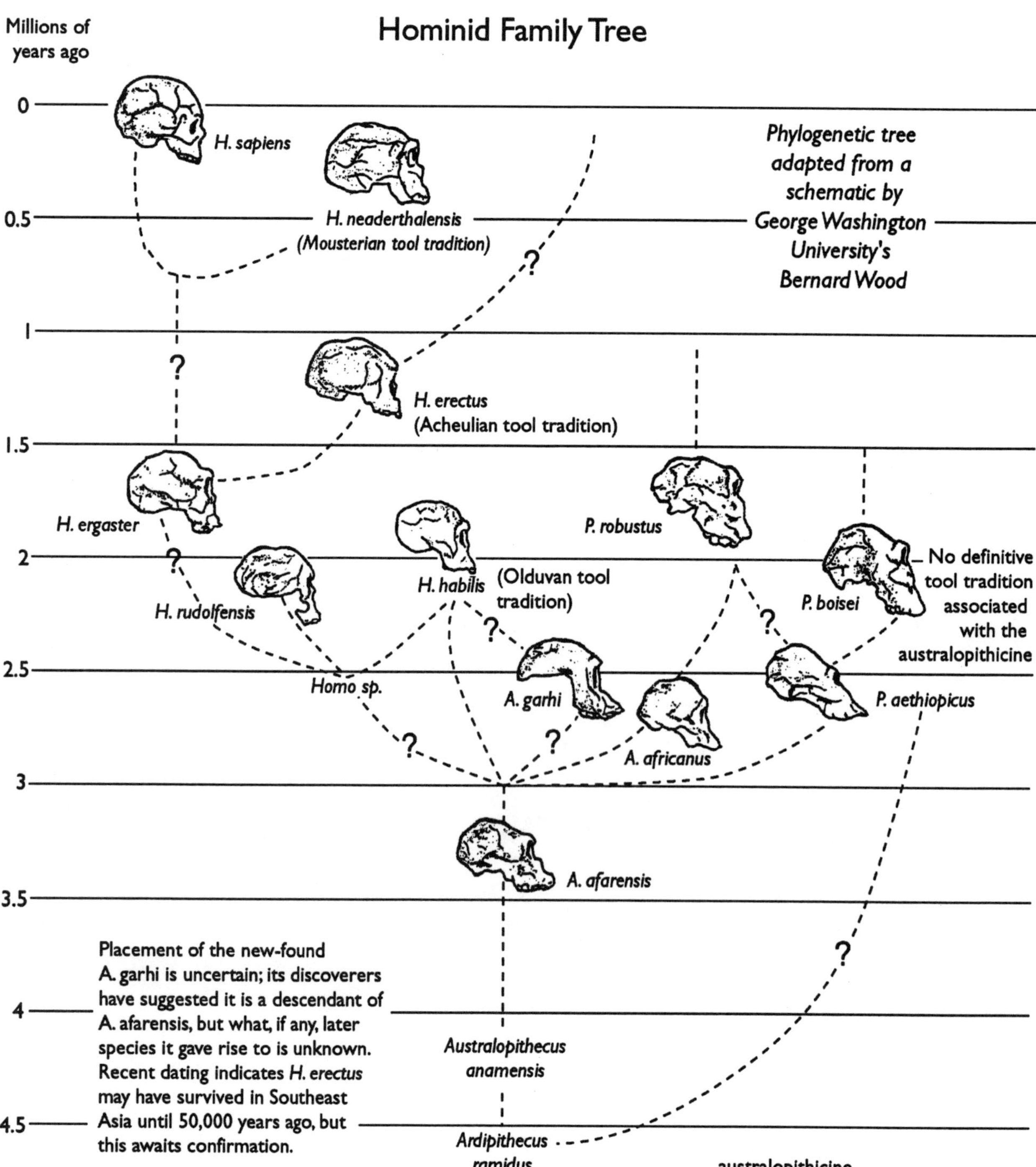
Millions of years ago
Hominid Family Tree
0
0.5
1
1.5
2
2.5
3
3.5
4
4.5
H. sapiens
H. neaderthalensis
(Mousterian tool tradition)
Phylogenetic tree adapted from a schematic by George Washington University's Bernard Wood
?
H. erectus
(Acheulian tool tradition)
H. ergaster
P. robustus
H. habilis
(Olduvan tool tradition)
H. rudolfensis
P. boisei
No definitive tool tradition associated with the australopithicine
Homo sp.
A. garhi
A. africanus
P. aethiopicus
A. afarensis
Placement of the new-found A. garhi is uncertain; its discoverers have suggested it is a descendant of A. afarensis, but what, if any, later species it gave rise to is unknown. Recent dating indicates H. erectus may have survived in Southeast Asia until 50,000 years ago, but this awaits confirmation.
Australopithecus anamensis
Ardipithecus ramidus
australopithicine

■ 5.2 Exercise: Hominid Phylogeny

How would this diagram differ depending upon the perspective of a lumper or a splitter?

5.3 *Rethinking Human Evolution*

Ian Tattersall

Fossil discoveries are readily proclaimed the "earliest this," and the "ancestral that," and credited with revolutionizing our knowledge all by themselves.

Fifty years ago the human fossil record was fairly sparse, and the dating of known specimens was limited to "older than/younger than" statements with a strong dose of uncertainty. The hominid status of the australopithecines (small-brained early bipeds) was already largely established, and it was known that *Homo erectus*, in the guise of Java Man and Peking Man, lay somehow intermediate between these early forms and the later Neandertals, a group already abundantly known from late Ice Age sites in Europe and western Asia. But the picture was still complicated by the specter of the Piltdown "fossil," an allegedly ancient, large-brained hominid whose fraudulence was proved only in 1953. There was also a plethora of species and genus names, applied liberally and capriciously to hominid fossils from around the Old World, that hampered attempts to make sense of the known record.

Little wonder that in this confusion paleoanthropologists welcomed Dobzhansky and Mayr's simplifying messages. Dobzhansky announced his view that only one kind of hominid could have existed at any time and that virtually all developments in human evolution since Java Man had taken place within the single, albeit variable, species *Homo sapiens*. Mayr touted the notion that at most three successive species could be discerned within the genus *Homo*: *H. transvaalensis* (the australopithecines), *H. erectus*, and *H. sapiens* (including the Neandertals). While few paleoanthropologists followed these pronouncements in all their details, schemas of hominid evolution routinely came to incorporate the synthesis' basic assumptions, whereby evolutionary change consisted simply of the gradual modification of lineages, usually no more than one, over long spans of time. Human evolution thus became the story of a long, single-minded struggle from primitiveness to perfection.

Fifty years later, our perspective on human evolution has changed beyond recognition. For one thing, we have made remarkable progress in our understanding of the evolutionary process, and in ways of analyzing the fossil record. And for another, the hominid fossil record itself has expanded wonderfully, as has the archaeological record that accompanies it.

Let's start with the theoretical perspectives. In the early 1970s paleoanthropologists began to recognize that, for all its strengths, the synthesis represented at best an incomplete account of the evolutionary process. The notion of gradual change implied that there would be few endpoints in the fossil record; instead, the vast majority of fossils—all that were not about to become extinct—were simply transitional to new forms. Yet, in practice, the fossil record was at least as famous for its lack of such intermediates as for its possession of them. Ever since Darwin, paleontologists had blamed this lack on the record's incompleteness. But now some started asking whether the notorious gaps in the fossil record might not be deficiencies after all, but might instead be telling us something. They began to recognize that any complete explanation of the evolutionary process needs to account for the origins of new species as well as for the accumulation of novelties within existing ones.

The practical consequences of this realization were profound. Previously the pursuit of paleoanthropology had been regarded essentially as a matter of discovery. Find enough fossils—enough links in the chain—and the course of evolution would somehow be revealed. But the alternative notion, that species have births through speciation (the budding off of a new one from an old one), histories of variable length, and deaths by extinction implied instead that the reconstruction of evolutionary histories required analysis. Once you accepted species as historical entities, instead of ephemera that would evolve themselves out of existence, you had to work out the relationships among them.

New branch of systematics, known as cladistics, suggested how to go about doing this. Fossils have a number of attributes. You know where they are found; thanks to new dating techniques, you know (you hope) how old they are; and you know what they look like (their morphology). All of these considerations once entered simultaneously—and confusingly—into assessments of the human fossil record. But of all of these attributes, it is only morphology that corresponds directly to evolutionary relationship; even then, it does so in a complex way. Morphological similarities among species can be of two kinds: primitive, i.e. inherited from a remote common ancestor (in which case they tell you nothing about proximate relationships), or derived, i.e. inherited from the immediate common ancestor. Only derived characteristics are useful in determining relationships between species. Paleoanthropologists have embraced the terminology of cladistics more enthusiastically than its spirit, but the search for derived characteristics has revivified the science, and at last it is fairly widely accepted that the human fossil record consists of many species whose number demands elucidation and whose relationships require analysis.

It is no longer universally taken for granted that paleoanthropology is the search for links in a chain. Nonetheless, this notion lingers quite tenaciously in some quarters, notably the media, which greet each new find with a hoopla rarely bestowed on theoretical advances. Fossil discoveries are readily proclaimed—the "earliest this," the "ancestral that"—and credited with revolutionizing our knowledge all by themselves. Rarely are such finds presented as what they really are: welcome new components in a large and complex system of related forms that requires analysis to be understood. Little wonder that new fossils often burst onto the scene with much hype and publicity, only to be forgotten when the next sensation comes along.

Still, there's no denying that the fossil record lies at the heart of paleoanthropology. A major reason why scholars have begun to realize how diverse the human fossil record is, is, quite simply, the amplification of the record itself. Over the past 50 years the sheer number of human fossils known and the variety of species these fossils represent have expanded enormously. It is impossible to enumerate these discoveries in a short article, but some demand mention. Louis and Mary Leakey's finds at Olduvai Gorge in the 1960s radically changed our perspective on early *Homo*, as did those by their son Richard in Kenya's Turkana Basin in the 1970s and 1980s. These discoveries showed that the picture of early *Homo* was much more complex than previously imagined. At about the same time as the latter, the discovery of "Lucy" and other fossils in Ethiopia's Afar region by Donald Johanson's group vastly enhanced our knowledge of the earliest australopithecines, knowledge very recently augmented by Meave Leakey's discoveries of 4.1-million-year-old bipeds in northern Kenya. More recently, there has been a steady trickle of discoveries in Java and China, while finds in Europe, the Levant, and Africa have transformed our perspectives on the emergence of modern humans 100,000 to 200,000 years ago.

What all of these discoveries have made clear is that, far from having been a single-minded linear struggle, a matter of constantly perfecting adaptation, the history of the hominid family has been one of repeated evolutionary trial and error: of new hominid species spawned, competing, and becoming extinct. We take it for granted that *Homo sapiens* is the lone hominid on Earth, but this is probably unusual. In the past, coexistence and competition among hominid species have quite likely been much more typical. This realization is salutary, for whereas our egotistical species likes to think of itself as the pinnacle of evolution, any accurate view of ourselves requires recognizing *Homo sapiens* as merely one more twig on a great branching bush of evolutionary experimentation.

Ian Tattersall, the author of numerous books including the recently released *Becoming Human*, is a curator of anthropology at the American Museum of Natural History.

5.4 *A New Human Ancestor?*

Elizabeth Culotta

Ethiopian fossils reveal a new branch on the hominid family tree: a small-brained hominid that is a candidate for the ancestor of our lineage.

About two and half million years ago, on a grassy plain bordering a shallow lake in what is now eastern Ethiopia, a humanlike creature began dismembering an antelope carcass. Nothing remains of the hominid, but the antelope bones show that it wrenched a leg off the carcass, then used a stone tool to slice off the meat and smash the bone. After several tries, it managed to break off both ends of the bone and scrape out the juicy marrow inside.

At just about the same time, two other hominids died near the lake. One, perhaps 1.4 meters tall, had long legs and a human gait but long, apelike forearms. The other, a male, lay some distance away. His limb bones are gone, but the remains of his skull show he had a small brain, big teeth, and an apelike face.

These new fossils give different glimpses of each hominid, and no one can be sure all three belonged to the same species. But even if not, their details are starting to fill in a mysterious chapter of human prehistory. According to the international team that made all three discoveries, the big-toothed skull represents an unusual new species that is the best candidate for the ancestor of our own genus, *Homo*. Not everyone in the contentious field of paleoanthropology agrees, but the new species, which Ethiopian anthropologist Berhane Asfaw and his colleagues have named *Australopithecus garhi* (*garhi* means "surprise" in the language spoken by the local Afar people), is certain to shake up views of the transition from the apelike australopithecines to humankind. And the scored bones from the first hominid's feast are the earliest recorded evidence of hominids butchering animals, bolstering the notion that meat eating was important in human evolution.

"They've put together a whole package here, so that you can say a fair amount about a time we don't know much about," says anthropologist F. Clark Howell of the University of California (UC), Berkeley. With its surprising mix of traits—primitive face and unusually big teeth—the new australopithecine doesn't match the profile many researchers expected for a human ancestor at this stage. "It's very exciting," says paleoanthropologist Alan Walker of Pennsylvania State University in University Park. "Until now it's all been just scraps of teeth and bits of mandible from this time. And this [morphology] is a surprise."

But this rare glimpse of a murky period in human evolution raises as many questions as it answers. *A. garhi* has few traits that definitively link it to *Homo*, and like other hominids from the same period, it may simply be an evolutionary dead end that brings us only slightly closer to understanding our own ancestors, says paleoanthropologist Bernard Wood of George Washington University in Washington, D.C. The debate is complicated by the fact that paleoanthropologists are deeply divided over who the first humans, or members of *Homo*, were, and indeed what makes a human. "These are magnificent fossils," says Wood, but he's not ready to admit *A. garhi* into the gallery of our ancestors. "At this point it's impossible to tell what's ancestral to what," he says. "This won't be the last surprise."

Anthropologists have long been itching to know just what East African hominids were doing between 2 million and 3 million years ago, says one of the team's leaders, paleoanthropologist Tim White of UC Berkeley. Decades of fieldwork and analysis have allowed researchers to identify many characters in the human evolutionary story (see diagram), starting with apelike species such as the 4.2-million-year-old *A. anamensis*. Next in line, known from 3.7 million to 3.0 million years ago, is *A. afarensis*, best known for the famed "Lucy" skeleton: a meter-tall, small-brained, upright hominid that retained apelike limb proportions and a protruding lower face.

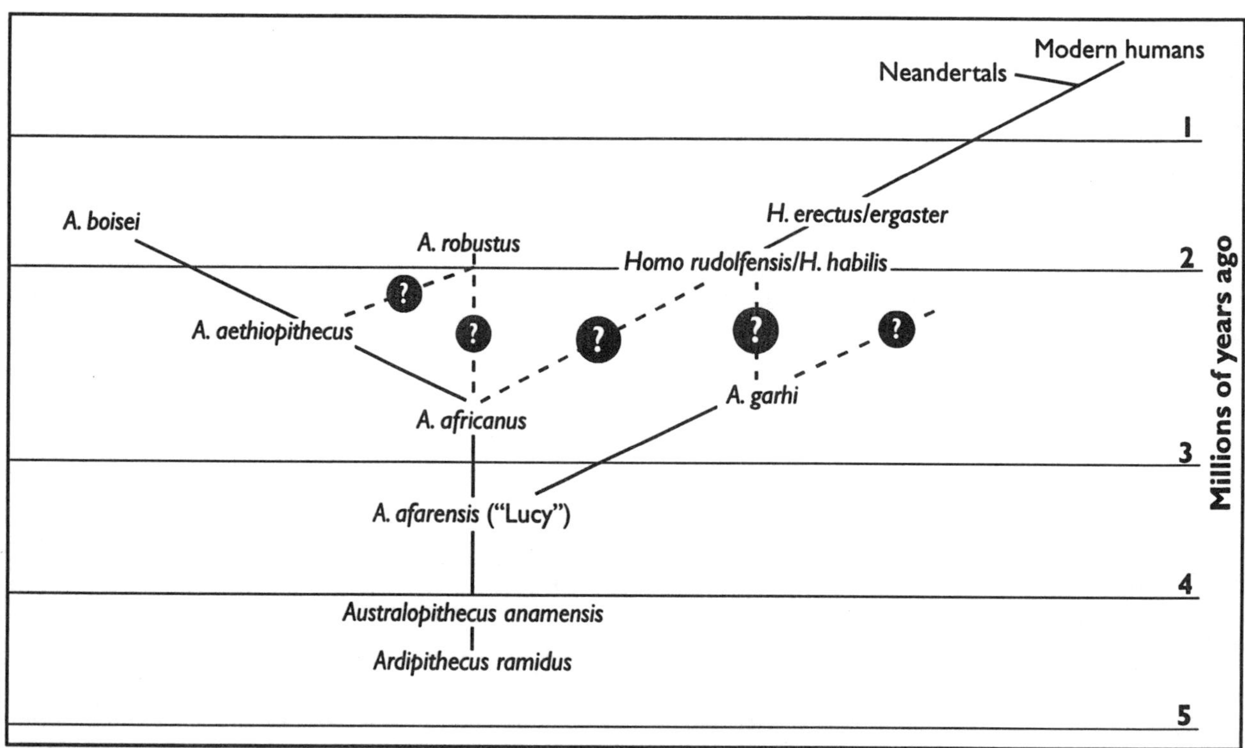

Untangling the family tree. Fossil finds suggest an outline of our evolutionary history, but the ancestor of our genus remains in question.

More than a million years separate Lucy from the first specimens usually considered to be part of our own genus, which appear in East Africa around 2 million years ago and tend to have larger brains and a more human face, although they are highly variable. In the interim, the South African fossil record is diverse and confusing, and the East African record has been sparse. The period includes three species that fall into the "robust" australopithecine group—heavy-jawed hominids with skull crests and large back teeth, perhaps for eating hard roots and tubers—that are not part of our own lineage. More promising for those seeking a human ancestor is *A. africanus*, known from South Africa starting at around 2.8 million years ago, which has a more humanlike face than the Lucy species.

But the *A. africanus* fossils were found half a continent away from the East African cradle of *Homo*, and some anthropologists have been hoping for a stronger candidate for the root of our lineage. "After the split with the robust lineage, we have very little evidence," says Walker. That's why White and his team zeroed in on sediments in the desert of Ethiopia's Afar depression. They struck gold with three separate discoveries, all dated securely to 2.5 million years ago by radiometric techniques on an underlying volcanic rock layer.

One dramatic find came in 1997, when El Niño-driven rains washed away stones and dirt on steep slopes near the village of Bouri. Berkeley graduate student Yohannes Haile-Selassie spotted fragments of the skull—the color and thickness of a coconut shell—on the surface. A closer look revealed teeth poking out of the ground. Much of the rest of the skull had washed down the hill, so the team, which includes 40 members from 13 countries, took the slope apart. They dug tons of material from the hill, then sieved it and picked through it for bone—twice. "It was probably the most difficult fossil recovery we've ever done," says White. "We spent 7 weeks on that slope." Although the delicate bones of the middle face were gone for good, the team found many more skull fragments.

After reconstructing the skull, the researchers were confronted with a face that is apelike in the lower part, with a protruding jaw resembling that of *A. afarensis*. The large size of the palate and teeth suggests that it is a male, with a small braincase of about 450 cubic centimeters. (A modern human brain is about 1400 cubic centimeters.) It is like no other hominid species and is clearly not a robust form. And in a few dental traits, such as the shape of the premolar and the size ratio of the canine teeth to the molars, *A. garhi* resembles specimens of early *Homo*.

But its molars are huge—the second molar is 17.7 millimeters across, even larger than the *A. robustus* average. "Selection was driving bigger teeth in both lineages—that's a big surprise," says Walker.

The other dramatic skeletal find had come a year earlier: leg and arm bones of a single ancient hominid individual, found together. The new hominid femur or upper leg bone is relatively long, like that of modern humans. But the forearm is long too, a condition found in apes and other australopithecines but not in humans. The fossils show that human proportions evolved in steps, with the legs lengthening before the forearms shortened, says co-author Owen Lovejoy of Kent State University in Ohio.

The third major find, at the same stratigraphic level and only a meter away from the skeletal bones, preserves dramatic evidence of hominid behavior: bones of antelopes, horses, and other animals bearing cut marks, suggesting that butchery may be the oldest human profession. One antelope bone, described by a team including archaeologist J. Desmond Clark of UC Berkeley and White, records a failed hammerstone blow, which scratched the bone slightly and caused a bone flake to fly off; a second blow was struck from exactly the same angle. Both ends of the bone were broken off, presumably to get at the marrow.

Similarly, an antelope jawbone bears three successive curved marks, apparently made as a hominid sliced out the tongue. In a cross section under the microscope, these marks show a parallel series of ragged V-shaped striations with rough inner walls—the telltale signature of a stone tool rather than a predator's teeth, says White. Marks on the leg bone of a three-toed horse show that hominids dismembered the animal and filleted the meat from the bone.

The Bouri sites yielded few of the stone tools the hominids must have used, perhaps because there is no local source of stone. The hominids "must have brought flakes and cobbles in from some distance, so that obviously shows quite a bit of forethought," says Clark. Tool use by this point is no surprise: At other sites, anthropologists have found tools dated to 2.6 million years ago. But there had been little hard evidence of what the oldest tools were used for. The new find shows that tools enabled hominids to get at "a whole new world of food"—bone marrow, says White.

Marrow is rich in fat, and few animals other than humans and hyenas can get at it. Anthropologists have theorized that just such a dietary breakthrough allowed the dramatic increase in brain size (*Science*, 29 May 1998, p. 1345), to perhaps 650 cc or larger, that took place in the *Homo* lineage by 2 million years ago. Two researchers recently proposed that cooked tubers were the crucial new food source (*Science*, 26 March, p. 2004), but most others have assumed it was meat. The cut marks present convincing evidence that they were right, says Yale University anthropologist Andrew Hill.

Whether or not the three finds can be connected, *A. garhi*, as based on the new skull, is now a prime candidate as an ancestor of our genus. The species is in the right place—East Africa—and the right time—between the time of *A. afarensis* and that of early *Homo*—says White. But making the link to the human lineage isn't easy, in part because the nature of "early *Homo*" is itself something of a mystery. White notes that some of the early *Homo* specimens have large teeth, and that in the teeth "there's not much change at all from *A. garhi* to those specimens of early *Homo*."

The link between *A. garhi* and *Homo* would be strengthened, of course, if researchers could show that the humanlike long bones come from *A. garhi* rather than from some other humanlike hominid. For now White is willing only to "make up a hypothesis to be tested": *A. garhi*, a small-brained, big-toothed hominid with humanlike leg proportions, began butchering animals by 2.5 million years ago. Thanks in part to the better diet, brain size rapidly increased to that seen in early *Homo*, and the trend toward large back teeth reversed—changes that quickly transformed other parts of the skull as well, such as flattening the protruding jaw.

But some other researchers don't buy that as a likely scenario. There's no reason to expect that every new branch on the hominid tree is our ancestor, says George Washington's Wood. He adds that he is not surprised by *A. garhi*'s mix of humanlike and robust features, because, given that climate was changing, "we should expect a variety of creatures with mixtures of adaptations at this time." Other researchers note that the dental data linking the species to *Homo* are weak. "Nothing here aligns *garhi* closely with *Homo*," says paleoanthropologist Fred Grine of the State University of New York, Stony Brook. "It's a possible candidate [for *Homo* ancestry], but no better than *africanus*."

Some anthropologists also say that there may not have been enough time for evolution to have transformed *A. garhi* into *Homo*. The oldest known specimen assigned to *Homo*, a 2.33-million-year-old palate from Hadar, Ethiopia, is more humanlike than *A. garhi*, with smaller teeth. That requires either a burst of evolution or some other explanation, such as sexual dimorphism, if *A. garhi* is to be considered part of our lineage, notes paleoanthropologist Juan Luis Arsuaga of the Universidad Complutense de Madrid in Spain. White says that only further discoveries and analysis will show just where the hominids of that long-vanished plain stand in relation to our own species: "*A. garhi* isn't the end; it's the first step."

5.4 Study Questions: A New Human Ancestor? — Elizabeth Culotta

1. What did a humanlike creature do to an antelope carcass in Ethiopia two and one half million years ago? How are the other two hominids near the lake described?

2. How has the big toothed skull been named?

3. Be aware of the fossil and time sequence of *A.anamensis*, *A.afarensis* and *A. africanus*.

4. In what ways does *A. garhi* resemble *Homo*? What do the molars tell us?

5. What have we learned from the "other dramatic skeletal find?"

6. What does the third major find tell us?

7. What is the significance of the fact that the Bouri sites yielded few of the stone tools?

8. What do the cut marks tell us regarding the controversy as to what brought about the dramatic increase in brain size?

5.5 *In Love With Lucy and All Her Relatives*

Frank Miele

An Interview with Paleoanthropologist Donald Johanson

Donald Johanson is perhaps the world's best known living paleoanthropologist. He is the founder and president of the Institute of Human Origin, (which recently relocated from Berkeley, CA, to Arizona State University in Tempe, AZ, where he also teaches at both the graduate and undergraduate level), discoverer of the Lucy skeleton that revolutionized our knowledge of human evolution, host of the acclaimed three-part PBS-Nova documentary In Search of Human Origins, *and the author of numerous scientific papers and five previous books:* Ancestors: In Search of Human Origins *(with Lenora Johanson and Blake Edgar);* Journey from the Dawn: Life with the World's First Family *(with Kevin O'Farrell);* Lucy's Child: The Discovery of a Human Ancestor *(with James Shreeve);* Lucy: The Beginnings of Humankind *(with Maitland Edey); and* Blueprints: Solving the Mystery of Evolution *(with Maitland Edey).*

Johanson's most recent book, From Lucy to Language *(with Blake Edgar, and special photography by David Brill, Simon and Schuster, 1997), grew from his commitment, in this time of neo-Fundamentalism, to provide the general public with access to the evidence the experts use in trying to reconstruct the story of human evolution. It provides the reader with a veritable home museum of human evolution. In addition to the informative and stimulating text, it includes beautiful life-sized photographs of every major fossil hominid skull that seem to almost jump out from the pages. One can only pray for it appear on CD-ROM (perhaps supplemented by numerical appendices which could be the source for countless future research articles, theses, and dissertations). With the publication of* From Lucy to Language, *creationists who try to foster doubt as to the fact of human evolution are finding themselves in the position of the defense team in the OJ civil trial after the photos of the Bruno Magli shoes surfaced.*

In this interview, Johanson tells Skeptic why he thought it was important to produce so special a book as From Lucy to Language, *responds to the religious, scientific, and literary criticisms of the search for human origins, sets forth the scientific and philosophical foundations of paleoanthropology, provides a great quick start guide to the latest findings in the search for our ancestors, tells us what he has learned in over two decades of field research in the Great Rift Valley of East Africa, and also shares his firsthand insights into the personalities who have shaped the ever exciting and ever controversial study of human evolution.*

Donald Johanson is clearly in love with the search for our origins, with Lucy and all of her relatives. Pick up a copy of From Lucy to Language *and you will be too.*

Skeptic: You've taken time out from digging in East Africa for Lucy's relatives, writing up your research for the professional journals, and running the Institute of Human Origins to bring us your latest book, *From Lucy to Language* (Johanson and Blake Edgar, with photography by David Brill, Simon and Schuster, 1997). In addition to the very readable and informative text, it includes remarkable photographs of what seems like every major fossil hominid skull. Why the commitment to popularization, in the best meaning of that word?

Johanson: We decided to produce this book mainly because there was nothing else available for undergraduates and the lay public that clearly presents the evidence paleoanthropologists use in trying to reconstruct the human evolutionary career. They often hear the criticism that we base our theories and conclusions about human evolution on fragmentary pieces of jaw or just a single tooth. *From Lucy to Language* contains life-sized, not postage stamp-size, photographs of what we consider the most critical and pivotal fossils that have shaped our understanding of the human evolutionary career. For the first time, the reader can look at the specimens in their absolute natural size and get an impression of the actual anatomy of these creatures. You can see how different a *Homo erectus* skull is from a Neandertal, or how a Neandertal skull differs from a modern human skull. We were especially fortunate in having the help of David Brill, who is the world's premier photographer when it comes to rendering these fossils in virtually three dimensions. Students have come to me recently and said, "I could almost reach out and touch a browridge or palpate the bone surface where a muscle is inserted." For those students and general readers who don't have access to the original fossils or even casts, our book provides a good substitute.

Skeptic: Let's examine those criticisms. On the one hand, you have creationists who claim that, "If you study the history of evolutionary anthropology you'll see that at one time they claimed Piltdown man was important, but now concede that it's a fraud. And then they claimed that *Ramapithecus* was the earliest homind, but now concede that it's really a fossil orangutan. All these bone peddlers do is change their line-up card as their supposed 'missing links' get successively ejected from the evolutionary game."

On the other hand, you have molecular evolutionists who say, "We already know a great deal from the comparative data, both anatomical and molecular. How would our knowledge of our evolution suffer if there was no hominid fossil record at all?" And most recently, we have literary deconstructionists who argue that, "Paleoanthropological theories are origin stories, just like other origin stories. Many of them are 'just so' stories. And in the past, some of them had unpleasant racist implications."

So why study human fossils at all? What do they prove? How do you deal with those criticisms?

Johanson: You've really dissected out the three major lines of criticism. The first comes from the so-called "Scientific Creationists," although that's really an oxymoron. But we do get that type of criticism from those who believe in the revealed truth of the Bible. They do exactly that. They *believe* in the Bible. They accept it on faith. They make no distinction between what we *know* from facts and what we *believe* by faith. The creationist issue, which has been beaten like a dead horse, essentially boils down to the fact that science and religion are two entirely different ways of looking at the universe. One is based on the presupposition that you have to invoke some sort of supernatural intelligence, or being, or force. That presupposition is based solely on belief, rather than on fact; whereas science looks at evidence which is immediately and instantaneously available to anyone who has the open mind to examine it. One doesn't have to invoke any supernatural cause to explain, say, the Lucy skeleton. The skeleton is there. Its a fact. It's dated at 3.2 million years bp (before the present). It comes from a geological stratum of that antiquity and the skeleton is associated with the remains of extinct animals. We don't need to invoke any supernatural understanding to simply accept that as a fact.

An example I often use in my class is that we don't, in a religious sense, *believe* in gravity; we *accept* gravity. We don't evaluate gravity in the same framework that we evaluate our personally held religious or spiritual ideas. Gravity isn't moral or immoral. It's simply a fact. As I was sorting through the stuff in my office, I came across a story about the creationism taught in fundamentalist private schools in California. There on the front page of the *San Francisco Chronicle* of December 17, 1996, was a 5-by-7 photo of a sign on the desk of a 10th grade biology teacher that read, "Darwin Is Dead and He Ain't Coming Back," which has now been turned into a bumper sticker. To which I responded in a letter to the editor of the newspaper, "Isn't it a shame that having nearly reached the millennium, we're still teaching ignorance to our students. Sir Isaac Newton is dead, but gravity ain't going away!" So maybe we can have *that* as a bumper sticker. We're just not going to change the minds of those who believe that the world is flat, that all the lunar landings were really staged in the Nevada desert and that we've never been in space. The only thing you can hope is that the United Airlines pilot who is flying you from San Francisco to London doesn't believe that the earth is flat, because he's never going to get you there.

Skeptic: Then let's consider the more intellectually serious criticisms. Your colleague Vincent Sarich, who is on our editorial board, and the late Allan Wilson upset the whole paleontological apple cart back in 1967 with their molecular dating of human evolution.

Johanson: Vince is always a provocative guy—and a terrific guy.

Skeptic: When I was in graduate school, you had to either accept the paleontologists' view that the fossil record showed that the apes and humans split maybe 15 to 20 mybp, or you could go by the molecular evidence, which said the split was much more recent, maybe 5 mybp. Eventually, the Sarich and Wilson viewpoint won. The interpretation of the fossil record then had to be brought into accord with the molecular evidence. Is that how you see it?

Johanson: This issue of molecules and anatomy tells us a great deal about the branching patterns and the levels at which various species, or genera, or families, or other higher-level taxa, separated. As we compare the molecular data, and this has been done extensively with proteins, with genes themselves, and with serum albumin as Sarich did, we develop an understanding of the branching sequence for the evolutionary history of the particular taxonomic group we are looking at. That methodology can be traced back to Morris Goodman's work in the late 1950s and 1960s. He alerted us to the fact that those taxa that were more recently related to one another would not only show tremendous similarities in anatomy, and possibly behavior, but they should also show a great deal of similarity at the molecular level.

What Sarich and Wilson did was to go from Goodman's insight and assume that the molecular clock was moving along and changing and mutating at a fairly constant rate, from which we could then calculate dates of separation. Their initial estimate was that humans and African apes separated something like 5 mybp, which others have since been pushed back somewhat in time. But their date was nothing like the 15 to 20 million years that most people looking at the fossil record in the 1960s proposed. Their prime candidate for a protohominid in the fossil record at that date was *Ramapithecus*.

Skeptic: Which the critics delight in pointing out now turns out to be a fossil orang.

Johanson: Right. But if we go back and examine the original evidence that was used to establish the *Ramapithecus* scenario, we now see that it was a "just-so" story. I don't think anybody can deny that. From a jaw fragment, it was inferred that a delayed dental eruption sequence, which meant extended childhood, which meant significant parental care, which meant enlarged brains, which meant stone tools, which meant bipedalism. That scenario involved huge leaps of faith. Before we can reconstruct our evolutionary history accurately, we need to start with the basics—determining the geological context in which the fossil was found, providing a purely anatomical description of the fossil, presenting a metrical, anatomical comparison of that fossil with others. We can then put that information into a less subjective and more objective cladogram, in which we simply look at the shared, derived features and ignore the ancestral, conservative features. Then, after we have accumulated enough of that type of information, we can try to construct a phylogeny that incorporates time, dates of divergence, dates of extinction, and the degree of diversity within the fossil species. Only later, much later, can we intelligently script the scenario of human evolution. I don't think we've reached that point yet.

But we're always tempted to look for a quick fix. The climate changed, so bang, we evolved from *Australopithecus* to *Homo*. We don't know if that was really the case. More and more evidence is coming along which says that it was not.

Let me return to your specific question about anatomy versus molecules. Without a fossil record, it would be very easy to support the idea that a Miocene ape simply stepped into the "Magic Tunnel of Evolution" and emerged as an upright, White, European male, which is what you see in the pages of so many magazines.

Skeptic: It was in my high school textbooks.

Johanson: Without the fossil record, we wouldn't know that the tree of evolution was very bushy, that there were many branches, and most of them went extinct, with only one survivor. That's essentially what Darwin said back in 1859—that the tree of life was is in fact a bush, that it was not an inexorable march from a primitive to an advanced or derived creature.

Without the fossil record, you'd never know of the existence of *Australopithecus boisei*. You wouldn't even know about the robust australopithecine radiation. They represent an extraordinary adaptation, that we are now beginning to suspect underwent parallel evolution in southern and eastern Africa—separately. So in eastern Africa, you had *Australopithecus aethiopicus*, and then *Australopithecus boisei*. While in southern Africa, you had *A. africanus* and *A. robustus*. Yet the two groups converged on the same anatomical adaptations. That tells us something about the richness of the fossil record. Today, it's a very impoverished record. We're the only species of hominid alive. From that perspective, it's a very uninteresting world. Think of how much more interesting it would have been 35,000 years ago when you were marching across the European landscape and you said, "Who are those guys? They must be the Neandertals. We'd better stay away from them!" or whatever.

The fossil record is extraordinarily important for revealing to us the various branches of evolution that went extinct. They provide us with a remarkably poignant perspective of our place in nature. Even the general public that accepts the fact of evolution often thinks that we are the pinnacle of evolution and that we've been around forever and that we'll last forever. We've probably been around for maybe 150,000 to

200,000 years. But the fossil record reveals to us the mini-adaptive radiation of the robust australopithecines that probably lived across most of Africa, though the best places to find their remains today are eastern and southern Africa. They lasted for almost a million-and-a-half years. And yet they went extinct! So without the fossil record, we'd never know about the richness of our family tree. This is what makes the whole human story, the story of our place in nature, so rich and so attractive.

If we go back to the case of *Ramapithecus* and examine the original material, the original upper jaw that was used to reconstruct what was termed the "parabolic arch," upon which that whole evolutionary scenario was built, we find out that the midline of the jaw wasn't even present on that specimen. The reconstruction of the "parabolic arch" was a flight of fancy. From that basic mistake, an entire scenario was concocted, without necessary prerequisites of first developing a cladistic analysis, fleshing it out with a phylogeny, and then testing the various possible cladograms and phylogenies. Looking back, what we now see is a convergence of the fossil record and the molecular evidence, which alerted us to the fact that we are remarkably closely related to the African apes and couldn't have separated from them as early as 15 to 20 mypb, but rather more recently. But the real resolution of the *Ramapithecus* controversy came not from the molecular evidence. It came from the fossil evidence.

When we went back and looked at the Yale Peabody Museum specimen, YPM 13799 and saw that there was no midline on that specimen, so you could reconstruct either a human-like parabolic arch or an ape-like parallel tooth row, the fossil evidence suggested something was wrong. Then when *afarensis* was found in the 1970s and described, we found that it has a very parallel-sided, rectangular, ape-like dental arch, not a human-like parabolic arch.

The entire *Ramapithecus* issue was finally resolved when a more complete specimen was found in Pakistan by David Pilbeam's team. Pilbeam and Elwyn Simons had been the principal proponents of *Ramapithecus* as a protohominid. The skull of that specimen looks very, very much like a living orang. But again the fossils tell us something in terms of the mode of evolutionary change. While the narrow interorbital septum, its lack of frontal sinuses, the sort of ski-slope to the face, and many other features look very much like those of a modern orang, the post-cranial material suggests a more generalized anatomy that is very different from what we see in orangs today. This means that in terms of the sequence of evolutionary change, the skull obtained its modern form first and only later did the adaptations of the post-cranial skeleton, similar to those seen in the modern orang, take place. So here again the fossil record is very important because it tells us something about, going back to good old George Gaylord Simpson, not only the tempo, but the mode of evolutionary change—what happened first, what happened second—what was the sequence of events. Whether bipedalisin came before big brains in the hominid line or big brains came before bipedalism was a huge issue that was not going to be settled in the test tube. Lucy and other fossils have given us the answer—we were upright long before our brains began to enlarge.

Skeptic: Let's take a quick look at that fossil with which your name will be forever linked. What does Lucy tell us about the evolution of our bodies and brains?

Johanson: In the book, we use Lucy as a metaphor for the whole species of *Australopithecus afarensis*. She tells us that at least as recently as 3.2 million years ago, the australopithecines were still quite ape-like in their general, overall anatomy. They had fairly long arms compared to their legs, which is probably evolutionary baggage left over from a more quadrupedal, arboreal, climbing ancestry, like we see in chimps today. We see that her pelvis has a very small pelvic outlet, which means that the brains of the newborns were very small. The adult brains were not anywhere near the size of modern humans. Very little of her braincase has been preserved, but fortunately we do have enough of the occipital (the back of the skull), to tell us that she might have had a braincase that was well under 400 cubic centimeters. Yet looking in detail at the pelvis, the knee, and the ankle, there's no question that the primary locomotor adaptation was different from that of a quadruped. Lucy was a biped, maybe not identical to us today in terms of locomotor mode, but one that had definitely made a significant shift in locomotor repertoire from quadrupedalism to bipedalism. The shape of her thorax is more of a pyramid (again, a primitive feature), rather than a broad barrel chest, seen in modern humans. Overall, Lucy presents an interesting amalgam of ape-like characteristics and more derived features, such as bipedalism.

Skeptic: A lot of evolutionists have fixed their eyes on the canine teeth.

Johanson: Canine teeth are very interesting and at the moment we have a somewhat enlarged sample

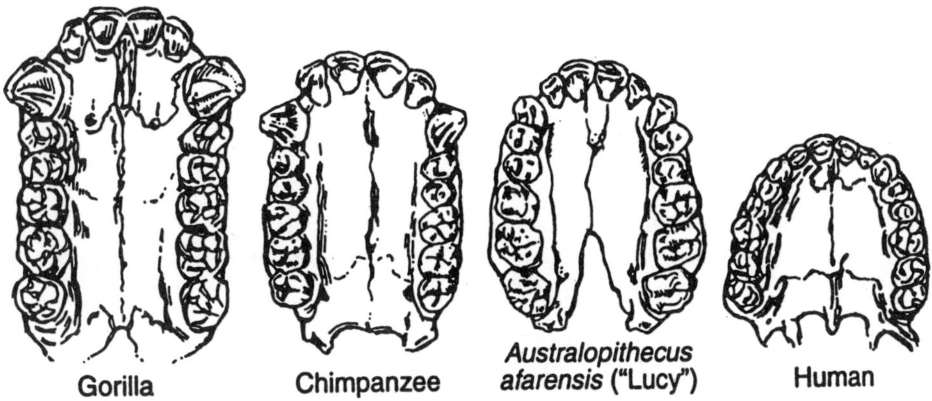

Figure 1. Shape of upper jaw and dental arch and size of canine teeth in gorilla, chimpanzee, *Australopithecus afarensis* ("Lucy") and human. Note that like humans, Lucy has much smaller canine teeth than the two ape species, who have large canines and parallel tooth rows. [Adapted from Howells, Fig. 27, p. 81 and Johanson & Edey, p. 265].

we're beginning to examine. There does not appear to be a very major difference in canine size between males and females in *afarensis*, as there would be in chimps or gorillas. Both male and female *afarensis* had feminized (i.e., reduced) canines. On the other hand, there is a tremendous degree of sexual dimorphism in body size. The males were much larger than Lucy. Many people wondered when Lucy was first found whether this was some sort of aberrant fossil, maybe that of a dwarf. No, it wasn't, because there's nothing abnormal about its anatomy to indicate that. So the question then arose, does she represent a different species from the larger specimens found at Hadar (Ethiopia), a hypothesis we initially entertained ourselves.

First, let me revisit your question about the creationists who say, "Well one year, the evolutionists say this, and next year they say that." That's one of the charms of doing science. That's one of the wonderful things about doing science. You go into the laboratory or out into the field and find something new, and all of a sudden, you have to change your mind. That just means you have a scientific approach, you have an open, inquiring mind. You have a *skeptical* mind that says, "I don't want to put all my eggs in this basket. I want to adopt the strategy more typical of an ostrich, who lays her eggs in different nests, so if lions destroy one nest, all her genes aren't gone because she's got eggs in other nests." We want to entertain a series of hypotheses. Even if we become very committed to one of them, something may come along and enlighten us to change our minds. That's one of the great rewards of participating in science. The more evidence that comes in, the more exciting

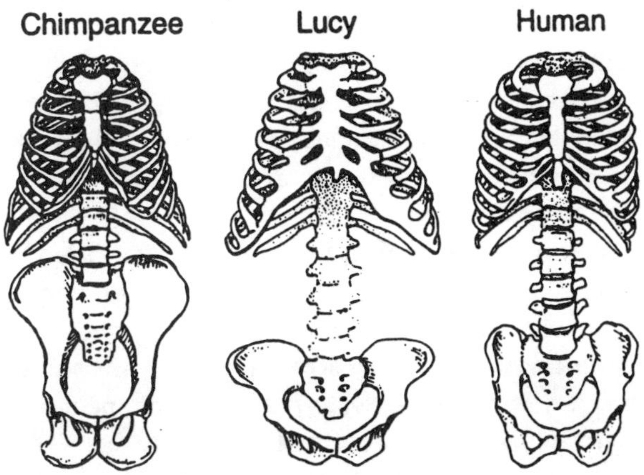

Figure 2. Rib cage and pelvis in chimpanzee, *Australopithecus afarensis* ("Lucy") and human. Lucy's rib cage is similar to the pyramidal shape of the chimp, while the pelvis is intermediate, with a small pelvic outlet. [Adapted from Howells, Fig. 25, p. 79].

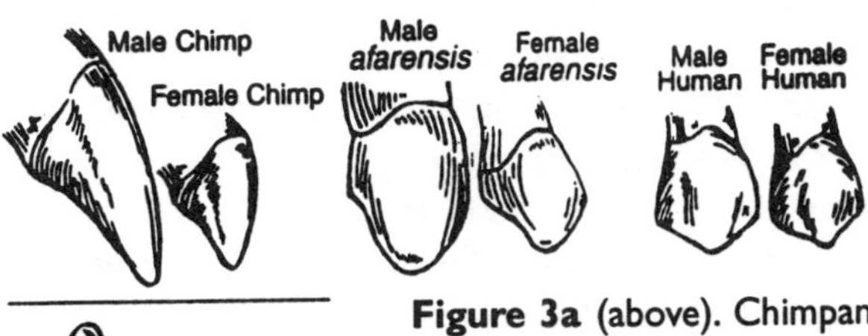

Figure 3a (above). Chimpanzees show much greater sexual dimorphism in canine tooth size (M>F) than either humans or *Australopithecus afarensis.*

afarensis canine
Chimpanzee canine
human canine

Figure 3b (above). Chimpanzee canines are larger in proportion to the rest of their teeth than either humans or *Australopithecus afarensis.* [Adapted from Johanson & Edey, p. 265].

it is for entertaining very different opportunities and possibilities. Not only is this not a criticism of science, it's one of its strengths—we can change our minds when new evidence comes to light and causes us to radically revise our way of looking at things.

Returning to sexual dimorphism, when we look at *afarensis*, we find a considerable amount of it. Lucy was 3½ feet tall, males were probably about 5 feet tall; Lucy was only 50 to 55 lbs., males 100 to 110 lbs. Males were almost twice the size of the females. This has been the focus of a number of scholars, because of Owen Lovejoy's hypothesis. (Lovejoy, 1993) Seeing that there was little difference between the canine teeth of males and females, he took that as evidence that males didn't need large canines to compete with other males for access to estrous females, and concluded that our ancestors were monogamous.

Skeptic: How do you evaluate Lovejoy's hypothesis against the evidence that most contemporary societies are not monogamous while the great apes are sexually dimorphic and show a variety of mating patterns.

Johanson: That's exactly the point. I prefer not to look at modern humans, because we're so derived and depend so much on culture that almost anything is possible. But when you look at a creature like Lucy who was, I'll use the term, more in tune with the natural world in which she lived, probably a great deal of her anatomy reflects the world she lived in. There is a considerable amount of criticism of the Lovejoy model, which is emerging more and more. A recent book on women in paleoanthropology by Laurie Hager (1997) includes substantial criticism by many primatologists and behavioral researchers who look at the size differences between males and females in *afarensis* and point out that monogamy is not the pattern we see in contemporary primate societies that have comparable degrees of sexual dimorphism. Instead, we see harem groups in gelada baboons or in gorillas, or we see polygynous groups, or we see multi-male—multi-female groups, where there's a mixture of mating combinations. So that it was a great leap of faith to go from just canine size to reduced aggression to monogamy.

Maybe there was reduced aggression in *afarensis.* But look at bonobos, where you have a significant male-female difference in canine size but a female-dominated society in which conflict is resolved by sexual behavior. This is totally different from what you would conclude simply by extrapolating from the relative tooth sizes. That's the danger of constructing evolutionary scenarios based on just one or a small number of features found in the fossil record.

Skeptic: In addition to sexual dimorphism, your book also illustrates the racial or populational variation in living humans. We also see that individuals change during development from childhood to adulthood, and we don't even know whether the trajectory of that change was the same in the fossils as it is today. So, being a good skeptic, when you examine a family tree, such as the one by Bernard Wood which you have adapted and shown on page 38 of your book, how do you decide whether what you're seeing in the fossil record is a real evolutionary difference, versus a difference between sexes, or a racial/populational difference, or a maturational difference?

Johanson: Almost every feature you've mentioned, Frank, was addressed many years ago by Le Gros Clark. He was extremely observant in his writing [see *The Antecedents of Man: An Introduction to the Evolution of Primates*, 1959] on the fossil evidence for human evolution, where he said you cannot take the Taung baby (an australopithecine fossil) and compare it to a grown-up chimpanzee, or compare a baby chimp to a fully grown human. You have to be aware of the ontogenetic age of your fossils and compare babies with babies and adults with adults. You also have to be well aware of pathologies, because some nutritional deficit may have influenced the shape of the teeth or the jaw. Males should be compared against males and females against females.

People sometimes ask why we have to go out and keep finding more fossils. As we build a collection of specimens, we find out about the range of variation within a species. If we look at a large collection of skeletons of chimpanzees or gorillas, we can use them as a baseline that tells us the variation in size and morphology within a single species. We can then use that statistic as a yardstick to evaluate what we find in the fossils.

When we first look at the very large variation in size in a sample like the *afarensis* material at Hadar, we immediately consider a couple of hypotheses. Hypothesis #1 is that the size differences are due to the fact that there are really two different species at the site. Hypothesis #2 is that there's only one sexually dimorphic species. To test those hypotheses, we examine more carefully the range of variation in tooth size, or jaw size, or the morphology and anatomy of the face. In the case of *afarensis*, we found that there was quite a difference in size, but it was comparable to what you find between male and female gorillas or chimps. It's just what's called an allometric difference, a scaling difference, where the features that identify the species are the same in both large and in small individuals.

That adds more strength to Hypothesis #2, that there was only one species at Hadar between 3 and 4 million years ago. But it's still only a hypothesis. There may be another species there. At the moment, however, most of the evidence suggests that there was only a single species. In the future we may find that there was significantly more diversity, but what we see now is consistent with the range of variation we see within a single species in living chimpanzees, or in gorillas, or even in collections of other fossil species.

This brings me back to your question about how skeptically we should look at the family tree shown on page 38. What stands out most to me in that representation is the period between four to three mybp. Look, there's only one species there. And that, to me, immediately raises a red flag. Are we missing a species somewhere? Was there another species living in a somewhat different habitat that we haven't discovered yet? Why did hominids become so speciose (i.e., species plentiful) after 3 mybp but so conservative between 4 and 3 million years? That is an issue. And I leave that more as a question, a source of inquiry, a stimulus to future discoveries and interpretations, because if you look at the period just before 4 mybp, it looks like there were two different taxa. So now, some scholars are suggesting that *Australopithecus anamensis* may have overlapped in time with *Ardipithecus ramidus.*

Skeptic: Following up on the question of how you interpret the fossil record and test competing hypotheses, Carleton Coon's book, *The Origin of Races*, presented his controversial view of human evolution, especially as regards the parallel evolution of the major human races. Current interpretations of the fossil record certainly do not support his view, which was controversial even at the time. However, his book presented a wealth of data with which others could test his hypothesis or develop and test hypotheses of their own. And the subject of the origin of racial or populational differences remains unresolved and controversial.

Johanson: When we were graduate students at the University of Chicago we read *The Origin of Races* and we were appalled by the misuse of the book. It was packed with data and information. And it was the first time that a book with that information

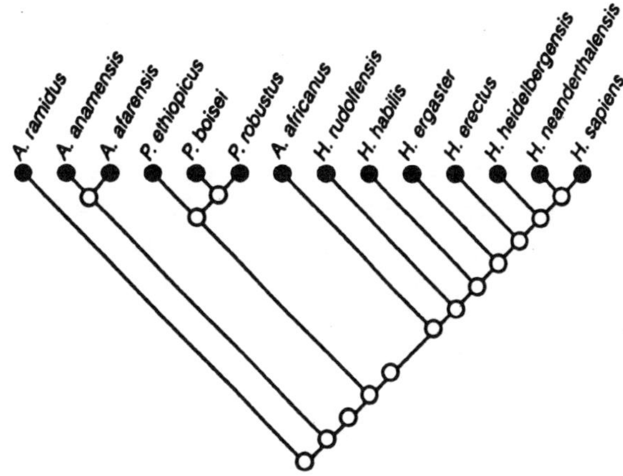

Figure 4a. Hominid cladogram—a branching diagram that shows shared anatomical features between fossils and living hominids, and sorts them into related groups. [Adapted from Johanson and Edgar, p. 38, after Tattersall].

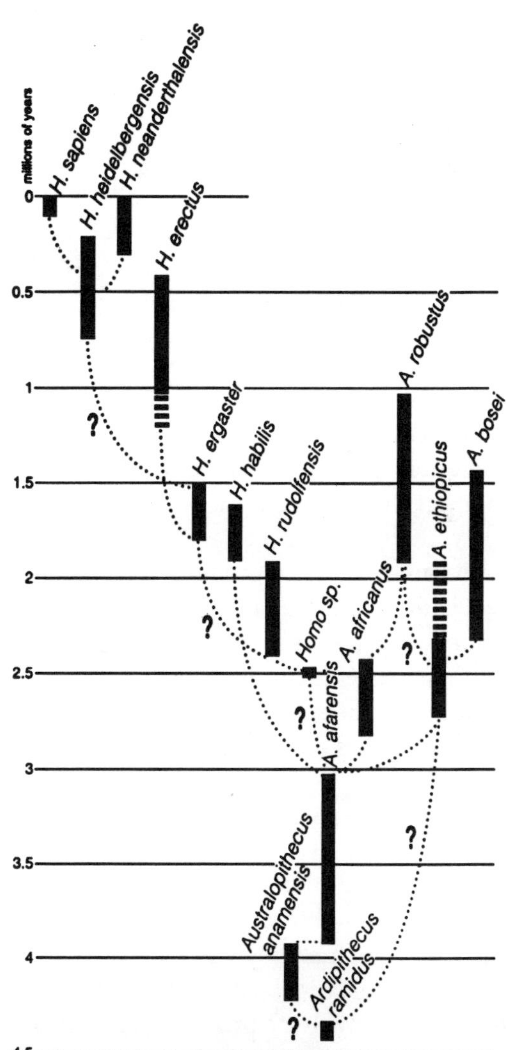

Figure 4b. A phylogenetic tree adds the dimension of time and proposes explicit evolutionary lineages. Note how only one species occupies the 4–3 million years before present period, suggesting there are more species yet to be found. [Adapted from Johanson and Edgar, p. 38, after Wood].

was made readily available. We tended to ignore all of the open nerves that were touched by misinterpretations of the book and realized how vital and important that book was.

***Skeptic*:** In your book you have a photograph of the Kow Swamp skull from Australia. It is a *Homo sapiens* skull from only about 10,000 years ago that has a much lower cranial capacity than the Neandertals. Kow Swamp also shows a number of conservative, ancestral features, such the brow ridge and a sloping forehead. You also can see those features in some living humans today. And we also see a broad range of cranial capacities in living humans, all of whom live in the modern technological world and lead thoroughly modern lives. So either the anatomical differences in living humans, either within groups or the average difference between groups, must mean something behaviorally, or how do you know those differences meant something when seen in the evolutionary record? If someone suddenly cloned a Neandertal, or a *Homo erectus*, or an *Australopithecus afarensis*, how do we know that they would be behaviorally different from people alive today?

Johanson: You've really sent up a balloon here. There's so much to consider. Let me go back to some very basic stuff about the *Homo sapiens* skulls we have illustrated. We've just chosen at random a group of skulls and illustrated them to show that there is a significant range of variation in modern humans. And there are clearly populational differences. Now, the population differences that we see between, say, people who live in Lapland and people who live in Australia are clearly discernible. But when we look at them in the overall behavioral context, we find out that whether you are a native Australian or a native Laplander, what's going on inside the braincase is essentially the same. They're capable of all the same sorts of behaviors as any living member of *Homo sapiens*.

We don't always have good answers to the question of why groups of living humans look different from one another. We can look at Eskimos, who live in very cold areas and tend to be cold adapted, and see that they have short, squat bodies which tend to conserve heat. As did Neandertals. So in both cases, body shape probably represents a very consistent micro-adaptation to the environment. On the other hand, why are there other populational differences today? I think that boils down to the fact that most Laplanders marry Laplanders, and most native Australians marry other native Australians. Generally, we tend to marry people who look very much like ourselves, our parents, our siblings. Until relatively recently, there was not much opportunity for as much gene flow as there is today. That's probably why we developed these different morphotypes, these different skull shapes. Some people now think that the shape of Kow Swamp skull, for example, also reflects a distortion due to cultural practices such as binding the skull.

***Skeptic*:** There are some anthropologists, however, Like Milford Wolpoff and Alan Thorne, who look at the brow ridges in the Australian samples and say that they reflect the continuity of, if not races as Carleton Coon believed, at least those morphological features. And some, like Eric Trinkhaus, argue that the pronounced nasal morphology of living European populations reflects a continuity from the Neandertals, while Out-of-Africa proponents like Christopher Stringer disagree.

Johanson: The issue of continuity has not been thoroughly resolved. I lean more toward the Out-of-Africa hypothesis, because the earliest *sapiens* that we have in the Middle East, like the Qafzeh specimen, show a more tropical, African type of build. And the earliest evidence we now have for anatomically modern humans comes from Israel and the Horn of Africa. So I believe *Homo sapiens* originated somewhere in that African arena. But I'm not totally closed to the idea that it could have happened in another place. Alan Mann at University of Pennsylvania and I have spoken about this a number times and there is a possibility of early *sapiens* in China. And if that is the case, maybe *Homo sapiens* first arose there.

***Skeptic*:** Can the molecular evidence resolve the issue? I read recently that analysis of some Neandertal DNA seemed to rule out the possibility that they contributed to the modern human gene pool (Kings, et al. 1997). Can you triangulate between the fossil record and the DNA data to test the various hypotheses?

Johanson: Yes. We need to look at the totality of evidence. When we develop a cladogram for our fossils, we obviously rely upon comparative skeletal anatomy. But when we deal with living species, we can use behavior, physiology, as well as the molecular data. In the past it wasn't possible to get molecular data from the fossil record. I find the Neandertal DNA evidence extraordinarily fascinating. I would be inclined to grab on to it as providing the ultimate proof that Neandertals did not leave genes in modern human populations. But it is, after all, the DNA of one individual. It is only mitochondrial DNA, not nuclear DNA. So it's another piece of evidence, but I don't think it slams that door completely shut. I think we're going to need a lot more DNA before we can make a really strong call. The people who promote the Out-of-Africa model have glommed on to the Neandertal mitochondrial DNA as the final nail in the coffin of the Multiregional model.

Skeptic: Some of them also glommed on to the argument of anatomist Philip Lieberman that his reconstruction of the anatomy of the Neandertal larynx ruled out the possibility of speech. But as you point out in the book, that one didn't hold up.

Johanson: Exactly. The hyoid bone found in the Kebara 2 specimen is virtually identical to that of a modern human, which may imply Neandertals were capable of speech. It's going to be very difficult, if not impossible, to determine the origin of language, which is an extraordinary adaptation. What's going on in language is going on inside our brain and how much do we really know about how the brain works? I'm fairly convinced that Chomsky and the others, who today are considered the bad guys, are right in their view that the ability to speak is hardwired into our brains. No matter which society or culture you grow up in, you speak that language perfectly, because the basic underlying structure necessary to learn language is already plugged into your brain.

Skeptic: Any guess as to when that module got slotted into the brain?

Johanson: I tend to favor a later arrival. Others like Phillip Tobias favor a younger arrival. Human language is part of a continuum of communication that ranges from body posture and hand motion to articulated speech. I think that modern syntactic language, as we are using it right now to symbolically represent ideas, emotions, whatever, is fairly late and associated with the Upper Paleolithic creative explosion. I think Neandertals were pretty good at what they did and undoubtedly had pretty good language, but they didn't have a lot of planning depth. They didn't have a way of symbolically representing the world around them to the degree that modern *Homo sapiens*, the Cro-Magnons who left the cave paintings did. And at the moment, that's the cultural, physical, artefactual evidence we can point to that shows a fairly rapid explosion occurred in the Upper Paleolithic. I see it as providing hard evidence that the Upper Paleolithic people were no longer living in a dark, murky world, but beginning to celebrate the world in which they lived.

Skeptic: Any speculation as to what, if it wasn't God zapping them, put that extra module in their brains?

Johanson: You know, I have no idea. I'm looking at my Macintosh sitting on my desk. Until you put in the software, it's like the paleolithic brain. It's essentially dead. But once you put in that software and communicate with the machine, and as it uses that software to perform certain tasks, it can perform all these wonderful functions. How that software got plugged into our brains 50 or 100,000 years ago, I just don't know.

Skeptic: Scholars have looked to things such as climate change, you've mentioned Lovejoy's hypothesis, Dean Falk has proposed the Radiator Hypothesis (i.e., that bipedalism evolved so we could dissipate heat more efficiently), to explain the changes we see in the fossil record. There's always this search for some external driver—if not God, then something in the environment. To what extent does culture drive itself? To what extent have we shaped our own evolution, once we started running that cultural software?

Johanson: That's an extremely powerful and useful way to look at human evolution. We tend to be very adaptable creatures. We can adapt to virtually any and every environment through cultural means. We also tend to be very adaptable in terms of our physiology. We're not highly adapted creatures. My favorite example that I use in my classes is Gary Larson's cartoon of the cows watching TV when the phone rings. One cow turns to the others and says, "There it goes again. And we just sit here without opposable thumbs."

Human evolution is not driven strictly by biology. It is not driven strictly by culture. It is really a co-evolution of biology and culture. There's a section in the book entitled, "Is Human Evolution Different?" It is different, because culture is a very major element in our evolutionary success. It is possible, as E.O. Wilson and Sherwood Washburn have argued, that culture takes on a very important role in shaping the species itself. When we look at the arrival of anatomically modern humans, it's not just biology that's driving their evolution. It's also culture.

I'm sure you're aware of the huge controversy in the anthropology department at Stanford University that was highlighted in *Science* a few months ago (Gibbons, 1997). There are some anthropologists who believe that when culture comes in the door, biology goes out the window. They believe that we were born with our minds a Lockean *tabula rasa*.

Skeptic: That the software runs with no hardware platform underneath it?

Johanson: Yes, that's what they're saying. But given the millions of years of natural selection that have shaped us, both biologically and behaviorally, there has to be an important element in our behavior that is related to the genes and based in biology, as E.O. Wilson and the sociobiologists and evolutionary psychologists have argued. So to really understand our evolution, we cannot look for the "magic bullet" that made us human, or assume that culture sprang up spontaneously. Human evolution took place through a series of events that ultimately expressed themselves in the interaction of biology and culture.

Skeptic: Finally, where in time and space do you think the next major advance in our knowledge of the human fossil record will take place? Will it be in the early part of the record, around the time where hominids and pongids split, or much later on when modern *Homo sapiens* appears and the racial or populational variation begins? Will it come from discoveries outside of Africa?

Johanson: One area that I think is very, very exciting is the study of the deposits that date earlier than 4 mypb. Tim White's work on *Ardipithecus ramidus* has opened that window for us. If we go back to the Miocene period, we see an incredible diversity of ape species. They occupied Europe and Asia, as well as Africa. David Pilbeam has written a very interesting and provocative article (Pilbeam, 1996) that puts forth a new view of what protohominid looked like. He argues that it would be very chimp-like, with thin dental enamel, which is very different from the prevailing view that it would have thick (i.e., human-like) dental enamel. But in fact, we don't have a really good, solid, protohominid ancestor from the Miocene. We need to go out and find one.

The other area I find intriguing is the transition from *Australopithecus* to *Homo*. Since the recent discovery at Hadar of the oldest well-dated evidence for the genus *Homo*, I'm more and more interested in reconstructing that link, which, I think, represents an extraordinarily important moment in human evolution. We should abandon trying to think up grand scenarios of global change and environmental desiccation to explain that transition. Instead, we have to go out and find the real evidence of the transitional forms between *Australopithecus* and early *Homo*. First we need to understand what those differences were and how they were expressed. Then we can build a cladogram, and after that develop a phylogeny. Only then should we try to paint the whole big picture. We may find out that, just as there were many different species of *Australopithecus*, there will also be many different species of *Homo*. We're beginning to get an insight into that looking at *Homo habilis*, *Homo ergaster*, and *Homo erectus*. It may be that the tree of evolution was very speciose (species plentiful) at that time, but that only one branch of tree survived to evolve into ourselves.

Skeptic: Thank you for talking with *Skeptic* and for making much clearer the complex story of our evolutionary history.

Bibliography

Asimov, N. 1996. "A Look Inside an Evangelical Classroom," *San Francisco Chronicle*. 17 December 1996, p. A-1.

Coon, C. S. 1962. *The Origin of Races*. New York: Knopf.

Falk, D. 1992. *Braindance: New Discoveries About Human Origins and Brain Evolution*. New York: Holt.

Gibbons, A. 1997. "Cultural Divide at Stanford," *Science*. 20 June pp. 1783–1784.

Hager, L. (ed.) 1997. *Women in Human Evolution*. New York: Routledge.

Johanson, D., and Edey, M. 1981. *Lucy: The Beginnings of Humankind*. New York: Simon and Schuster.

Johanson, D., and Edgar, B. 1997. *From Lucy to Language*. New York: Simon and Schuster.

Krings, M., Stone, K. A., Schmitz, R. W, Krainitzki, H., Stoneking, M., & Paabo, S. 1997. "Neandertal DNA sequences and the origin of modern humans." *Cell*, 90:19–30.

Le Gros Clark, W. 1963. *Antecedents of Man*. New York: Harper.

Lovejoy, O. 1993. "Modeling Human Origins: Are We Sexy Because We're Smart or Smart Because We're Sexy?" pp. 1–29 in D. T. Rasmussen (ed). *The Origin and Evolution of Humans and Humaness*. Sudbury, MA: Jones and Bartlett.

Pilbeam, D. 1996. "Genetic and Morphological Records of the *Hominoidea* and Hominid Origins: A Synthesis." *Molecular Phylogenetics and Evolution*. V.5, No. 1, pp. 155–168.

Simpson, G., 1949. *Tempo and Mode in Evolution*. New York: Columbia University Press.

Stringer, C., and McVie, C. 1997. *African Exodus: The Origins of Modern Humans.* New York: Holt.

Tattersall, I. 1995. *The Fossil Trail.* New York: Oxford.

Trinkhaus, E. and Shipman, P. 1993. *The Neandertals: Changing the Image of Mankind.* New York: Knopf.

Wolpoff, M. and Caspari, R. 1997. *Race and Human Evolution: A Fatal Attraction.* New York: Simon and Schuster.

Wood, B. 1994. "The Oldest Hominid Yet." *Nature,* 371:280–281.

5.5 Study Questions: In Love with Lucy and All Her Relatives — Frank Miele

1. What are the main differences between science and creationism, according to Don Johanson? How does the concept of gravity highlight the differences?

2. Read the ensuing passages for a general understanding of molecular dating, how paleoanthropologists script the scenario of human evolution and why the tree of human evolution is seen as more "bushy" today.

3. What general conclusions can be drawn about *Australopithecus afarensis* just from looking at Lucy?

4. With respect to Lucy specifically, and *A. afarensis* in general, how does Johanson assess canine size and body size?

5. How does Johanson respond to the creationist critics regarding the changes in evolutionary theory?

6. Why does Johanson think that the size differences seen in *A. afarensis* represent sexual dimorphism rather than a diversity of species?

5.6 *A New Face for Human Ancestors*

Ann Gibbons

An 800,000-year-old species from Spain takes its place on the human family tree, and these first Europeans may be ancestral to both modern humans and Neandertals.

More than 780,000 years ago, a boy with a remarkably modern face lived near a warren of caves in the red limestone Atapuerca hills of northern Spain. He died young, possibly the victim of cannibalism, and today only part of his face remains. But that part is stunning, because despite its antiquity, it "is exactly like ours," says paleoanthropologist Antonio Rosas of the National Museum of Natural Sciences in Madrid, Spain. Rosas and his colleagues, who found the remains of the boy and five other early humans in a railway cut, suggest that these people—the oldest known Europeans—were members of a new species of early humans directly ancestral to us.

The Spanish team has named this first new member of the human family in over a decade *Homo antecessor*, from the Latin word meaning explorer or one who goes first. They say that the species's unusual mix of traits—in particular, the boy's modern face set between a primitive jaw and brow—shows that it gave rise to both modern humans and Neandertals, the heavyset species that lived in Ice Age Europe until about 28,000 years ago.

Other paleoanthropologists are impressed by the finds—more than 80 fossils, including skulls, jaws, teeth, and other parts of the skeleton—that offer new insight into a mysterious time and place in human evolution. "We now have a better window on the first peopling of the European continent," says paleoanthropologist Philip Rightmire of the State University of New York (SUNY), Binghamton. But identifying these people as a new species, not to mention claiming them as a key human ancestor, is highly controversial. "I think many of my colleagues will be uncomfortable with creating a new species, because it is mainly based on the facial features of one juvenile," says paleoanthropologist Jean-Jacques Hublin of the National Center for Scientific Research (CNRS) in Paris. What's more, if *H. antecessor* is indeed the last common ancestor of Neandertals and modern humans, it could bump two other favored contenders—*H. erectus* and *H. heidelbergensis*—off the main line of descent leading to modern humans, making them side limbs on an increasingly bushy human family tree.

That's too drastic a revision for many researchers to swallow. Some, however, think the new family tree with all its offshoots helps explain an increasingly diverse fossil record. "It's further evidence for the complexity that we're finding all the way down the story of the evolution of *Homo*," says Chris Stringer, a paleoanthropologist at the Natural History Museum, London.

■ Seeing a Familiar Face

Only a decade ago, the textbook view of the evolution of *Homo* was that of a gradual, straightforward progression, with one species unfolding into another—a pattern quite different from the diversity seen in other animals. First came *H. habilis*, the toolmaker, arising more than 2 million years ago from apelike australopithecines. Then came *H. erectus*, the upright walker who trekked across Africa and Asia about 1.8 million years ago. It gave rise in the past 500,000 years to a relatively robust ancestor called archaic *H. sapiens*, which led to both our species and Neandertals.

But in the past decade, new fossils and reanalysis of old ones have prompted researchers to rewrite this script and add more characters, including several different types of early *Homo* in Africa (*Science*, 22 November 1996, p. 1298). And they also have changed the cast in the final acts. Notably, half-million-year-old African and European fossils once described as

Reprinted with permission from *Science* 276, May 30, 1997, pp. 1331–33.

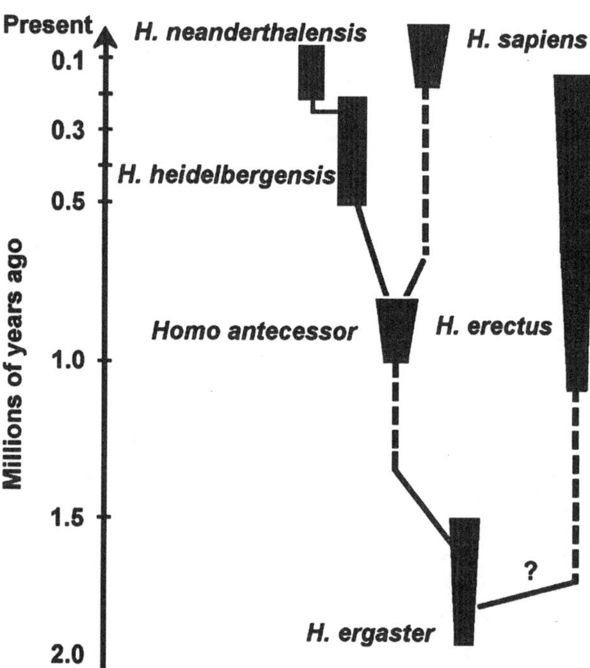

A new relative. *Homo antecessor* claims a key spot on the human family tree.

archaic *H. sapiens* now are attributed to the species *H. heidelbergensis*, which many think was ancestral to Neandertals and modern humans.

This view has been hard to test, however, because of huge gaps at critical times in the fossil record of Europe. From the time the first humans left Africa about 1.8 million years ago until some 500,000 years ago, not a single bone had been found in Europe. Then, in 1994, new excavations in Spain uncovered fragments of hominid bones and teeth at a site called Gran Dolina, where railroad workers blasting through Atapuerca Hill in the 19th century had exposed cross sections of bone-filled limestone caverns. The layers containing human fossils were dated using periodic shifts in Earth's magnetic field to more than 780,000 years old (*Science*, 11 August, 1995, pp. 754, 826, and 830). That makes these "exciting because they are the earliest well-dated fossils from Europe," says University of Michigan paleoanthropologist Milford Wolpoff.

Subsequent field seasons yielded simple stone tools and more fossils from at least six individuals. And as soon as the Spanish scientists cleaned up the fossils—particularly the face of the boy—they knew they had found something special. The face had familiar modern features, such as sunken cheekbones with a horizontal rather than vertical ridge where the upper teeth attach, and a projecting nose and midface. "We realized right away it was modern looking," says paleoanthropologist Juan Luis Arsuaga of the Universidad Complutense in Madrid, co-leader of the team with paleoanthropologist José Bermúdez de Castro of the National Museum of Natural Sciences, Madrid, and archaeologist Eudald Carbonell of the University of Tarragona.

But the fossils also had primitive features, such as a prominent brow ridge and multiple roots for premolars. It all added up to an unusual mosaic of modern and primitive features that just didn't fit any known species. "We tried to put them in *H. heidelbergensis*, but they were so different that we could not," says Arsuaga. And so they set the fossils apart as a new species.

Next, the team tried to solve the problem of where *H. antecessor* sits in the human family tree. And here the researchers go out on a limb, relying on a few dental and cranial features to suggest that *H. antecessor* is close kin to 1.6-million-year-old fossils from East Africa, which some researchers identify as *H. ergaster*. This species resembles *H. erectus*—indeed, some consider it part of *H. erectus*—but others have proposed that only the African *H. ergaster* is ancestral to modern humans, while the Asian *H. erectus* went down a different evolutionary path. The Spanish team supports this view by noting traits that link *H. antecessor* to *H. ergaster* and other traits that separate it from *H. erectus*. That would bump *H. erectus*—or at least the Asian form—off the direct line to modern humans, making it a separate lineage that went extinct without descendants.

At the same time, *H. antecessor* shows enough similarities to fossils identified as *H. heidelbergensis* to be an ancestor of that species, which most paleoanthropologists agree led to Neandertals. Yet *H. antecessor* also shares more traits with modern humans than do European *H. heidelbergensis* fossils. The Spanish team therefore argues that *H. antecessor* is a key central player that ultimately gave rise to modern humans and to Neandertals—thus deposing *H. heidelbergensis* from its position as the last common ancestor of both (see family tree). The new species's midface traits are "exactly the morphology we would imagine in the common ancestor of modern humans and Neandertals, if we were to close our eyes," says Rosas. To make sense of these clues, the Spanish team proposes that *H. ergaster* gave rise to *H. antecessor*, probably in Africa, although the new species has only been found at Atapuerca. They speculate that members of *H. antecessor* began to spread out about 1 million years ago and eventually headed north to Europe, leaving the 800,000-year-old fossils found at Atapuerca. As time passed, some members of the species evolved into *H. heidelbergensis* (and may have left the 300,000-old fossils at Atapuerca; see sidebar). These humans headed farther north into Europe, where they in turn led to Neandertals—but not to modern humans.

Meanwhile, the southern members of *H. antecessor*, probably still in Africa, gave rise to modern humans by way of another, as yet unidentified transitional species, according to the Spanish team's view. This middle player may include fossils already discovered in Africa that look ancestral to modern humans and are now attributed to *H. heidelbergensis*. These include a massive skull from Bodo, Ethiopia, dated to 600,000 years, and a more recent cranium from Kabwe, Zambia.

Face-off

That scenario is speculative, however, and not everyone welcomes the entrance of the new species—and its retinue of still-unknown relatives. "Given the evidence presented here, I'm reluctant to endorse a new species," says SUNY's Rightmire. Otherwise, "you end up littering the taxonomic landscape with all sorts of names that may turn out to be less useful later on." Most troublesome to Rightmire, CNRS's Hublin, London's Stringer, and Michigan's Wolpoff is that the designation of the new species rests primarily on the modern features found in the boy's face. They worry that some of those features are juvenile traits that weren't present in adults, and perhaps were also found in the young of other species. More comparison of the boy's face with Atapuercan adults and juveniles of other species is needed, they say.

Rosas responds that fragmentary facial bones from Atapuercan adults do show some of the modern-looking features found in the boy's face, such as hollowed cheekbones. And the Nariokotome boy who lived 1.6 million years ago in Kenya and is often identified as *H. ergaster* does not share these modern traits. Nor do the faces of 300,000-year-old *H. heidelbergensis* youths from the younger beds at Atapuerca. "We think we have enough information to define it in the proper sense of a new species," says Rosas. "But people are probably going to need some time to accommodate this proposal."

It may take more than just time, however, to convince other paleoanthropologists that *H. erectus* and *H. heidelbergensis* are not on the lines of modern humans. For one, researchers such as Rightmire think fossils designated as *H. ergaster* in Africa are really *H. erectus*—and so are ancestral to modern humans in almost any scenario. But even if *H. ergaster* is considered a distinct species, says Rightmire, its link to *H. antecessor* rests on thin evidence—"the morphology of the root system of premolars, and that's just one trait," he says. Nor does Rightmire

Into the Pit of Human History

In 1976, Spanish paleontologist Trinidad Torres was searching for bear fossils in well-known beds at Atapuerca, near the city of Burgos in northern Spain, and found a human bone instead. This search had uncovered what turned out to be the world's largest known repository of fossil humans from the period 780,000 to 127,000 years ago, the Middle Pleistocene. The locality's importance for human prehistory became clear in the early 1990s, after additional excavation at one particular site, a 14-meter shaft inside a cave known as Sima de los Huesos (Cave of Bones).

Inside this pit, researchers have found at least 32 individuals who lived 300,000 years ago. In a special 300-page issue of the *Journal of Human Evolution* the Spanish team suggests that these skeletons are from a species called *Homo heidelbergensis*—a group that many paleoanthropologists regard as ancestral to both Neandertals and modern humans. Much older fossils from another part of Atapuerca, however, may have bumped *H. heidelbergensis* off the line to modern humans, says team co-leader Juan Luis Arsuaga of the Universidad Complutense in Madrid.

The fossils in the pit present a mystery. They come mainly from male and female teenagers and young adults, who were generally in good health when they died, although one remarkably complete skull is scarred with osteitis, a bone inflammatory disease, and another is from a person who apparently was deaf. What—or who—killed them? Many bones show evidence of chewing by carnivores, but animals would not selectively kill young adults and no other prey are in the pit. And the animal bones show that it's not a burial site, although Arsuaga speculates that other humans might have dumped the remains there. Researchers are now doing detailed analyses of the ages of the individuals at death, to see if they can tell whether all died in a single catastrophe.—A.G.

think *H. heidelbergensis* should be removed from our ancestral lineage, because he believes it includes the Bodo skull and other recent African fossils that have ties to modern humans. "I'm going to stick to my guns and support *H. heidelbergensis* [not the new species] as the antecedent to Neandertals and recent humans."

On the other hand, others find the new order a pleasing solution to the fact that *H. heidelbergensis* is something of a "wastebasket taxa" that includes widely varying African and European fossils, as Leslie Aiello, a paleoanthropologist at University College, London, describes it. Reserving the name *H. heidelbergensis* for the European fossils and considering African fossils to be the as yet unnamed descendants of *H. antecessor* "makes things nice and neat," she says.

Regardless of where the new fossils fit in the family tree, Wolpoff and others hope the site will eventually reveal what kind of technology or behavior allowed these early humans to persist in the hostile European climate before 500,000 years ago. So far, it's hard to tell, because the tool kit found with them included only simple cutting flakes, not the more sophisticated tools found elsewhere at this time. One additional, bizarre clue is that the bones were covered with cut marks, indicating that their bodies were defleshed and processed like those of animals killed for meat (*Science*, 19 January 1996, p. 277). Bermúdez de Castro and his colleagues have suggested that this could be cannibalism, but researchers such as Peter Andrews of the Natural History Museum, London, warn that cut marks alone don't prove cannibalism.

So although the fossils give paleoanthropologists a new view of an obscure time in history, they also raise a whole crop of new questions. "That's the main contribution of the Atapuerca fossils," says Hublin. "They give us an idea of the amazing variation in *Homo*." And that diversity, notes Arsuaga, shows "that human evolution is like that of other groups. We're not so different."

5.6 Study Questions: A New Face for Human Ancestors —Ann Gibbons

1. How does this hominid, identified as *Homo antecessor*, fit in with the hominid phylogeny?

2. Do you feel there is evidence to create a new species, and why?

3. What are the primitive characteristics expressed by this species?

4. What derived (advance) physical characteristics are being expressed?

5. How will the analysis of the species differ according to lumpers and splitters?

6. Discuss the migration pattern for this species.

7. How does this find impact how paleoanthropologists view our evolutionary relationship to *Homo erectus*?

8. Describe the tool kit of *Homo antecessor*.

5.7 The Fate of the Neanderthals

Paul Mellars

Between about 30,000 and 40,000 years ago, the Neanderthals in Europe were replaced by populations of behaviourally and biologically modern humans. What happened during that period?

The Neanderthals have had a chequered scientific career. Berated throughout the first half of the century as distinctly retarded, they were suddenly elevated in the 1960s to having been only marginally less accomplished in biological and behavioural terms than modern *Homo sapiens.*[1] But in the late 1980s they were again relegated to an extinct side-line of human evolution,[2,3] and this was confirmed a couple of years ago[4] by the recovery of surprisingly well-preserved mitochondrial DNA from the original Neanderthal skeleton (from Neanderthal itself). European Neanderthals are thought to have diverged from the lineage that eventually gave rise to modern humans at least half a million years ago. Then, around 30,000–40,000 years ago, the Neanderthals were replaced by modern populations—probably from an ultimately African source.[5]

Now that the evolutionary fate of the Neanderthals has been clinched by DNA evidence, the debate concerns how this process of population replacement came about. In particular, what was the extent of contact between the final Neanderthals and the earliest modern humans?[6] This theme dominated a conference held in August to commemorate the discovery of a fossil Neanderthal skull at Forbes Quarry in Gibraltar in 1848. Any process of population dispersal and replacement must involve some degree of coexistence and potential interaction between the two populations, but do we measure this in decades or millennia? Did the two groups occupy essentially the same, or sharply separated, territories? And how and why did one population, the Neanderthals, eventually dwindle to the point of extinction?

On one point, at least, there seems to be a consensus—that in the southern part of the Spanish peninsula, roughly to the south of the Ebro valley, the local Neanderthals survived for at least 5,000–10,000 years after the arrival of modern populations in the adjacent parts of northern Spain and the Mediterranean coast. A typical Neanderthal lower jaw from the site of Zafarraya in Andalusia has been dated by two separate methods (radiocarbon and uranium series) to around 30,000 years before present (BP).

Equally typical 'Mousterian' Neanderthal technologies have been dated at sites in both southern Spain and Portugal to a similarly late period (J. Zilhao, Natl Inst. Archaeol., Lisbon; L. Raposo, Natl Mus. Archaeol., Lisbon). By contrast, characteristically modern 'Aurignacian' technologies, almost certainly manufactured by anatomically modern humans, have been dated at several sites in northern Spain to around 38,000–40,000 years BP.

The most likely explanation for the prolonged coexistence of these two populations lies in ecological differences between the northern and southern parts of the Iberian Peninsula. The Ebro Valley seems to act as a sharp ecological boundary for several other species, so the biological and behavioural adaptations of the expanding modern populations were probably not adequate to compete with the local Neanderthals—at least until the modern populations had time to develop their own adaptations to cope with the conditions (A. Currant, Nat. Hist. Mus., London; C. Finlayson, Gibraltar Mus.). Interestingly, despite the prolonged period of coexistence, there is no archaeological evidence that the late Neanderthal populations in southern Spain adopted any behavioural tricks or technological innovations from their new, more technologically advanced neighbours immediately to the north.

A very different pattern emerges to the north of the Pyrenees. Here, the final Neanderthal populations (as represented, for example, at Saint-Césaire in Aquitaine or at Arcy-sur-Cure in northern Burgundy) started to show remarkably similar behavioural patterns to those of the first anatomically modern populations. The Neanderthals produced simple bone tools, perforated animal teeth and other forms of personal decoration, and scattered powdered red ochre across the floors of their living areas.[6,7] But were these new patterns of behaviour simply copied from contemporaneous modern populations, immediately to the south, or did the Neanderthal populations in this region invent them independently, at almost exactly the same time as the modern human populations were dispersing across Europe?

Many participants at the conference found it hard to accept the hypothesis that this evolution of modern human behaviour was totally independent and coincidental. They pointed to direct dating evidence, which seems to show that the new behavioural patterns among the final Neanderthals emerged only after around 38,000 years BP—that is, only after the modern populations were already established in northern Spain (J.-J. Hublin, Musée de l'Homme, Paris; Fig. 1). It was argued that the combination of exceptionally high Neanderthal population densities in western France (reflected in the high densities of archaeological sites in this region), together with the conditions in this area (which were cooler, with more open vegetation than in the Mediterranean areas further to the south), delayed colonization by modern human groups. In any event, evidence from both north and south of the Pyrenees shows that population replacement was by no means an overnight event, and seems to have depended on local ecological conditions, as well as on the specific behavioural adaptations of the two groups.[8]

The alternative picture—of an independent, coincidental evolution of typically 'modern' behaviour by the final Neanderthal populations, considerably before modern humans arrived in western Europe—would have dramatic implications. We would have to admit that the behavioural and

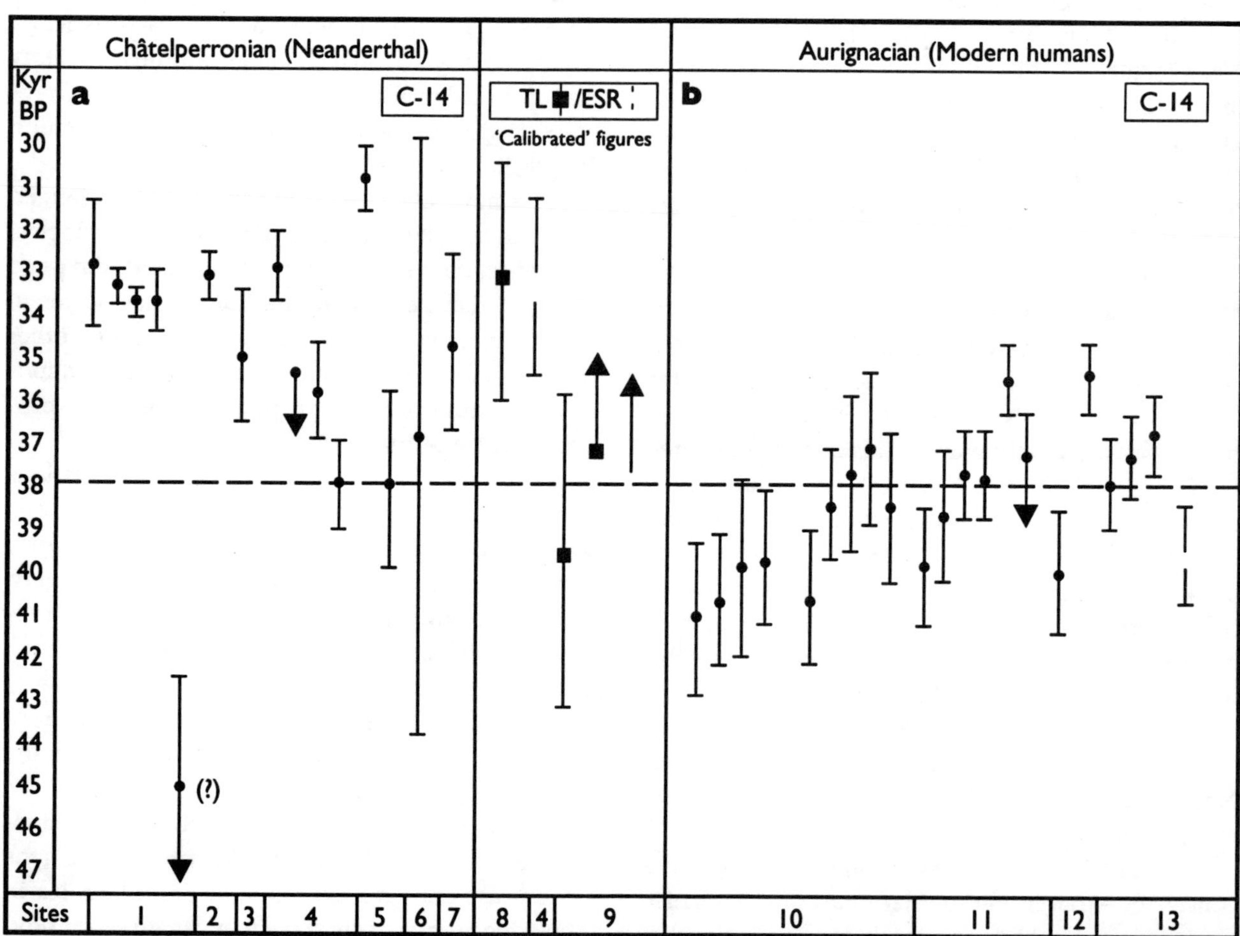

Figure 1. Radiocarbon (C-14) and other absolute age measurements for late Neanderthal and early modern human sites. a, Late Neanderthal, 'Châtelperronian' sites in France. b, Early modern human 'Aurignacian' sites in northern Spain. Note the marked overlap in the age ranges,[10] and that the thermoluminescence (TL) and electron spin resonance (ESR) dates have been 'calibrated' by subtracting 3,000 years to allow for the known offset between radiocarbon and other dating methods in this time range.[11,13]

cognitive capacities of the Neanderthals were every bit as advanced as those of modern humans. Not only that, but also that technological, social and cognitive 'modernity' could erupt at different times and places, presumably in response to some as-yet-unidentified cause. The sceptics in the audience pointed to the statistical improbability of this kind of occurrence, and to the conflicts between this picture and the rapidly accumulating dating evidence (O. Bar-Yosef, Harvard Univ.; C. Gamble, Southampton Univ.).

Aside from these debates, studies of Neanderthal skeletal remains reinforce the conclusion that they were a divergent lineage, which probably made no contribution to the evolution of anatomically modern humans. A range of anatomical features is unique to the Eurasian Neanderthals, from the detailed form of the lower jaw to the complex morphology of the inner ear. These must have evolved after the Neanderthals separated from the ancestors of modern humans (Y. Rak, Tel Aviv Univ.; M. Ponce de León, C. Zollikofer & R. Martin, Zurich Irchel Univ.). Distinctively Neanderthal features have been identified in the 35 individuals from the Sima de los Huesos (Atapuerca) in northern Spain, at least 300,000 years BP, and in even earlier skeletons from Petralona in Greece and Arago in southern France (J.-L. Arsuaga, Complutense Univ., Madrid).

All of this is consistent with the DNA evidence that the two lineages separated at least half a million years ago,[4] and even longer divergence times are favoured by some workers. But how much of this divergent development can be attributed to climatic contrasts between Eurasia and Africa? Only the relatively short, stocky bodies of the Neanderthals stand out as a classically climatic adaptation, yet much of their ecological range was in relatively temperate areas of southern Eurasia, as opposed to the periglacial north. Their notoriously large noses and faces were probably due to the pressures of heavy chewing and use of the jaws as tools, rather than to any climatic adaptation to warming up cold air streams in the nasal passages. Most of the other 'robust' features of the Neanderthal skeleton seem to be related directly to their massive body weight, although the morphology of the upper limb bones does seem to reflect exceptionally heavy stresses in the use of the arms and hands (E. Trinkaus, Washington Univ., St Louis).

At the end of the conference we were left with the impression that the Neanderthals really were very different—well adapted to survive in the harsh glacial environments of Europe, perhaps, but with distinct anatomical and behavioural patterns from their modern human successors. Whether these contrasts reflect different mental abilities remains the 64,000 dollar question. But it could be argued that if the Neanderthals followed a separate evolutionary trajectory from the one that led to modern humans over at least half a million years, it would hardly be surprising if related divergences in cognitive capacities (such as language or intelligence) had evolved over this time.[9] The eagerness of some scientists to claim close kinship with the Neanderthals could come close to denying that human evolution actually took place.

Paul Mellars is in the Department of Archaeology, University of Cambridge, Downing Street, Cambridge CB2 3DZ, UK.

References

1. Trinkaus, E. & Shipman, P. *The Neandertals* (Cape, London, 1993).

2. Cann, R. L, Stoneking, M. & Wilson, A. C. *Nature* 235, 31–36 (1987).

3.`Stoneking, M. & Cann, R. L. in *The Human Revolution* (eds Mellars, P. & Stringer, C.) 17–30 (Edinburgh Univ. Pres, 1989).

4. Krings, M. *et al. Cell* 90, 19–30 (1997).

5. Stringer, C. B. & Mackie, R. *African Exodus: The Origins of Modern Humanity* (Cape, London, 1996).

6. d'Errico, F., Zilhao, J., Julien, M., Baffier, D. & Pelegrin, J. *Curr. Anthropol.* 39, S1–S44 (1998).

7. Bahn, P. G. *Nature* 394, 719–720 (1998).

8. Mellars, P. A. in *Neandertals and Modern Humans in Western Asia* (eds Akazawa, T., Aoki, K. & Bar-Yosef, O.) 493–507 (Plenum, New York, 1998).

9. Mithen, S. *The Prehistory of the Mind* (Thames & Hudson, London, 1996).

10. Mellars, P. *Curr. Anthropol.* (in the press).

11. Bard, E., Hamelin, B., Fairbanks, R. G. & Zindler, A. *Nature* 354, 405–410 (1990).

12. Laj, C., Mazaud, A. & Duplessy, J. C. *Geophys. Res. Lett.* 23, 2045–2048 (1996).

5.7 Study Questions: The Fate of the Neaderthals — Paul Mellars

1. In what part of Europe were Neanderthals and modern humans existing simultaneously?

2. What proof do researchers have that the two species existed at the same location for at least 5,000 years?

3. How were behavioral patterns between the two species similar? Different?

4. Does the author of this article suggest that modern humans evolved from Neanderthals, and why? How has DNA evidence confirmed the authors' hypothesis?

5. What is meant by coincidental evolution?

6. What are the classical features associated with Neanderthals?

7. Do Neanderthals exist today? (This question can be tricky—the answer should mention interbreeding with modern humans, rather than mentioning the current people from Neander Valley.)

5.8 Neanderthal: Case Closed?

Catherine E. Martin

A colleague comes rushing into the office in Arizona; another calls from Los Angeles. Did you hear the news? The examination of Neanderthal DNA showed it differed from that of modern humans! These results settle once and for all an almost 150 year old controversy surrounding Neanderthal's status as a recent ancestor of some, if not all, human populations today. Or did they?

Followers of physical (biological) anthropology are hardly surprised by the controversy and the changing interpretations occasioned by the new data or paradigms! In the days of Louis Leakey, for instance, headlines periodically announced the discovery of the oldest hominid ancestor yet. The declaration that *Homo habilis* was the first member of our genus and our only early ancestor remained in dispute for many years. After the discovery of Lucy in Ethiopia, media coverage featured the debate between the Leakeys and Don Johanson over her role in our early evolution. How was Lucy (given a new species name, *Australopithecus afarensis*, by Johanson and White) related to Mary Leakey's finds at Laetoli (including jaws and the famous footprints)? How many species of *Australopithecus* were there? The focus on punctuated equilibrium, with its emphasis on branching and rapid changes rather than the gradualist, unilineal evolutionary models previously more in vogue, suggested the possibility of a number of different species.

But the role of Neanderthal in the evolution of modern *Homo sapiens* remained unclear. For some anthropologists, Neanderthal was too similar to modern humans not to have been closely involved in our evolution, either as a direct ancestor or a slightly specialized cousin interbreeding with immigrating populations, especially in Europe. From the first discovery of a Neanderthal skeleton in Gibraltar in 1848 to the naming of Neanderthal for the 1856 find in Germany (after the Neander Valley or Thal, later changed to Tal in the German spelling of valley) the importance of this hominid was not clear. Was Neanderthal merely a somewhat aberrant member of our species? Or were the caricatures of Neanderthal as a stooped and hairy caveman (based on Boule's early reconstructions) with a very different sort of brain—as portrayed in Jean Auel's *Clan of the Cave Bear*, for instance—more accurate?

Physical anthropology is affected by scientific discoveries and by changing interpretive frameworks that, in some cases, can be related to social and political trends in society. Was Neanderthal to be cast off as a brute? Did this hominid represent our "bestial" side? Or were we to include this ancestor as one of our own? The 1960's, unsurprisingly, was the prominence of this last viewpoint. The work of Erik Trinkaus, however, once again portrays Neanderthal as very different.

The 1980's was characterized by an explosion in research on genetics and the use of mitochondrial DNA for exploring how populations are related. Mitochondrial DNA is found outside the nucleus of the cell, in the powerhouse or mitochondria. Because males transmit primarily nuclear DNA in their sperm—whereas females pass on mitochondria in the cytoplasm of their cells—children inherit their mitochondrial DNA maternally and it continues through the female line. Mitochondrial DNA involves fewer base pairs than nuclear DNA and can be compared to determine the number of differences between individuals or populations. These variations result from changes, mutations in the genetic code, which are claimed to accumulate over time at a constant rate. Using this method, genetic researchers at the University of California at Berkeley (Mark Stoneking, Linda Vigilant, Rebecca Cann and leader Allan Wilson) suggested in 1987 that modern humans all have a recent common ancestor living approximately 200,000 years ago in Africa. Later studies supported this conclusion and the date of divergence was revised to reflect a more recent split. The variation in modern populations is greatest among African populations themselves, suggesting that they began to diversify before migration to Asia, Europe and the New World.

The model involving evolution from this population of "mitochondrial Eve" became known as the "out of Africa" hypothesis and has been supported by a number of researchers, notably Christopher Stringer at the Natural History Museum in London and, using archaeological evidence, Richard Klein. The "Eve" theory fits in well with current political correctness, the idea that there is little difference among "racial" or population groups today. Neanderthals lived for many thousand years near modern humans, especially in the Near East. In Europe they coexisted until sometime before 30,000 years ago, when they died out, the result perhaps of superior adaptations of Cro-Magnon populations. On the other hand, the "multiregional hypothesis" continues to hold sway with many anthropologists, including Milford Wolpoff of the University of Michigan and Alan Templeton of Washington University in St. Louis. These scholars claim that the fossil evidence supports the earlier divergence of populations, with subsequent adaptation and evolution in different geographic areas. New fossil evidence from Spain announced just this May was attributed to an early common ancestor of Neanderthals and modern humans. A third view argues that both independent evolution and migration with intermixture are involved, but this claim is seen to conflict with the continuity reflected by mitochondrial DNA.

It was bound to happen. On July 11, 1997, the British journal *Cell* announced the results of a direct comparison of the mitochondrial DNA extracted from Neanderthal remains with that of modern humans. Research was conducted by Svante Paabo and his coworkers at the University of Munich and confirmed by testing at Pennsylvania Sate University. Once and for all, Neanderthal was eliminated as a human ancestor. Or was he/she?

Seldom in biological anthropology do results—no matter how "conclusive"—remain uncriticized. While the study is of great interest, does it resolve "the Neanderthal problem?" The analysis was carried out on a small sample of material from the upper arm bone of the Neander skeleton from Germany. Based on 378 nucleotides, more than three times the number of differences was found compared to variation within modern human population. But how representative is this sample? Might additional analyses show that some populations of Neanderthal are more similar to us? Could some of the Neanderthal characteristics have disappeared through later evolution? Are modern populations similar because of recent adaptation or intermixture? Were early modern populations variable in their mitochondrial DNA? Are these conclusions supported by other genetic studies? Obviously, more research needs to be done. Nonetheless, the results of these studies are exciting and suggestive, in keeping with the dynamic nature of physical anthropology.

Selected References

Auel, Jean
1980 The Clan of the Cave Bear. Toronto: Bantam Books.

Boule, M. and H. Vallois
1957 Fossil Men. London: Thames and Hudson.

Klein, Richard G.
1992 The archeology of modern human origins. Evolutionary anthropology 1 (1):5–14

Leakey, Richard and Roger Lewin
1992 Origins Reconsidered. New York: Doubleday

Lewin, Roger
1993 The Origin of Modern Humans. New York: Scientific American Library (Distributed by W.H. Freeman and Company.)

Mellars, P. and C. Stringer, eds.
1989 The Human Revolution: Behavioral and Biological Perspectives on the Origins of Modern Humans. Edinburgh: Edinburgh University Press.

Shreeve, James
1995 The Neandertal Enigma: Solving the Mystery of Modern Human Origins. New York: William Morrow and Company.

Stringer, Christopher and Clive Gamble
1993 In Search of the Neanderthals: Solving the Puzzle of Human Origins. New York: Thames and Hudson.

Templeton, A.R.
1993 The "Eve" Hypothesisis: A Genetic Critique and Reanalysis. American Anthropologist 95:51–72.

Trinkaus, Erik and Pat Shipman
1993 The Neandertals: Changing the Image of Mankind. New York: Alfred A. Knopf.

5.8 Study Questions: Neanderthal: Case Closed? — Catherine E. Martin

1. What is meant by the "Eve" theory?

2. How does this model differ from Wolpoff's "multiregional hypothesis?"

5.9 *Did Neanderthals and Modern Humans Interbreed?*

Reuters

St. Louis, April 19—A 24,500-year-old skeleton found in Portugal with characteristics of both early modern humans and Neanderthals shows the two groups interbred and may be ancestors of modern humans.

The hybrid skeleton of what was likely a 4-year-old boy refuted the widely held theory that early humans emigrated from Africa and displaced the Neanderthal population without interbreeding, Washington University anthropologist Erik Trinkaus said.

The hybrid skeleton was the first evidence ever found that populations of early modern humans and Neanderthals interacted and interbred, Trinkaus said.

"This skeleton shows a mixture of features that are features of modern man," he said in a telephone interview on Monday.

Many anthropologists support the so-called "Out of Africa" theory of human origins that says modern humans evolved in Africa and spread across the world about 100,000 years ago.

There is considerable evidence that Cro-Magnon people, who became modern humans, lived side-by-side with and interacted with Neanderthals, which died out about 30,000 years ago.

"This find refutes strict replacement models of modern human origins—that early modern humans all emerged from Africa and wiped out the Neanderthal population," Trinkaus said.

Radiocarbon Dating

Radiocarbon dating of the skeleton excavated in December showed it lived about 24,500 years ago, or 4,000 years after the time that early modern humans migrated across the Pyrenees and into the Iberian Peninsula where Neanderthals were already living, he said.

"This skeleton, which has some characteristics of Neanderthals and others of early modern humans, demonstrates that early modern humans and Neanderthals are not all that different. They intermixed, interbred and produced offspring," Trinkaus said.

'Not a Love Child'

He said the skeleton could not be dismissed as just a product of some unlikely, rare affair between members of the two groups.

"This is not a love child," he continued. "The results of admixture were there in the population 4,000 years after Neanderthals and early modern humans first met on the Iberian Peninsula."

A study published in 1997 of DNA taken from the Neanderthal skeleton discovered in Germany's Neander valley in 1856 indicated it was too distant genetically to have been an ancestor of modern humans.

But Trinkaus said that merely proved that Neanderthals were not modern man, which was already known.

Though the skeleton's skull was crushed when a farmer bulldozed the then-undiscovered site six years ago, Portuguese archaeologists led by Portugal's director of antiquities, Joao Zilhao, subsequently found the well-preserved body and the intact lower jaw preserved in red ochre a few inches below the surface.

The prominent chin was characteristic of early modern humans while the stocky trunk and short limbs reflected its Neanderthal origins, Trinkaus said. Other arm bones pointed to early modern human parentage.

The skeleton was found when an archaeologist stuck his hand down a rabbit hole and pulled out the well-preserved skeleton's left forearm. The body was buried in red ochre, with a pierced shell, indicating a ritual burial, Trinkaus said.

The site is on a hillside near Leiria, Portugal, in the Lapedo Valley 80 miles north of Lisbon and 19 miles off the Atlantic Coast.

5.9 Study Questions: Did Neanderthals and Modern Humans Interbreed?

1. What does the hybrid skeleton from Portugal seem to reveal? Explain the interpretation.

2. How does this find fit in with the hypotheses raised during studies conducted on DNA from Neandertals and modern humans?

3. What is meant by a "love child?"

■ 5.10 Exercise: Hominid Traits

Complete the following study sheets for each member of the hominid phylogeny. Please be aware that there may be instances where information is still unknown or that the category may not pertain to a particular species. Be sure to indicate that on your answer sheets.

Ardipithecus ramidus

location of remains:

time period of existence:

names of specific finds:

associated researchers:

locomotion pattern:

dentition:

cranial capacity:

morphology of skull:

post-cranial remains:

diet: (scavenging, hunting-gathering)

tools:

culture:

Australopithecus anamensis

location of remains:

time period of existence:

names of specific finds:

associated researchers:

locomotion pattern:

dentition:

cranial capacity:

morphology of skull:

post-cranial remains:

diet: (scavenging, hunting-gathering)

tools:

culture:

Australopithecus afarensis

location of remains:

time period of existence:

names of specific finds:

associated researchers:

locomotion pattern:

dentition:

cranial capacity:

morphology of skull:

post-cranial remains:

diet: (scavenging, hunting-gathering)

tools:

culture:

Australopithecus garhi

location of remains:

time period of existence:

names of specific finds:

associated researchers:

locomotion pattern:

dentition:

cranial capacity:

morphology of skull:

post-cranial remains:

diet: (scavenging, hunting-gathering)

tools:

culture:

Australopithecus aethiopicus

location of remains:

time period of existence:

names of specific finds:

associated researchers:

locomotion pattern:

dentition:

cranial capacity:

morphology of skull:

post-cranial remains:

diet: (scavenging, hunting-gathering)

tools:

culture:

Australopithecus boisei

location of remains:

time period of existence:

names of specific finds:

associated researchers:

locomotion pattern:

dentition:

cranial capacity:

morphology of skull:

post-cranial remains:

diet: (scavenging, hunting-gathering)

tools:

culture:

Australopithecus robustus

location of remains:

time period of existence:

names of specific finds:

associated researchers:

locomotion pattern:

dentition:

cranial capacity:

morphology of skull:

post-cranial remains:

diet: (scavenging, hunting-gathering)

tools:

culture:

Australopithecus africanus

location of remains:

time period of existence:

names of specific finds:

associated researchers:

locomotion pattern:

dentition:

cranial capacity:

morphology of skull:

post-cranial remains:

diet: (scavenging, hunting-gathering)

tools:

culture:

Homo habilis

location of remains:

time period of existence:

names of specific finds:

associated researchers:

locomotion pattern:

dentition:

cranial capacity:

morphology of skull:

post-cranial remains:

diet: (scavenging, hunting-gathering)

tools:

culture:

Homo erectus

location of remains:

time period of existence:

names of specific finds:

associated researchers:

locomotion pattern:

dentition:

cranial capacity:

morphology of skull:

post-cranial remains:

diet: (scavenging, hunting-gathering)

tools:

culture:

Homo neandertalensis

location of remains:

time period of existence:

names of specific finds:

associated researchers:

locomotion pattern:

dentition:

cranial capacity:

morphology of skull:

post-cranial remains:

diet: (scavenging, hunting-gathering)

tools:

culture:

Archaic Homo sapiens

location of remains:

time period of existence:

names of specific finds:

associated researchers:

locomotion pattern:

dentition:

cranial capacity:

morphology of skull:

post-cranial remains:

diet: (scavenging, hunting-gathering)

tools:

culture:

Homo sapiens

location of remains:

time period of existence:

names of specific finds:

associated researchers:

locomotion pattern:

dentition:

cranial capacity:

morphology of skull:

post-cranial remains:

diet: (scavenging, hunting-gathering)

tools:

culture:

	Homo rudolfensis	*Homo ergaster*	*Homo antecessor*
location of remains:			
time period of existence:			
names of specific finds:			
associated researchers:			
locomotion pattern:			
dentition:			
cranial capacity:			
morphology of skull:			
post-cranial remains:			
diet: (scavenging, hunting-gathering)			
tools:			
culture:			

■ 5.11 Exercise: Fossil Comparisons

Answer the following questions pertaining to the biological illustrations provided on the following pages.

1. Compare and contrast the illustrations of *Australopithecus africanus* and *Australopithecus boisei*. What similarities do you see? What are the differences? What factors led to these differences between the species?

2. Compare the above two species to the gorilla drawing. Describe the similarities and differences.

3. Compare the australopithicines to *Homo habilis*. What are the similarities and differences between the species?

4. Discuss the similarities between *Homo erectus* and *Homo sapiens*. Differentiate between the primitive and derived physical characteristics of each.

■ 5.12 Diagram: Illustrations of Fossil Remains

Gorilla, Male

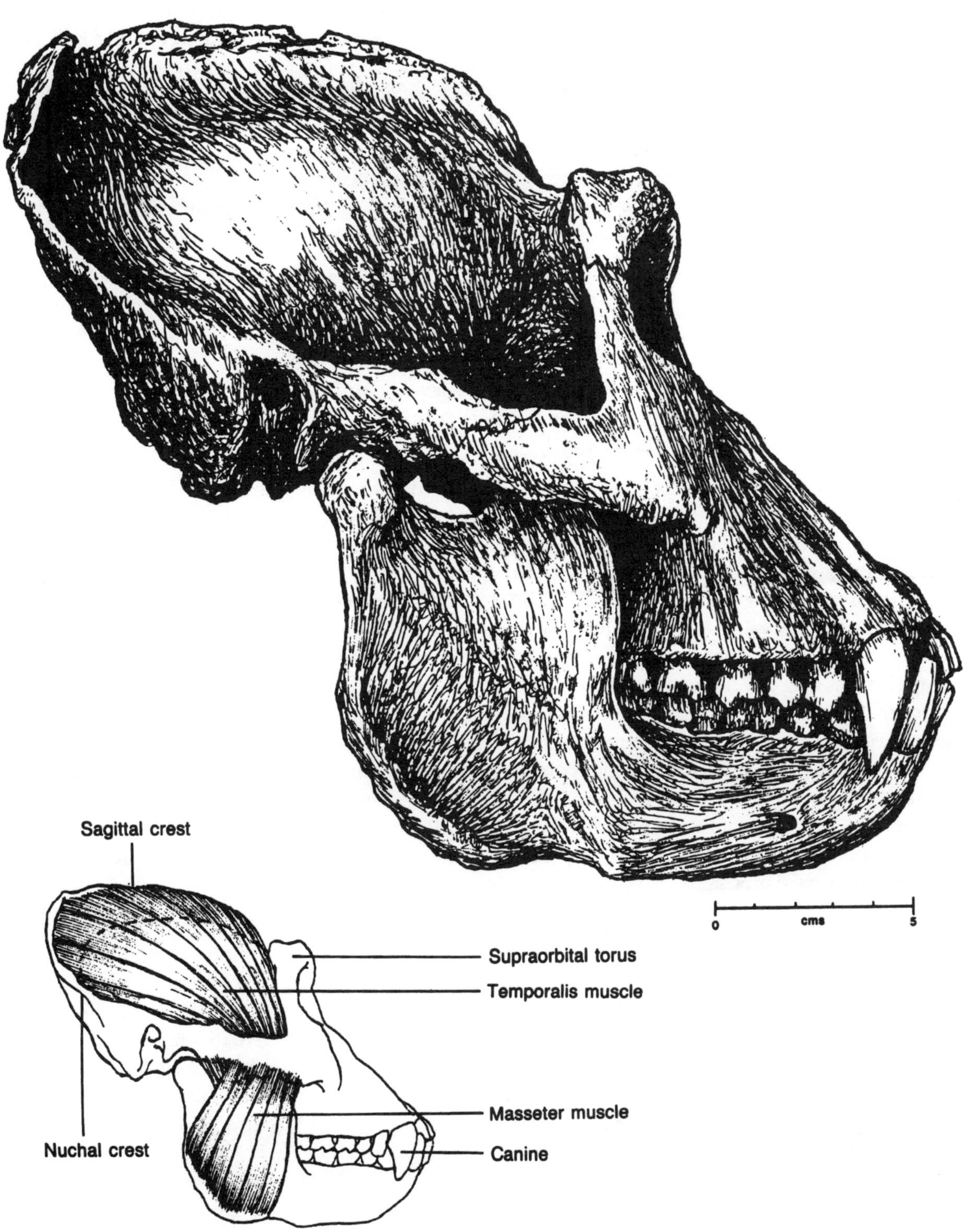

A.L. 288-1

Specimen: **A. L. 288-1 ("Lucy")**
Geographic location: Hadar, Ethiopia
Taxonomic affiliation: *Australopithecus afarensis*
Dating: Middle Pliocene (3.0 myBP)

General description: Discovered in 1974 by D. Johanson and T. Gray, this 40% complete fossil hominid skeleton represents one of the most complete individual remains of an australopithecine. The individual is a very small female, weighing about 60 pounds and standing not much greater than three and a half feet in stature. In addition to being short, this individual possesses a suite of features that are very different from that of living humans. The bones are extraordinarily thick, reflecting a demanding, strenuous lifestyle. The relative elongation of the bodies of the thoracic vertebra reflect heavy use of the back, such as climbing, lifting, and carrying. The relative lengths of the arms and legs are different from those of modern humans. William Jungers contends that these differences reflect a hominid that had attained arm proportions similar to modern humans, but the legs were much shorter. This implies that this hominid had a short stride length, thus requiring more steps to move the same distance relative to a modern human.

The curved hand and foot phalanges are reminiscent of those of living apes. Stern and Susman (1983) have remarked that the curvature of the Hadar proximal hand phalanges—like chimpanzees—is very pronounced, well outside of the range of living humans. Study of the tarsal-metatarsal joint articulation of the first or great toe of *A. afarensis*, however, shows lack of grasping capabilities seen in all extant apes. It is unlikely, therefore, that these early hominids possessed the same level or kind of commitment to arboreality as the living apes. The curvature of the fingers suggest, however, that *A. afarensis* may have been a competent tree climber.

It is the consensus among paleoanthropologists that one differentiating (and perhaps most important) feature of hominids is their habitual and efficient bipedal locomotion. In addition to characteristics described above, there are other indicators of bipedality in the Lucy postcranial skeleton. In the drawing it can be seen that although the form of bipedalism may have been different from later hominids, the pelvis exhibits a number of morphological adaptations that are more similar to a modern human than to a quadrupedal ape, such as the chimpanzee. In particular, the ilium of Lucy is short and broad and flares outward, thus providing for muscle and bone positions compatible with habitual bipedality. In contrast to this configuration, the ape ilium is long and narrow. The angle formed at the knee region (bicondylar angle) in Lucy is also like that of the modern biped. In the chimpanzee, the angle is much straighter than in either *A. afarensis* or modern *Homo sapiens*. That is, the long axis of the femur is nearly parallel to the vertical axis; in modern humans, the long axis of the femur is not parallel to the vertical axis, but instead, forms a distinct angle. Note also the variation in position of the knees relative to each other in the chimpanzee, Lucy, and modern *Homo sapiens*. The knees of the chimpanzee are much further apart than those of either of the two bipeds. These anatomical details, coupled with footprint patterns from Laetoli, provide irrefutable proof that these early hominids were bipedal.

References: Johanson and Edey, 1981; Johanson, Lovejoy, Kimbel, White, Ward, Bush, Latimer, and Coppens, 1982; Bush, Lovejoy, Johanson, and Coppens, 1982; Skinner and Sperber, 1982; Cherfas, 1983; Cook, Buikstra, DeRousseau, and Johanson, 1983; Jungers, 1982, 1988; Jungers and Stern, 1983; Stern and Susman, 1983; Susman, Stern, and Jungers, 1984, 1985; Wolpoff, 1983a, 1983b, 1998; Lovejoy, 1974, 1981, 1984, 1988; Lewin, 1983a, 1983b, 1987; Lamy, 1983; Berge, Orban-Segebarth, and Schmid, 1984; Tague and Lovejoy, 1986; McHenry, 1986; White and Suwa, 1987; Ruff, 1988; Tuttle, 1988; Latimer and Lovejoy, 1989, 1990; Simons, 1989; Ruff, 1991; Skelton and McHenry, 1992; Gebo, 1992, 1996; Häusler and Schmid, 1995; Simpson, 1996.

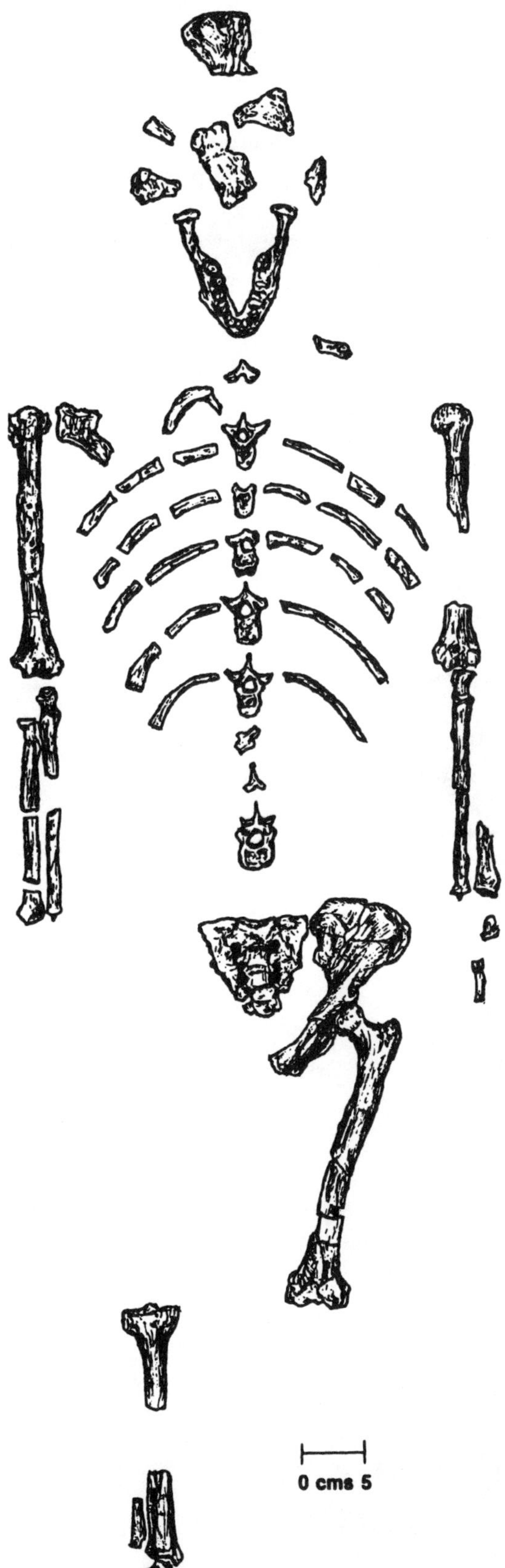
A.L. 288-1
0 cms 5

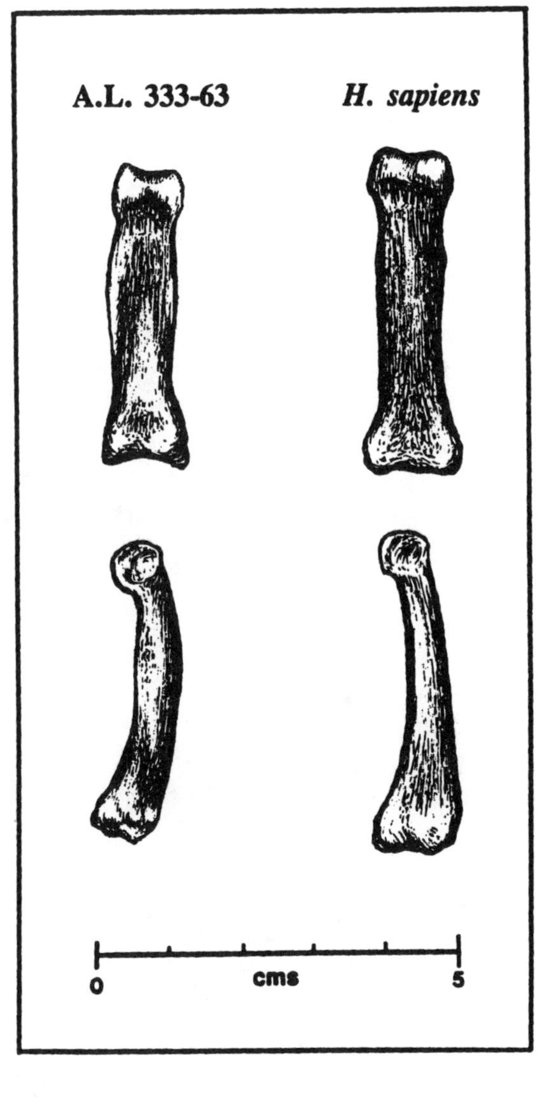
A.L. 333-63
H. sapiens
0
cms
5

STS 5

Specimen: **STS 5**
Geographic location: Sterkfontein, Republic of South Africa

Taxonomic affiliation: *Australopithecus africanus*
Dating: Upper Pliocene (2.3–2.8 myBP)

General description: Discovered in 1947 by Robert Broom and John T. Robinson, this nearly complete adult cranium (nicknamed "Mrs. Ples"), is the most complete australopithecine cranium. This specimen shows a number of important cranial morphological features that are associated with *A. africanus*: small endocranial capacity (about 450 cc), lightly constructed cranium, reduced postorbital constriction, lower facial projection, and relatively wide, dished face.

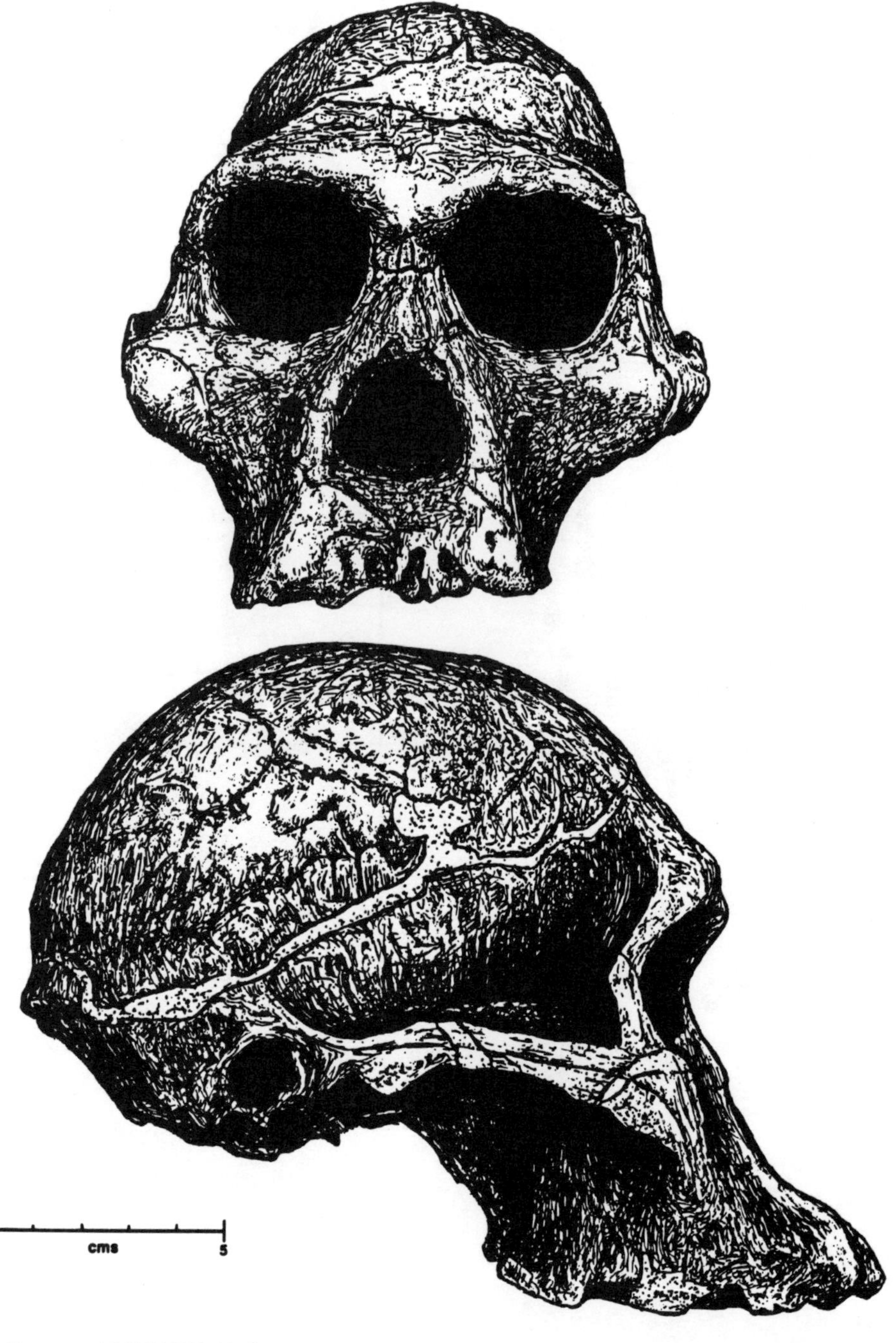

References: Broom, 1947, 1950; Robinson, 1962; Howell, 1978; Reed, 1983; Rak, 1983; Kuman, 1994; Clarke, 1994; Conroy, 1997.

O.H. 5

Specimen: **O.H. 5**
Geographic location: Olduvai Gorge, Tanzania
Taxonomic affiliation: *Australopithecus boisei*
Dating: Late Pliocene—early Pleistocene (1.8 myBP)

General description: This nearly complete cranium (known as "Zinj" after the original genus name, "*Zinjanthropus*") was discovered by Mary Leakey in 1959 and subsequently described by P. Tobias. Both the size of the attachment areas for the masticatory muscles—note the well developed sagittal crest—and the molars are massive. In addition, the premolars are enlarged (molarized), effectively increasing the chewing surface of the cheek teeth from three to five teeth on each side of the jaw, upper and lower. Note the relatively tiny incisors and the flat occlusal wear pattern of the teeth, including the canines. The enamel is thick. The face is massive and a diamond shape. These features characterize this taxon of hominid. The method of dating of this specimen (potassium argon) was important in that it provided an extremely old date, and it represented the first reliable chronometric assessment of an early hominid.

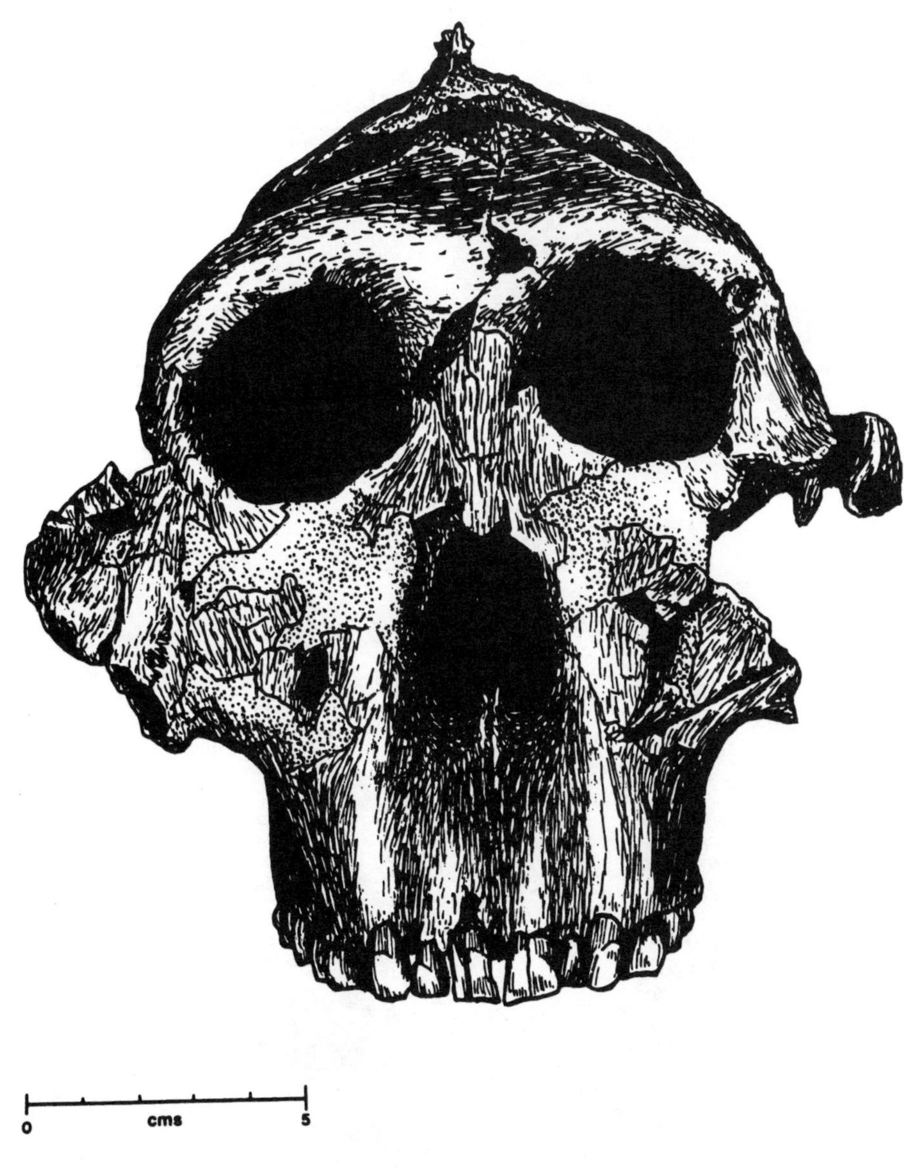

0 cms 5

References: L. Leakey, 1960; Robinson, 1960; Tobias, 1967; Johanson and Edey, 1981; Rak, 1983; M. D. Leakey, 1984; Grine, 1988; Demes and Creel, 1988.

O.H. 5

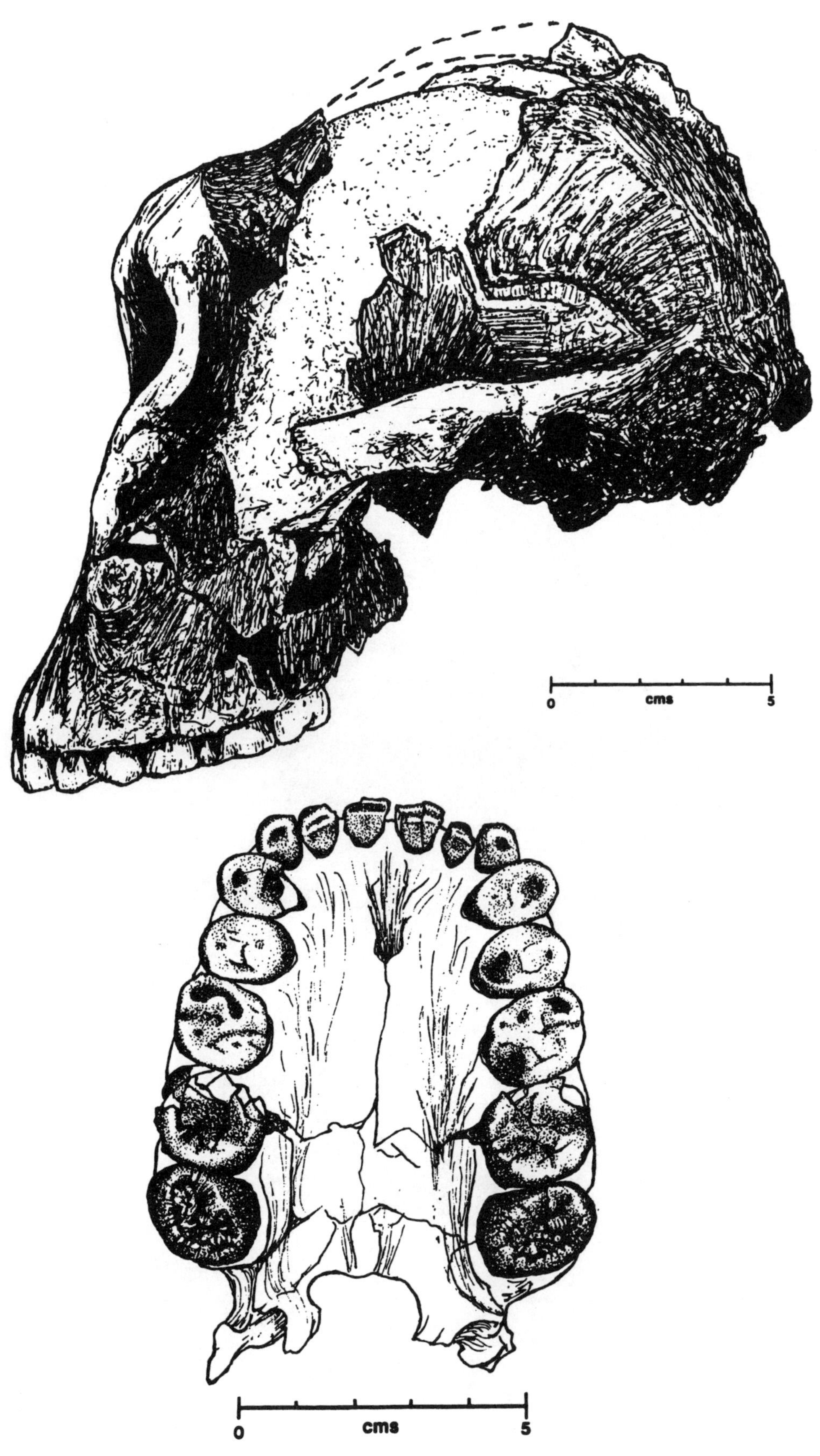

O.H. 24

Specimen: **O.H. 24**
Geographic location: Olduvai Gorge, Tanzania
Taxonomic affiliation: *Homo habilis*
Dating: Late Pliocene-early Pleistocene (1.75–2.0 myBP)

General description: Discovered by P. Nzube in 1968, the specimen had been exposed and badly weathered for a number of years. Restoration and reconstruction by R. J. Clarke yielded a specimen consisting of the better part of a cranial vault, and part of the face and dentition is present as well. Although some paleoanthropologists include it in the australopithecines, most agree that the presence of reduced postorbital constriction, a lighter-built cranium, expanded brain size (about 600 cc), and generally smaller teeth align it most closely with the genus *Homo*.

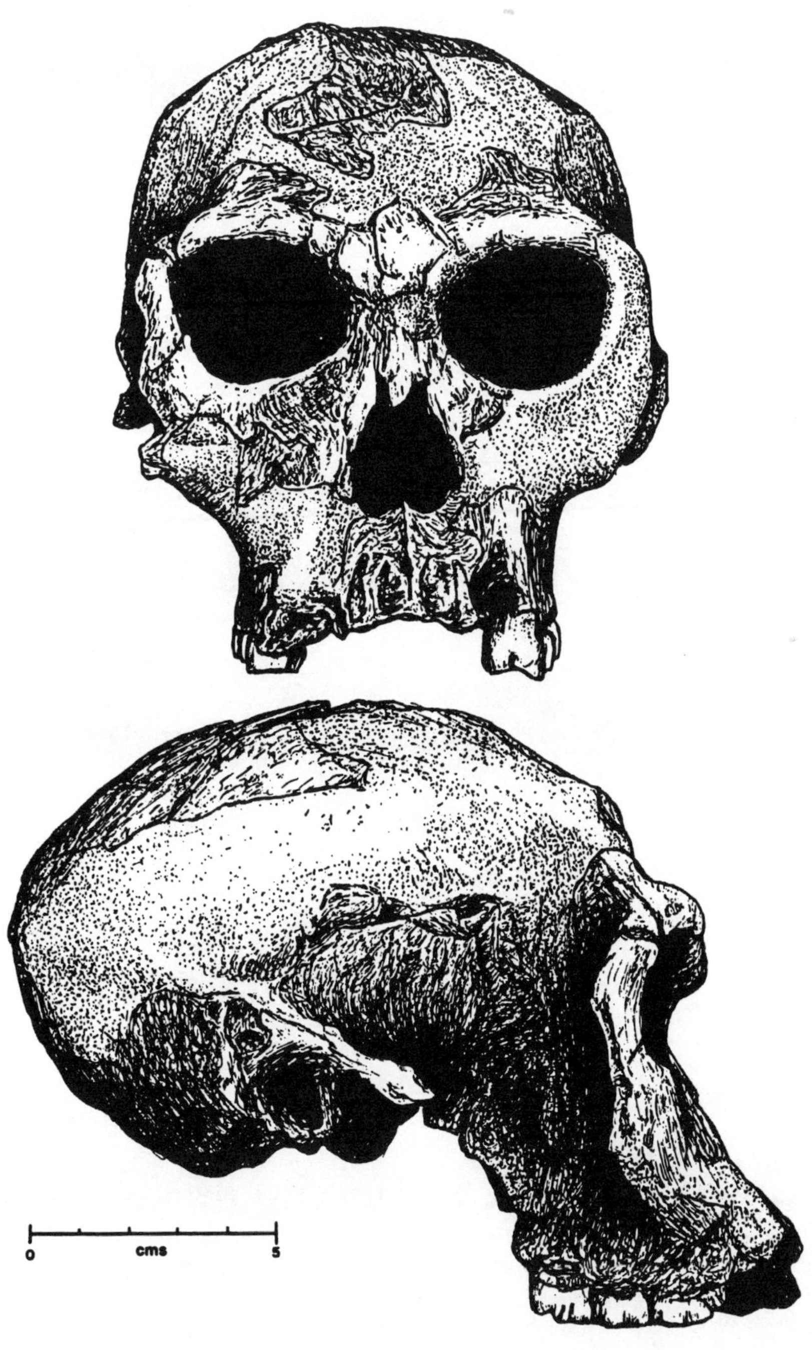

References: M. D. Leakey, Clarke, and L. Leakey, 1971; Tobias, 1972,1991; Howell, 1978.

Zhoukoudian

Specimen: **Zhoukoudian skull reconstruction**
Geographic location: Locality 1, Zhoukoudian (formerly Choukoutien), People's Republic of China
Taxonomic affiliation: *Homo erectus*
Dating: Middle Pleistocene (300,000–550,000 yBP)

General description: The composite reconstruction by Franz Weidenreich was based on cranial materials recovered from the site prior to World War II. The reconstruction of the face is conjectural because few facial bones were found at the site. The later finding of *Homo erectus* crania with faces at other sites, however, suggests that the reconstruction is essentially accurate. The cranium is long and low with thick cranial bones. The forehead is higher and more filled out relative to those of earlier hominids.

The site is of tremendous importance in paleoanthropology, primarily because a large collection of hominid remains, faunal remains, and tools, as well as other evidence of prehistoric occupation that was associated with *Homo erectus* were recovered from a series of well-dated stratigraphic layers. With the exception of materials collected from Zhoukoudian by Chinese paleontologists and archaeologists after World War II, all other remains disappeared in 1941 at the outbreak of World War II. Fortunately, while still in Beijing, Franz Weidenreich made complete sets of cast reproductions of the hominid materials before their disappearance. These casts, in addition to a series of detailed reports, has made it possible to continue study of this valuable fossil sample.

References: Black, 1933; Weidenreich, 1935, 1936a, 1936b, 1937, 1939, 1943; de Terra, 1941; Chang, 1962; Chiu Chung-lang, Ku Yu-min, Chang Yin-yun, and Chang Sen-shui, 1973; Shapiro, 1974; Howells, 1977; Institute of Vertebrate Paleontology and Paleoanthropology (Chinese Academy of Sciences), 1980; Jia Lanpo, 1980; Mann, 1981; Trinkaus, 1982b; Wu Rukang, 1985; Wu Rukang and Dong Xingren, 1983, 1985; Wu Rukang and Lin Shenglong, 1983; Liu Ze-Chun, 1983; Pope, 1988; Brooks and Wood, 1990; Rightmire, 1990; Wu and Poirier, 1995; Tattersall and Sawyer, 1996; Wolpoff, 1996; Etler, 1996; Grün, 1997.

Zhoukoudian

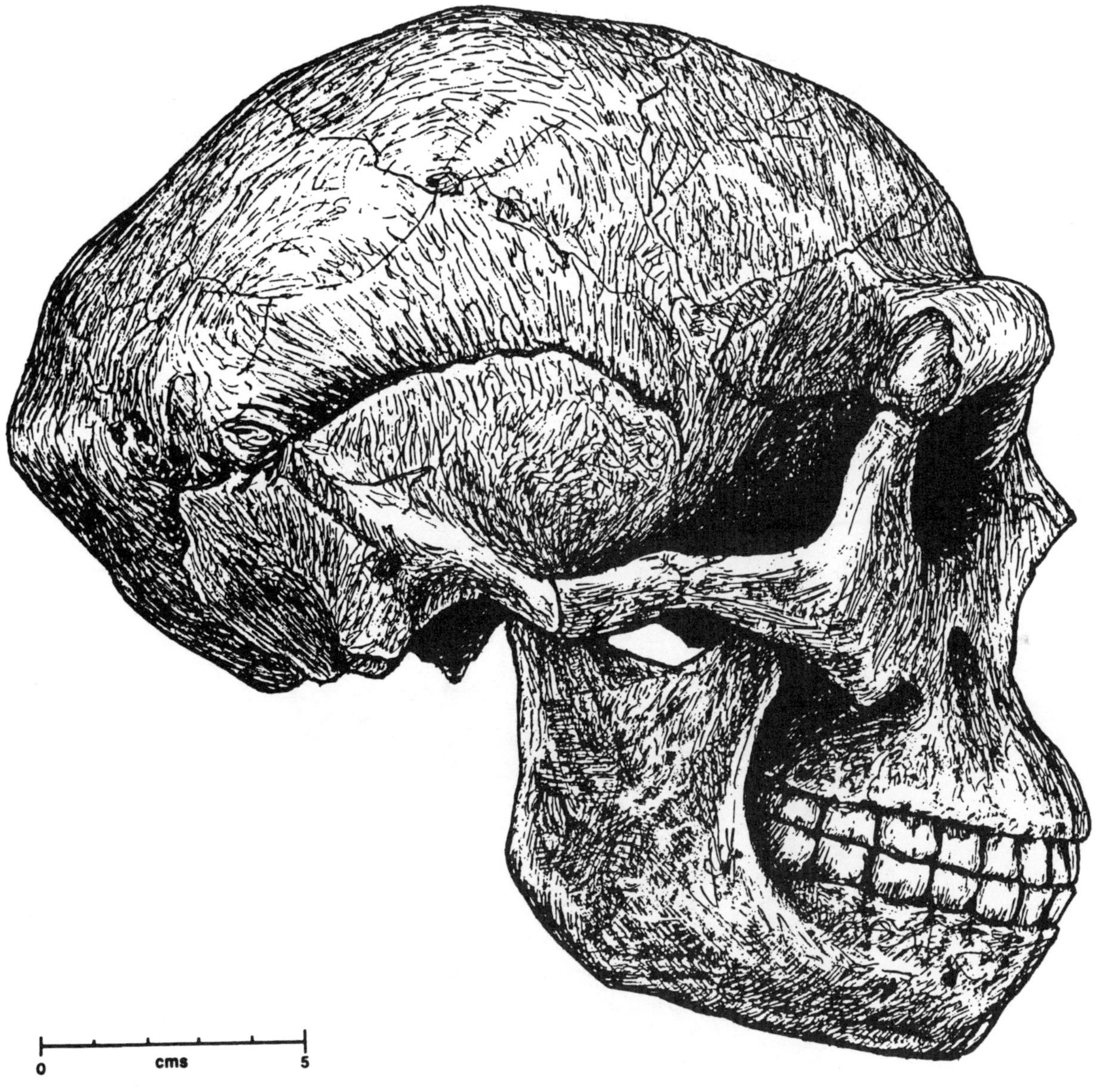

Cro-Magnon I

Specimen: **Cro-Magnon 1**
Geographic location: Les Eyzies, Dordogne, France

Taxonomic affiliation: *Homo sapiens*
Dating: Upper Pleistocene (23,000–27,000 yBP)

General description: Popularly known as the "Old Man" of Cro-Magnon, this individual was discovered in 1868 by workmen and removed from the site by L. Lartet along with the remains of three other adults and four children. This skull exhibits a series of features that characterize the emergence of fully modern *Homo sapiens* in western Europe. Note in particular the broad, high face, the high, vertical forehead, small browridges, relatively narrow nasal aperture, and prominent chin. The projecting nasal bones are reminiscent of the earlier archaic *Homo sapiens* of western Europe. The lower face is quite small. In part, the diminutive size of the lower face may be associated with reduction in facial bone mass that is often associated with the aging process, particularly in older adults.

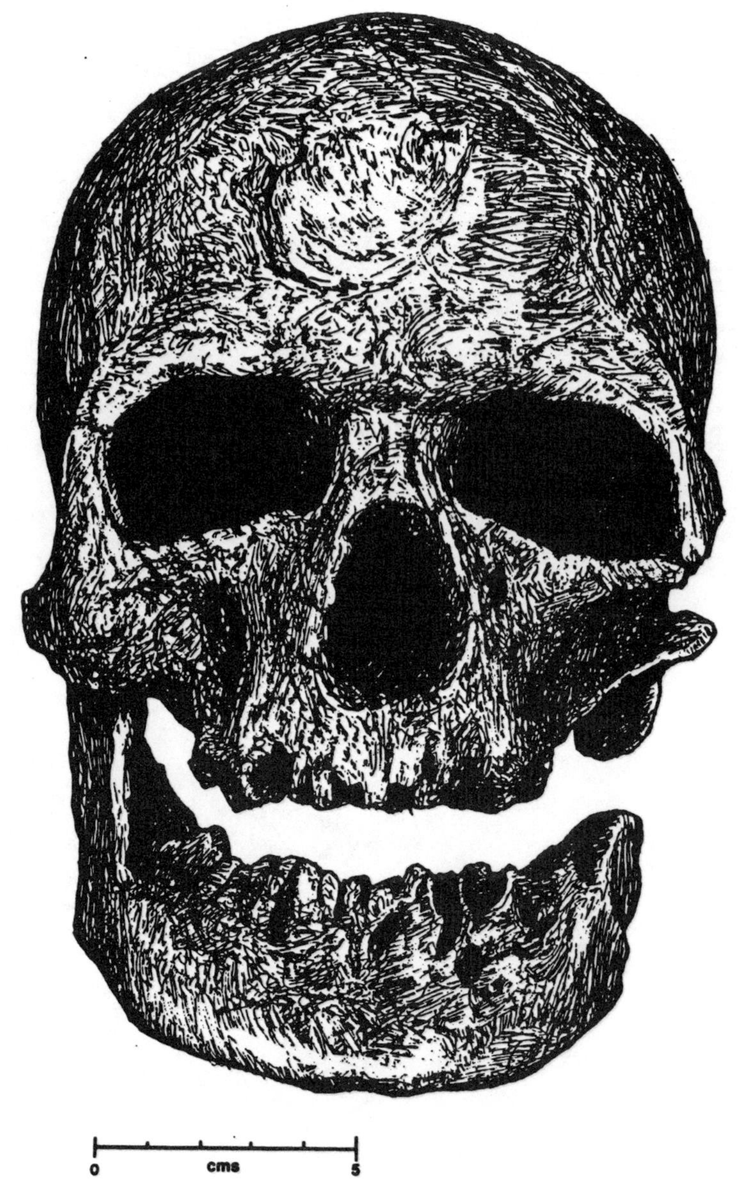

0 cms 5

References: Vallois and Billy, 1965; Camps and Olivier, 1970; Brace and Montagu, 1977; Frayer, 1978; Stringer, Hublin, and Vandermeersch, 1984; Gambier, 1989; Wolpoff, 1998.

Cro-Magnon I

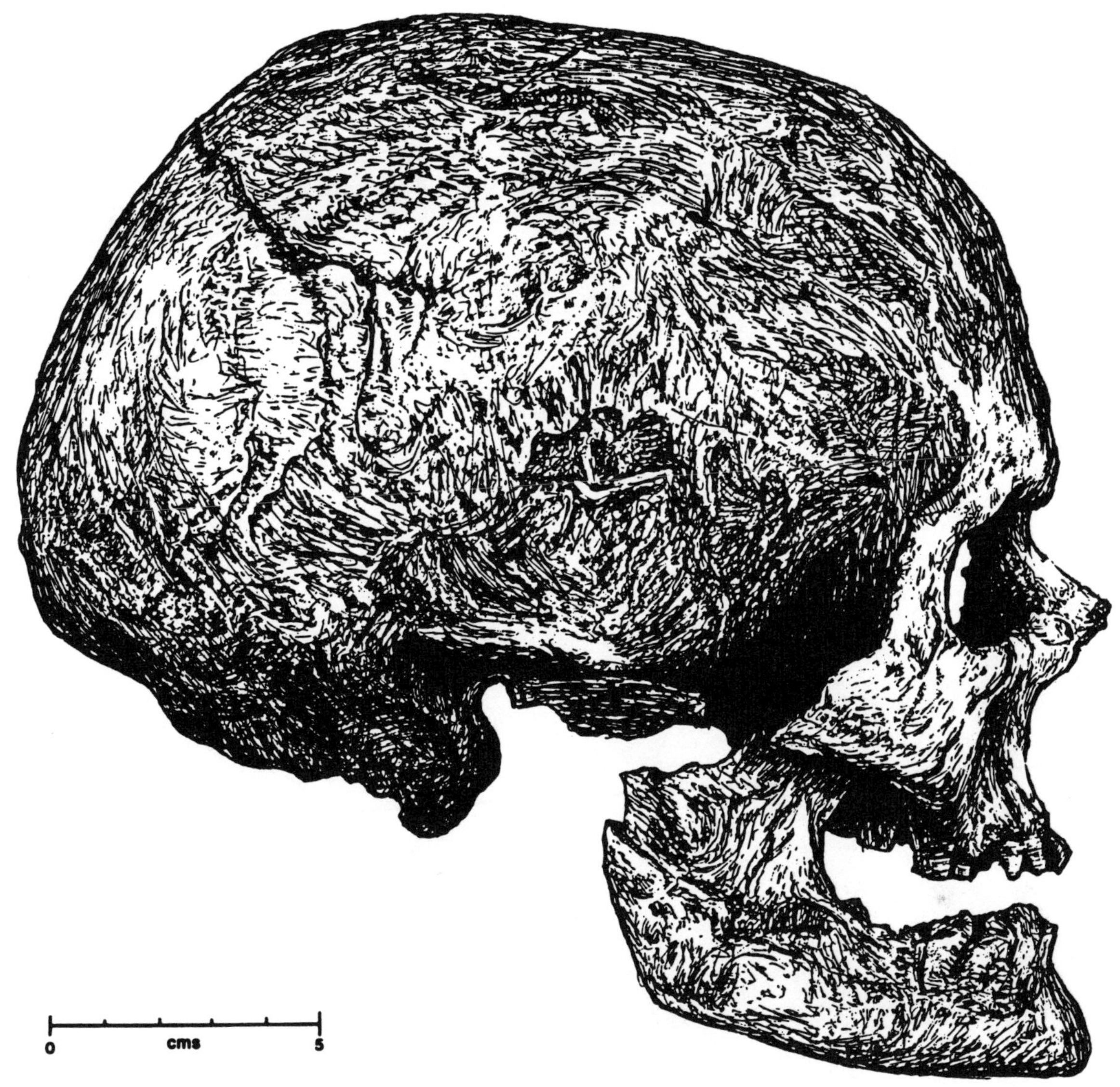

■ 5.13 Exercise: Where Did We Come From?

Differentiate between each of the following interpretations concerning the origins of *Homo sapiens sapiens*. What data are used to support each model? How does *Homo neandertalensis* fit into each of these models?

Complete Replacement Model:

Partial Replacement Model:

Regional Continuity Model (Multiregional evolution model):

5.14 Web Sites

Hominid Evolution

The Human Evolutionary Record

Summarizing the hominid fossil record and hypothesized lines of human evolution.
http://www.handprint.com/LS/ANC/evol.html

Hominid Evolution

A definitive survey of the current state of knowledge regarding human origins, with bibliography.
http://www.geocities.com/SoHo/Atrium/1381/

Hominid Species

All hominid species are discussed here.
http://www.talkorigins.org/faqs/homs/species.html

Prominent Hominid Fossils

All of the major fossil hominids are discussed.
http://www.talkorigins.org/faqs/homs/specimen.html

The Institute of Human Origins

A non-profit, multidisciplinary research organization affiliated with Arizona State University, dedicated to the recovery and analysis of the fossil evidence for human evolution.
http://www.asu.edu/clas/iho/

Human Evolution

From the On-Line Biology Book.
http://gened.emc.maricopa.edu/Bio/BIO181/BIOBK/BioBookHumEvol. html

Human Evolution

A Virtual Tour of the Smithsonian exhibit on the evolution of humans.
http://nmnhwww.si.edu/VirtualTour/Tour/First/Human/

Fossil Skulls

Interactive fossil skulls from the American Museum of Natural History.
http://www.amnh.org/enews/iskulls.html

Hunterian Museum Hominid Evolution

Hominid Evolution QTVR Web Site
http://www.dcs.gla.ac.uk/~hunterd/hominid/evol.html

Guided Tour of Hominid Evolution
http://info.gla.ac.uk/Museum/guided/Hominid/

Origins of Humankind

A comprehensive internet resource for the human evolution community.
http://www.pro-am.com/origins/

Human Prehistory

An overview of human evolution and prehistory with a particular emphasis on early human developments in the Old World.
http://users.hol.gr/~dilos/prehis.htm

6 Applied Anthropology and Current Issues

6.1 Introduction to Hands-On Research Strategies

Physical anthropologists are best known for their work using ancient bones and stone tools to interpret hominid evolution. Yet, the work conducted by physical anthropologists is much more complex than what is commonly believed. This text has hopefully demonstrated the prominent role which genetics, primatology and reproductive biology play in the interpretation of the hominid phylogeny. Yet, while this research is important, physical anthropologists are also interested in current issues that impact field research. This includes issues such as nutrition, disease, social stratification, economics, race, archaeology and forensics. **Applied anthropology** refers to the utilization of anthropological methodology, knowledge and theories by which to solve current dilemmas. How can physical anthropologists solve various problems, assist the people they meet, while also conducting field research?

An example of applied anthropology is seen with the collaborative, cross-discipline team of experts associated with the African Bushmeat Project. While the consumption of meat supplied by the poaching of endangered species is not unique to Africa, we will be focusing on this particular dilemma.

Currently, anthropologists have worked in association with conservationists, photographers, virologists, primatologists, psychologists, economists, politicians, zoologists, etc. to find a solution to this dilemma. African animals, including the African great apes (chimps, bonobos and gorillas) are being killed for food. This is not traditional subsistence hunting, but rather commercialized poaching. The meat is then sold to restaurants, as well as at open markets throughout Africa and into Europe. As many as 2,000 gorillas may be killed each year; the number of chimps killed each year seems to be even higher. While these animals are protected under the 'Endangered Species Act,' there are simply not enough financial resources and rangers available to protect the animals from poachers.

Subsistence hunting has occurred for hundreds of generations without causing a mass eradication of animals. Hunters and gatherers are familiar with the territory and the animals that share their environment. Yet, these individuals are currently being given guns (instead of arrows) and are being told to provide food for the large number of people associated with the timber industry—those same individuals that are clearing their forests. Can we ask innocent people to change their cultural ways of foraging in order to protect endangered species? Should researchers offer options to take the place of hunting for all of the individuals involved?

A byproduct of this commercialized hunting is orphaned animals. While some of these infants may be kept as pets, others may be fortunate to find themselves in the care of conservationists and zoo personnel. Many of these animals lose their lives to diseases, poor nutrition and even to despair.

For more information on this issue, where you can read currently published articles, see photographs and link to related sites, contact Anthony Rose, Executive Director of the Bushmeat Project at http://biosynergy.org/bushmeat/. The American Zoological Association (AZA) has also created a task force to offer solutions to this dilemma, to focus the public's attention on this issue as well as to lobby Congress concerning the plight of these animals and the people affected by the commercialization of hunting. Please contact the AZA's web-site for additional information.

This is only one example where researchers have collectively worked in hopes of solving an urgent dilemma that impacts both human and non-human primate populations. Read the following articles and then ask yourself, "what would I do if placed in a similar situation?"

6.2 *Sampling Rapidly Dwindling Chimpanzee Populations*

Pascal Gagneux

In the course of an on-going study of the population genetics of west African chimpanzees[1,2,3] we collected samples from wild chimpanzee populations in west Africa. We sampled shed hair collected from night nests which chimpanzees build in a new location at the end of each day. The hair-root cells of those shed hair contain DNA which can be analyzed using the Polymerase Chain Reaction (PCR). This method uses a heat-stable enzyme found in microorganisms living in natural hot springs, and allows researchers to obtain large numbers of identical copies of selected short stretches of the original DNA of a study organism (markers). Researchers can now study the genetics of wild animals non invasively by extracting DNA from shed hair, feces, chewed pieces of food and even museum skins.[4,5,6]

Visiting many different chimpanzee habitats has made the author very pessimistic about the survival chances of our closest living relative in west Africa. Marchesi et. al.[7] conducted a survey of chimpanzee populations of Côte d'Ivoire in 1991. Based on their findings, we visited a subset of the census sites in 1993–94 and again in 1995 (13 different sites). We found chimpanzees at each of the sites within two days. We also found massive evidence of hunting at every site. Our local guides were always villagers, usually hunters, all of whom readily admitted having hunted chimpanzees. We were shocked by the amount of hunting we witnessed, even inside the National Parks. In two of them (Taï and Comoé National Park) we had to hide from poachers on three different occasions. Denis Lia, the African assistant who had participated in the 1991 census with the Marchesis was very impressed by how much lower the density of chimpanzee nests was compared to three years earlier when he had helped conduct the survey. Richard Barnes, who just returned from doing an elephant survey in the Marahoue National Park, central Côte d'Ivoire, did not see a single chimpanzee nest, where the Marchesis had found the highest density of nests in the course of their census only six years eaxlier (Barnes pers. com.). Even in Western Mali, in the Fauna Reserve of Bafing, where Moore[8] had conducted chimpanzee surveys and had reported that chimpanzees were unlikely to be hunted, because the Muslim faith of most inhabitants prohibits the consumption of primate meat, we found three local hunters who admitted having killed chimpanzees for food recently. One dramatic occurrence in the coastal forests of south-western Côte d'Ivoire, illustrates the situation well: sitting in a day-old chimpanzee nest the author could see villagers slashing and burning the forest on one side and hear buses drive by at high speeds on the newly paved coastal road on the other side. The same road which allows hunters to market their bush meat in the capital as it is now only four hours away. Because chimpanzees tend to be very noisy during daily bouts of social excitement, they make a very easy target for hunters who can readily find them. When their numbers are decimated to just a few individuals they are likely to remain silent and may survive for many years even in heavily disturbed habitat. The presence of such relic populations can easily give the illusion of "populations" of chimpanzees still remaining in an area.

Thus, while sampling chimpanzees appears to be relatively easy, if one has information on their distribution, the strong pressure exerted on chimpanzee populations by humans, directly by hunting, or indirectly by habitat destruction will most likely destroy the remaining wild chimpanzee populations in west Africa. Even if the habitat becomes very well protected, unless there is a rigorous enforcement of wildlife protection, i.e. a total ban of hunting, and regular enforcement on site, chimpanzees and most other large mammals will be shot out of even the most consistently protected forests. Recent surveys in the Taï National Park have shown that the presence of long-term research sites is the most efficient way of limiting poaching, as in the case of the Taï chimpanzee project. However, even the regular presence of field researchers is no safeguard against continuous low intensity hunting pressure. The proximity of natural chimpanzee populations to cacao and other fields leads to crop-raiding by the chimpanzees. Many of them are killed by farmers who are protecting their crops. In the course of our sampling trips we saw several cacao plantations located within official forest reserves. When political instability forces researchers to temporarily abandon their research sites, the study populations instantly become highly vulnerable because of their habituation.

Currently, population genetic studies such as ours run the danger of becoming "instant paleontology". After just a few years we are now in the possession of samples belonging to extinct regional populations. Several researchers have sampled and are still sampling natural chimpanzee populations. Jim Moore and Phillip Morin[9] sampled in Mali and Tanzania, Rosalind Alp has provided samples from one community in Tenkere, Sierra Leone, Tony Goldberg[10] and Babette Fahey have sampled chimpanzees in Uganda and Zaire, Anne Pusey and her colleagues are sampling in Gombe, Katie Gonder[11] is currently sampling in Nigeria and Cameroun. Very little remains known on the distribution and the population genetics of central African chimpanzees in Cameroun, Gabon, CAR and Zaire. These regions are known for their people's traditional fondness for bush meat. War and political instability only contribute to the desperate need to find cheap animal protein or sources for cash (bush meat as a cash crop).

Recently, a Population and Habitat Viability Assessment (PHVA) project has been proposed for west African chimpanzees. The idea is to bring together African and Non-African specialists, wildlife managers and conservationists in order to design an action plan for the conservation of west African chimpanzees. A PHVA meeting organized by the Conservation Breeding Specialist Group (CBSG) in Uganda early this year has proved rather successful. Unlike the situation in Uganda, however, most west African Nations have long-lasting traditions of bush meat consumption. The issue of bush meat cannot be resolved by moralizing attitudes held by activists from industrial nations. Rather, we need culturally sensitive approaches to the problem.

The importance of primate hunting and consumption for human food and the transfer of dangerous infectious diseases has become increasingly clear in recent years. Between 1994 and 1996 there were three independent Ebola outbreaks in Gabon, all of which were associated with hunters and the deaths of non human primates.[12] The WHO in collaboration with several other organizations is currently conducting a search for the natural reservoir species of the Ebola virus in the Taï National Park, Côte d'Ivoire. The death of several habituated chimpanzees there in 1992 and 1994, and the subsequent infection of a Swiss researcher have alerted the medical community. Even though some may advocate using the fact that killing chimpanzees can infect people with Ebola and/or possibly SIV/HIV as a propaganda tool against the consumption of primates, one needs to be cautious, for such information could easily backfire. People could all too suddenly decide that killing as many chimpanzees as possible is a way of getting rid of dangerous diseases.

Pleading for the protection of chimpanzees based on the fact that they are our close relatives seems rather futile considering the lack of compassion that we regularly show even towards our fellow humans. There are utilitarian arguments for the conservation of chimpanzees: Studies of natural chimpanzee communities across Africa have profoundly changed our views on human nature and human evolution. Chimpanzees have great potential value for attracting ecotourism. The medicinal use of forest plants by chimpanzees as documented by Huffman and others,[13] promises to reveal new drugs based on pharmaceutical compounds found in such plants. Finally, there is the fact that chimpanzees in their natural habitat may harbor the solution to several medical problems of global importance. The very different ways in which our closest living relative is coping with diseases affecting our species, ranging from malaria and cholera to HIV, could teach us much about those diseases.

In summary: there is ample reason to be very pessimistic about the future of wild chimpanzees in west Africa. Efforts to organize a Population and Habitat Viability Assessment workshop in west Africa are being made and there will not be many more opportunities for such a project.

References

1. Gagneux, P., Woodruff, D.S., Boesch, C. 1997. Furtive Female Chimpanzees, *Nature* 387:358–359.

2. Gagneux, P., Woodruff, D.S., Boesch, C. 1997. Microsatellite Scoring errors associated with noninvasive genotyping based on nuclear DNA amplified from shed hair. *Molecular Ecology* 6, 861–868.

3. Gagneux, P., Woodruff, D.S., Boesch, C. Female reproductive strategies, paternity and community structure in a community of wild west African chimpanzees. *Animal Behavior* in press.

4. Takasaki, H., Takenaka, O. (1991) Paternity testing in chimpanzees with DNA amplification from hairs and buccal cells in wadges. A preliminary note. In: *Primatology Today: Proceedings of the 13th Congress of the International Primatological Society*. (eds. Ehara, A., Kinura, T., Takenaka, O., Iwamoto, M.), pp. 613–616. Elsevier, Amsterdam.

5. Morin, P.A., Woodruff, D.S., 1996. Non invasive genotyping for vertebrate conservation. In: *Molecular Genetic Approaches in Conservation* (eds. Smith, T.B., Wayne, R.K.). Oxford: Oxford University Press, pp. 298–313.

6. Mundy, N.I., Winchell, C.S., Woodruff, D.S. 1997. Genetic differences between the endangered San Clemente Island loggerhead shrike *Lanius ludovicianus mearnsi* and two neighbouring subspecies demonstrated by mtDNA control region and cytochrome *b* sequence variation. *Molecular Ecology* 6, 29–37.

7. Marchesi, P., Marchesi, N., Fruth, B., Boesch, C. 1995. Census and distribution of chimpanzees in Ivory Coast. *Primates*, 4, 591–607.

8. Moore, J.J. 1985. Chimpanzee Survey in Mali, West Africa. *Primate Conservation* 6, 59–63.

9. Morin P.A., Moore J.J., Chakraborty, R., Jin, L., Goodall, J., Woodruff, D.S. (1994a) Kin selection, social structure, gene flow, and the evolution of chimpanzees. *Science* 265, 1193–1201.

10. Goldberg, T.L, Ruvolo, M. 1997. Molecular phylogenetics and historical biogeography of east African chimpanzees. *Biol. J Linnean Soc.* 61, 301–324.

11. Gonder, M.K, Oates, J.F., Disotell, T.R., Forstner, M.R.J., Morales, J.C., Melnick, D.J. 1997. A new west African chimpanzee subspecies. *Nature*, 388, 337.

12. Georges-Courbot, M-C., Sanchez, A., Lu, C.Y. *et al* 1997. Isolation and Phylogenetic Characterization of Ebola Viruses Causing Different Outbreaks in Gabon. *Emerging Infectious Diseases* 3, National Center for Infectious Diseases, Center for Disease Control and Prevention, Atlanta, GA. URL://www.cdc.goc/ncidod/vol3no1/courbot2.htm.

13. Huffman, M.A, Wrangham, R.W. 1994. The diversity of medicinal plant use by chimpanzees in the wild. In *Chimpanzee Cultures*, Harvard University Press, Cambridge, Massachusetts, pp. 129-148.

6.2 Study Questions: Studying Rapidly Dwindling Chimpanzee Populations — Pascal Gagneux

1. Be familiar with the indicators of massive hunting of the chimpanzees of Cote d'Ivoire.

2. How does road-building seem to contribute to the decline of chimpanzees? What makes them an easy target? What illusion is created by relic populations?

3. What seems to be the most efficient way of limiting poaching? Why is even this not a complete safeguard?

4. How do war and political instability contribute to the danger to chimpanzees?

5. Why does "moralizing" not work?

6. Why must caution be used in warning people about the spread of infectious diseases?

7. Why does the use of compassion for our close relatives not work?

8. What are the utilitarian arguments for the conservation of chimpanzees?

6.3 Protecting and Preserving Primates

Noel Rowe

Most primates live in tropical, developing countries, and humans compete with them for resources. In many parts of the world, primates are exploited for food, "medicine," and commercial trade. Primates that raid crops are shot or poisoned. The forest habitat that is home to most species is being logged and cleared at an alarming rate by commercial loggers and subsistence farmers for land and firewood. The fate of several primate species will be decided in the next five years. If we humans collectively and as individuals do not act to protect these endangered primates and their habitats, they both will disappear—lost forever! We should not be lulled into complacency by another upbeat report from the media. We must get involved, write letters, educate others, and help the local communities that live near the forest to preserve their wildlife.

Sustainable development is defined as "increasing or maintaining productivity at levels that are economically viable, ecologically sound, and culturally acceptable, through the efficient management of resources with minimum damage to the environment or human health." This is the current theoretical phrase used by governments, international funding agencies, and conservation organizations for their programs to save endangered species and help the local people who will decide the fate of those species. The key word is "sustainable." We must be vigilant to see that what is called sustainable really is sustainable in the long term. What is *not* needed is more big development schemes that exacerbate the problem and lead to further destruction of forest habitats.

"Protection" is the word that must be stressed in regard to the conservation of primates. Both the individuals and their forest home must be protected with laws and enforcement. Monkeys are often a hunter's main target, because they are the largest diurnal mammal that is easy to detect and shoot. Females with infants are the preferred quarry, and their loss hastens population decline. Many endangered primates live only in primary forest, which has the most valuable timber. In many countries, including the United States, primary forest exists only where it has been protected. Primary forest is a productive biological system from which valuable forest products can sustainably be obtained. Most of the nutrients of tropical forests reside in the vegetation, not in the soils. Thus, once the trees are cut, the few nutrients in the soil are depleted by human cultivation in a few seasons. Primary forest will survive only if people who understand its true value educate others and together they defend the forests from the forces of greed.

Captive conservation and release is another avenue that has been tried recently with the golden lion tamarin (*Leontopithecus rosalia*). The program was a limited success but had an enormous cost for each individual released. Clearly it would be cheaper for us and better for the primates if they are protected in their natural habitat, where they can be viewed as integral members of their habitat rather than as bored captives. If a primate species exists only in captivity, it is no longer a part of a natural evolutionary system but a living specimen in a museum.

The individual primates that are lucky enough to survive and be rescued from illegal poachers and traffickers should be the only source of primates used for captive breeding and display. They must be the ambassadors for their species. From them, we can learn about their species and appreciate their uniqueness—and our own.

Ten Things You Can Do for Primate Conservation

1. Call, write, or fax your U.S. congressional representative (U.S. House of Representatives, Washington, DC 20515; 202-224-3121) and senators (U.S. Senate, Washington, DC: 202-224-3121) and urge them to support legislation that:

- protects endangered species and their habitats.
- increases funding for foreign aid programs that specifically address sustainable development and the conservation of global biodiversity.
- increases enforcement of wildlife trade laws to stop the smuggling of endangered species.
- curtails the use of primates in inhumane experiments.
- encourages family planning and discourages human population growth. The earth has finite resources—we must control ourselves.

2. Call, write, or fax the president of the United States (The White House, Washington, DC 20500: 202-456-1414) and ask that the United States impose sanctions on countries that do not enforce their endangered species laws or that violate international wildlife treaties.
3. Register to vote, and vote for candidates who support the protection of the environment, biodiversity, and endangered species.
4. Write to the president of the World Bank (1818 H Street NW, Washington, DC 20433) and ask that the World Bank make its loans to countries conditional on their protection of their national parks, biodiversity, and endangered species.
5. Ask your local zoo to adopt a park in a developing tropical country and provide it with supplies for educating local people about their endangered wildlife.
6. Get your local school to adopt a park or reserve or a school in a community near a park and share information and ideas about your wildlife and theirs.
7. Join the Peace Corps, which has many environmental and wildlife conservation projects in habitat countries.
8. Take a working vacation with Earthwatch (680 Mount Auburn Street, Box 403, Watertown, MA 02272-9104; 800-776-0188; http://www.earthwatch.org) and get actively involved in primate field research in a habitat country.
9. Be an ecotourist rather than a sightseer. Be sure the tour company you choose follows the principles of ecotourism set forth by the Ecotourism Society (802-447-2121). The idea is to ensure that part of the money you spend will benefit the local community.
10. Join and support in any way you can some of the following organizations, which support the conservation of primates.

Bonobo Protection and Conservation Fund
Georgia State University Foundation
University Plaza
Georgia State University
Atlanta, GA 30303

Conservation International
1015 18th Street NW, Suite 1000
Washington, DC 20036

Dian Fossey Gorilla Fund
800 Cherokee Avenue SE
Atlanta, GA 30315

Dian Fossey Gorilla Fund-Europe
110 Gloucester Avenue
London NW1 8HX
United Kingdom

Flora and Fauna Preservation Society
1 Kensington Gore
London SW7 2AR
United Kingdom

International Primate Protection League
P.O. Box 766
Summerville, SC 29484

Jane Goodall Institute
P.O. Box 599
Ridgefield, CT 06877

Jane Goodall Institute (UK)
15 Clarendon Park
Lymington, Hants SO41 8AX
United Kingdom

The Nature Conservancy International
1815 North Lynn Street
Arlington, VA 22209

Orangutan Foundation International
824 South Wellesley Avenue
Los Angeles, CA 90049

Primate Conservation, Inc.
163 Town Lane
East Hampton, NY 11937

Wildlife Conservation Society—International
Wildlife Conservation Society—Bronx Zoo
Bronx, NY 10460

Wildlife Preservation Trust International
3400 West Girard Avenue
Philadelphia, PA 19104

World Wildlife Fund
1250 24th Street NW
Washington, DC 20037

6.3 Study Questions: Protecting and Preserving Primates — Noel Rowe

1. In what ways are primates exploited in many parts of the world?

2. What is happening to the forest habitat?

3. What is meant by "sustainable development?" Why is "sustainable" the key word?

4. How must protection be ensured?

5. Why are monkeys often the hunters' main target? Which species are preferred?

6. Describe the importance of the "primary forest" and why it must be protected. Why would this be preferable to captive conservation and release programs?

7. What should be the only source of primates for captive breeding and display?

6.4 *From* Dancing Skeletons: *Of Worms and Other Parasites*

Katherine Dettwyler

Ordinary is what you are used to. This may not seem ordinary to you now, but after a time it will. It will become ordinary.

—*Margaret Atwood*

The rain fell in great sheets, sluicing off the roof, filling the courtyard with swirling brown water. The water snuck under the front door and edged across the tile floors of the living room. We chased it back outside with brooms and buckets, then crossed the courtyard through ankle-deep water and climbed up on the wall to view the havoc on the other side. Nothing looked familiar. The broad dirt road, with its open sewer (usually stagnant) running along the far side, had been replaced by a raging torrent, sweeping sewage, garbage, mud, and other debris downhill, toward the river. Children perched in the lower branches of trees, and we watched as the water carried a chicken, squawking piteously and flapping its wings, past our doorway.

"Welcome to Mali!" I shouted to Heather Katz, an undergraduate from Texas A&M who had arrived the day before to spend the fall semester working as my unpaid research assistant. Clinging to the wall, water streaming down her face, she looked over at me and grinned, then turned her face toward the sky.

The next day we learned that in rural areas of the country, entire villages of mud huts and herds of sheep and goats were swept away, never to be heard from again. It was late August, and the extraordinary storm signaled the end to the three-month-long rainy season. Following the rains, we would have months of glorious, practically unvarying weather, cool in the mornings, sunny and hot by the afternoon.

After having taken several anthropology courses, Heather was eager to get started with "the real thing." Early the next morning, following a breakfast of coffee and freshly baked bread (crisp *baguettes*, one of the few positive legacies of French colonialism) we set out to Magnambougou to finish up the final stage of my research project on intestinal parasites. First we walked a mile along the river toward the main road, the "airport road," that connected the capital city of Bamako, across the river to the west, with the airport to the east.

Once we reached the main road, we headed away from the river and walked, looking back over our shoulders for oncoming *baches* (baa-shays) that might be headed to Magnambougou. I exchanged hand signals with several bache drivers, searching for one with spare room headed for Magnambougou. Finally, one pulled over and we clambered up the step and squeezed in among the passengers, trying to avoid the uncomfortable corner seats, where your legs get cramped.

A bache is a small pickup truck with the tailgate removed. The interior of the truck bed is furnished with hard wooden benches around the periphery, covered by a metal framework that partially encloses the back and keeps out the sun and rain (more or less). Officially, 15 or 16 people can fit in the back of the bache, but often 20 or more are crammed in, not to mention babies in mothers' laps, live chickens and guinea fowl, huge enamel bowls full of cooked food or market vegetables, bundles of firewood, fresh fish, not so fresh fish, anything you can imagine, and then some.

Toubabs are often offered the seats up front next to the driver because these seats are considered more genteel. In reailty, it is cooler and more pleasant to ride in the back, where you at least have the benefit of the breeze to offset the smell of sweaty bodies and old fish. Besides, the drivers always turned off their engines at every opportunity—waiting for passengers to load, in traffic jams, going downhill—thinking they were saving gas by doing so, and it annoyed me intensely. No amount of explaining would convince people that it took more gas to start the engine than it took to keep it running for a minute.

People were surprised to see toubabs riding the public transportation system. Most American and French expatriates had cars of their own, and consultants and other short-time visitors usually rode in Embassy or A.I.D. cars or taxis. Only Peace Corps volunteers and anthropologists regularly rode the baches. One problem for the neophyte is that it is very difficult to figure out where a particular bache is headed, how much it should cost, or when and whom you pay. You must be taught all of the intricacies by a friendly (and honest) expert.

We jounced along, trying to keep our balance as the driver swerved around a herd of cows in the road, then careened off onto the dirt shoulder to pick up more people. There are no marked bus stops, though there are some usual, but unmarked, stopping places. You can also get a bache to stop for you anywhere along the road if you know the system of signals, and if the driver has any room.

As always, the seat next to the door was occupied by a young boy who worked for the driver, collecting fares and telling the driver when to stop and let someone off. He swung wildly off the back of bache, dragging his sandalled feet on the ground and waving to other bache boys going the other direction. He also acted as a watchdog, keeping an eye out for policemen, who like to stop overloaded baches and collect fines.

Toward the end of the line, the boy collected the fares. There are standard fares for certain distances, but no one will tell you what they are if you don't know. You can try to see what other people are paying, but that is difficult because the boy usually has to collect money from a number of people before he can make change for people who don't have the exact fare. I was amazed at the ability of the bache boys to keep track of who had paid what, who needed change, and who hadn't paid yet because they were still fumbling around with their money. Women, especially, always waited until they were asked for the fare to start digging out their money, sometimes a major process.

Women in Mali don't carry purses—they would be too easy for someone to steal. Many an unsuspecting toubab has been relieved of their wallet or coin purse on a bache, and people were always telling me to zip up my bag. Most people carry their money knotted in one corner of their long flowing robes (men) or in the corner of the cloth they use to tie their babies onto their backs (women). Thus, it takes several minutes to locate the money and maneuver it to where it can be reached and several more to untie the knot, search for the fare, and hand it over.

As often happened, the boy tried to cheat me, telling me that the fare was ten times higher than it really was, but since I knew the customary price, I just handed him the correct fare and ignored his rantings. "He thinks we're dumb toubabs!" I said first to Heather in English, then to the crowd in Bambara, earning chuckles and a round of greetings from our fellow passengers, and a lopsided grin from the bache boy, as if to say "You can't blame me for trying!"

My ability to speak Bambara, and the incongruity between that ability and my skin color, was a source of great pleasure to me because I could use it to make people laugh. I sometimes hid my ability to speak Bambara, then made jokes by revealing that I did, in fact, both understand and speak it. I might climb onto the bache and settle in without saying anything, then if the bache was weaving erratically all over the road (not a rare occurrence), I would casually comment, "This driver is a fool!" Or I would listen while several women discussed who I might be and why a toubab was riding the bache, then say, in Bambara, holding out my arm for their inspection "Look, I'm not a toubab, I'm a *fara fin* (black-skinned person), just like you!"

More than anything else, Malians like to laugh—at themselves, at each other, certainly at toubabs ("Only a white man would pay money for a dog! Ha ha ha!"), at the ludicrous world in which they find themselves living—and I liked to make them laugh. I also enjoyed participating in their rituals of respect and kindness, as another way of showing that I was interested in, and sympathetic to, their cultural beliefs and practices.

Giving alms to beggars, blind men, lepers, and mothers of twins are all ways of attaining grace in the eyes of God (Allah). Whenever possible, Malians like to help those in need, as they benefit themselves spiritually as well. However, the sheer numbers of beggars and lepers in the capital city could be overwhelming. As with everything else, there were rules of etiquette for giving alms. To avoid the crush of beggars in downtown Bamako, it is best to pick out one particular person and always give that one some money. "This is *my* leper," I explained to Heather, as I pointed out an old woman with no fingers or toes, sitting on the sidewalk near Dibida, the vegetable market. We exchanged greetings, I dropped some coins into her bowl, and she gave me her blessings in return. "Pick one for yourself,

Heather, and the others will leave you alone. You just have to remember to always carry small change, and remember to give something to your leper, but not any of the others, every time you pass by here. The others will respect your choice and not bother you. Likewise, I have my particular mother of twins near the bank. I always give her money and the others know not to ask." "Gee," Heather joked, uncomfortable with the entire situation, "I never had my very own leper before!" "Yes, well, there but for the grace of God . . ." I responded.

Another way of attaining grace was to show respect for old men and women in various ways. Respect for elders is part and parcel of daily life in Mali; all important decisions are made by councils of old men, and a man isn't truly in charge of his own affairs until his father and all of his older brothers have died. When Steven's 84-year-old grandmother visited us in Mali in 1982, wherever she went, people spontaneously dropped to their knees and bowed their heads in respect of her great age (much to her consternation).

One way of attaining grace and showing respect for your elders is by paying their fare on the bache. This is not something the casual tourist is likely to find out about, let alone practice. When we rode the bache with an elderly man or woman, we always paid their fare along with our own, indicating by gestures to the bache boy who else was included in our largesse. This simple action evoked smiles, exclamations of gratitude, prayers to Allah to bless us with many children, and the respect and appreciation of our fellow passengers.

The early morning ride to Magnambougou took about 10 minutes. We jumped off before the end of the line to avoid being crushed by the hordes of people trying to get on for the return trip to Bamako. People pushed onto the bache from the back or climbed in through the side windows (even women with children strapped to their backs!), and you risked your life trying to disembark without getting crushed if you rode to the end of the line. Even my most colorful cussing in Bambara wouldn't stop the pushing and shoving of people eager to get into town for work or school.

"What are we going to do first?" Heather asked as we walked down a side street toward Moussa's house. "First we have to get Moussa. I seldom do any research without him. Then, just for today, we're collecting the final round of urine and stool specimens for my project on intestinal parasites and taking them out to the Vet Lab for analysis," I explained. "Tomorrow we'll go back to measuring and interviewing."

Having Heather along helped me see Magnambougou with fresh eyes. After only a few months, I had already gotten used to the piles of goats' heads on the edge of the market, little kids squatting along the edge of the road to relieve themselves, and the teenager who had polio as an infant, crab-walking his way to a friend's house, waving at us with one sandalled hand.

"Why exactly are you collecting these specimens?" Heather asked. I explained as we continued on our way. This part of my research was designed to figure out whether intestinal parasites, thought to be common in most Third World communities, could be contributing to the poor growth of the children. One of the graduate students at Texas A&M (Karl Reinhard, who went on to the University of Nebraska) was enamored of intestinal parasites as a potential explanation for just about everything. His own research involved looking for signs of parasitic infection in the preserved remains of human feces (known as coprolites) from archeological sites. Imagine Karl at a party, when someone asks, "So, what do you study?" Karl often pestered me to include parasite analyses in my research, so I added it to my list of projects.

Early on, I had contacted the veterinary parasitologists at the Bamako Veterinary Laboratory. I went there (rather than to medical doctors) because the Vet Lab in Bamako is staffed by Malian alumni of Texas A&M's College of Veterinary Medicine. Because of the "Aggie" connection, I knew they were well trained, and I was able to negotiate a good rate for the laboratory analyses of the specimens. The lab provided small plastic bottles for collection, and set up a schedule for me to bring specimens to the lab the same day they were collected. The specimens were analyzed immediately, eliminating the need for chemical preservatives or refrigerated storage.

I expected people in Magnambougou to think I was bizarre, asking for feces and urine in little bottles, but everyone took my requests in stride. Maybe it was because I explained that they would be getting free testing for parasites, as well as medicine to cure any infections that were uncovered. Or maybe it was because Malians are a lot more relaxed and casual about bodily functions than most people in the United States. The first time Moussa said to me, "Excuse me, I have to go shit," I thought I must have misunderstood. Conversely, he didn't understand American reticence or our use of euphemisms: "Everyone does it. And everyone knows exactly what you mean even if you say you're going to the 'little girls' room,' so why don't you just say what you, mean?" he wondered.

Only a few people declined to participate in this phase of the research, which I began with 10 families. On one day we distributed the labelled bottles, two per child, and explained what (and how much) was needed. The next morning we collected the specimen bottles. Sometimes the child would not have been able to provide a specimen yet, and we sat around chatting while he or she tried again. It became obvious, early on, that many children had diarrhea and very dark, cloudy urine.

After gathering all 20 bottles for the day, I carefully tucked them in my monogrammed Lands' End attache bag (wouldn't that make a memorable advertisement?) and hopped on the bache for the long trip out to the lab, careful not to let anyone jostle my bag as I pushed and shoved my way aboard, fearing that the bottles would crack or pop open. Odd comments and looks were common; I smelled vaguely offensive. Pretending that I didn't speak Bambara, I was treated to such remarks as "Maybe it's that strange toubab—do you think she's the one who smells?" "No, it can't be her; maybe someone stepped in something rotten." Bouncing along, I looked nonchalantly out the side of the truck, pretending that nothing was going on.

I rode all the way across the river, to the main bache station in Bamako, then transferred to another line that took me about 10 kilometers north of town. From the end of the line it was still a hike of another mile to the Vet Lab, where I dropped off the filled bottles, picked up 20 clean ones, and hiked back to catch the bache back into town.

On the last trip out to the lab to deliver specimens, Heather was along, and the other occupants carried on a lengthy and derogatory discussion about the odor emanating from our corner of the bache. As we neared the end of the line, I blurted out in Bambara, "The smell is because my bag is full of little bottles of shit!"

Everyone laughed and looked around, surprised to discover that I could speak Bambara, chagrined that I had understood their comments, and amazed at my admission. There was a flurry of activity as people squished themselves as far away as possible. One old man was skeptical and, in my defense, suggested that I couldn't speak Bambara very well and had said something I didn't mean to. I carefully opened my bag, reached in, pulled out one of the bottles, and waved it in his direction. "No, it really is shit. Sorry about the smell. We're on our way to the Vet Lab." No one said a word. The old man pulled part of his robe up over his mouth and nose, and turned to gaze out at the roadway, muttering about how weird toubabs could be.

Out of the total of 68 specimens of feces I collected, only 4 showed any signs of the six most common intestinal parasites for which we searched—2 had *Ascaris*, another had hookworm, and the last one had a tapeworm. These children were each treated and their parents told how to avoid reinfection. The girl with the tapeworm, Aminata, had been part of my original research study. In fact, she was the only truly fat child under five years of age that I ever saw in Mali. In my 1989 research, I used photos of well-nourished, and mildly, moderately, and severely malnourished children, to elicit reactions from people as part of a project to understand traditional perceptions of nutritional status. Aminata's photo, taken in 1983 when she was three years old, was my example of a "well-nourished" Malian child.

I returned to Aminata's compound in early August of 1989 to remeasure her and see how she had fared during my six-year absence. After the usual greetings and small talk with her mother and the co-wife, I asked if Aminata was still alive (not a question one would normally ask an acquaintance in the United States—"So, is your daughter still alive?"—but perfectly understandable and acceptable in Mali, where many children die).

Her mother pointed out a short, thin, apathetic looking child, standing shyly behind the group of children who had lined up to stare at me. She looked much younger than the nine years Aminata should have been. At first I didn't believe it was the same child. I rechecked her name in my notes, then pulled out the photo of her when she was three years old and said, "Maybe I have the name wrong; this is who I mean."

Her mother just laughed and said, "Yes, I know she looks different—she was really fat when you knew her before. She's been sick for about four years."

"But she always used to eat so much!" I exclaimed. "You told me that she 'ate like a chicken'—all day long. She even went to the neighbors looking for food. What happened?"

"Oh, she still eats like that, more than anyone else in the family! Every day we give her money to buy meat in the market. Even today she had some."

"Then why is she so skinny?"

"Because she's been sick for so long," her mother replied, speaking slowly and patiently, as though dealing with someone who wasn't too bright. "Everyone knows that you can eat a lot and still be skinny."

Although I hadn't intended to include Aminata in the fecal/urine study, I decided on the spot that intestinal parasites might account for her stomach pains and slow growth in spite of a healthy appetite. "Have you ever seen worms in her feces?" I inquired. "Well, no," her mother replied, "but she uses the pit latrine, not a plastic cup like an infant."

We left the plastic bottles for the specimens and returned the next day to collect them. Results came back from the lab: positive for a tapeworm. Since most Malians are Muslim and don't eat pork, it was probably a beef tapeworm, acquired most likely from eating undercooked beef "kebabs" from the marketplace.

I brought her the appropriate medicine, and watched to make sure she took it. It used to be that tapeworm medicine merely killed the tapeworm, and it would then be excreted, so that one could actually see it, and even measure its length. The new treatment, however, not only kills the tapeworm, but renders it digestible by the intestines, so that nothing obvious comes out in the feces. Thus, we weren't able to confirm that the medicine had definitively killed the tapeworm, but in the weeks that followed, Aminata's symptoms (bad stomach pains, cramps, lack of energy, lethargy) all disappeared. We cautioned her against eating beef from the market. She continued to have a remarkable appetite. She should recoup some, if not all, of the growth she lost during the tapeworm's four year occupation of her body.

Aminata's experience reminded me that the connection between food intake and health is not at all obvious for people repeatedly subjected to a variety of illnesses and intestinal parasites. Here was the one "fat" child from the community, who always ate prodigious amounts of food. Nevertheless, over the course of several years, she lost her baby fat and stopped growing.

Besides Aminata's tapeworm, only three other children's fecal specimens tested positive for intestinal parasites. However, out of 68 specimens of urine, 34 were positive for eggs of *Schistosoma*, the parasite that causes schistosomiasis (also called "black water fever"). "Schisto" is a disease caused by parasites that burrow through the skin around the ankles and calves when you wade in infected waters, where they have passed part of their life cycle in the bodies of snails. The parasites travel through the body, ending up in the epithelial lining of the walls of the urinary tract. They cause bleeding, which imparts a reddish tinge to the urine. In the long run, schistosomiasis is fatal, but the symptoms may take many years to develop; in the interim, the disease weakens you and causes anemia.

The children in Magnambougou pick up schisto from wading and playing in the Fla-bla-bla ("put them down two by two") Creek, which passes along the northern boundary of the community on its way to the Niger River. Dry for much of the year, the creek contains water during the rainy season and is a favorite place for children to splash and play on hot afternoons.

An unintended consequence of using diapers for infants, then graduating to flush toilets, is that Americans have ample opportunity to see their own and their children's urine and feces. In Mali, children never wear diapers and are trained at an early age to go to the bathroom outside in the bush or to use the deep pit latrine found in the corner of almost every compound. This means that older, more responsible members of the compound, such as parents, do not often see either the urine or the feces of young children. Worms in the feces, or blood in the urine, may go unnoticed and thus untreated (the definitive ethnographic study of beliefs and practices surrounding defecation and urination cross-culturally has yet to be written).

Moussa's nephew, a teenaged boy who accompanied us one day on our rounds to collect specimen bottles, turned out to have the worst case of schisto in the sample. He came with us because he was bored that day and wanted to know what his uncle did when he went "out and about" with the toubab. At one busy and crowded compound, the young child who was supposed to have provided the specimens had been sick and was sleeping when we stopped by. I didn't want to bother him, but neither did I want to "waste" the bottles, so I suggested that Moussa's nephew run into the latrine and provide us with at least a urine specimen.

He was happy to oblige and returned in a few minutes with what appeared to be a bottle full of blood. Moussa and I looked with dismay, first at the bottle, then at him, and his smile of accomplishment turned into a look of consternation and confusion. "What's the matter?" he asked.

"Does your urine always look like this?" I responded.

"Yes. what's the matter? Isn't it supposed to? Doesn't everyone's?"

The lab analysis of his specimen revealed over 500 *Schistosoma* eggs per milliliter, the highest count allowed under the technique used. Upon questioning, the boy said that his urine always looked red; so did that of his friends, he told us, and he had never thought to ask anyone if it was normal or not. He knew that infants had yellow urine but thought the change to red was just part of growing up.

Several months later, I was working in the Macina region of northern Mali with a group of Malian health workers from a CARE project, and we discussed schistosomiasis late one afternoon at the end of a long, hot day. We were being poled across the river in a large pirogue, and I was chastising Mariam, one of the nurses, for dangling her legs over the side of the boat into the water. Mariam was from the Bozo tribe of river fishermen. She told me that in some Bozo communities, the first appearance of red urine in a young boy traditionally was thought to be equivalent to the first menstrual period (menarche) in a young girl. Just as menarche was recognized as a sign that a young girl was sexually mature and could become pregnant, red urine in a young boy was thought to be a sign that he was sexually mature, capable of impregnating a woman.

In Bozo communities, the river is their life, and practically everyone gets infected at an early age. Because schistosomiasis can take a number of years to develop to the stage where blood can be seen in the urine, most boys start showing this symptom during puberty. According to Mariam, many Bozo communities held celebratory rites of passage for boys when they reached this milestone. "Today," she said, as she continued washing her legs in the river, "everyone knows that this is a disease that comes from the river."

Even though the Bozo have been told that going in the river can lead to schistosomiasis, they continue to do it. Partly, it is because the span of time from initial infection to the appearance of early symptoms and eventually death takes so many years. Like the links between food and health, sex and AIDS, smoking and lung cancer, some people find them difficult to believe. Others believe, but still don't change their behavior—the consequences are just too remote. Perhaps even more importantly for the Bozo, to give up the river would be to give up their entire way of life.

At the completion of this part of the research, we delivered the appropriate medicine to each of the children who tested positive for intestinal parasites or *Schistosoma* and warned parents of the dangers of playing in the Fla-bla-bla. Even as I spoke, I knew that it would be almost impossible to keep children out of the water, that reinfection was almost certain, and that parents couldn't afford the medicine. In one sense, the money spent on expensive medicine for schisto was just thrown away, but I felt it was the least I could do in return for the time and effort taken by the parents, and in return for the data necessary to satisfy my own curiosity (and my friend Karl's insistent questions) about the problems of parasites.

The next project on the agenda was to add new children and adults to the study of growth and development and to conduct extended interviews with women and other caretakers about infant feeding, weaning, and child health, as well as intrafamilial distribution of food resources and the decision-making processes involved in food purchases. I was glad the parasite project was finished. I looked forward to meeting new people and spending time sitting under the trees talking, instead of spending hours riding the baches with my bag full of smelly little bottles.

6.5 Farmers and Baboons in the Taita Hills: Inter-Species Warfare in Southeastern Kenya

Jim Bell

Abstract: *In a mountainous region of southeastern Kenya, horticulturalists and troops of wandering baboons have engaged in inter-species warfare for countless generations. Such warfare has been over food and territory. Often, the battles are not just confined to elements of protecting or stealing food from garden plots, or capturing territories, but they are psychological contests involving a show of will and "clever" strategies in which mankind does not necessarily prevail. This paper is a humorous view of a confrontation between one set of men and a single baboon troop in the East African bush, an insight into conflict resolution between man and monkey in modern times.*

Introduction

East Africa, ancestral origin of humankind, has long served as a battleground between animal species in their quest for survival. This region's river valleys, plateau plains, rift valley, seemingly endless savannahs, and deep upland forests have all witnessed the daily aggression and mortal combat between those animals that are hunted and those that hunt. Among the most successful animal populations to survive such aggression through the millennia in East Africa have been various primate species.

Paleontologists suggest that primate species may have a long history of violent competition between one another for the nutritional resources of a local area. And, as their territories become smaller in contemporary times, zoologists and primatologists discuss food competition between modern primate species. Of course, topping the list of successful primate competitors at the moment is *Homo sapiens.*

One can easily observe that human beings have overwhelming control of the earth's food resources, especially those resources in East Africa, where other primate species live. There is, however, at least one of these other species who seems not in total agreement with this observation: the common, or savannah, baboon. Baboons usually view all food stuffs within the troop's range as theirs. This simple, yet irritating, fact was made clear to me while investigating the affects of local socialization practices on the academic performance of primary school children in southeastern Kenya.

On several occasions during my research, I had an opportunity to observe first-hand the foraging methods of baboons as they went into local garden plots and stole crops intended for humans. On one such occasion, I had the misfortune of being part of this inter-species warfare: a confrontation as old as the domestication of plants in the region and, perhaps, as old as the two species themselves.

The following is offered as a sometimes humorous view of a rather serious aspect of life in the bush-lands of East Africa. Such conflict between these particular anthropoids does provide some indication as to mankind's rise above the lower primates and, at the same time, serves to illustrate how the alleged domination of our species over these other animals may owe more to dumb luck than to brain size or superior intellect and fighting skills.

The Setting

The Taita Hills are a cluster of mountain groups located in the southern portion of Kenya, slightly less than 192 miles (309 kilometers) southeast of the nation's capital of Nairobi and where the eastern-most fingers of the Serengeti extend into the western edge of the coastal plateau. Here, too, lies Kenya's famous Tsavo National Game Park. Free-roaming baboon troops constantly wander away from the game park and raid *shambas* (garden plots) of the people living in, and around, the Taita Hills. The residents of these isolated inselbergs in the midst of the plateau plains refer to themselves as *Wataita, Taita,* or "The People." Their native language, Kitaita, is one of several Bantu tongues common to this part of East Africa. Owing to their colonial past, many Wataita are proficient in English, and all are fluent in Kiswahili as well.

Originally published in *California Anthropologist*, Vol. 19, No. 1, 1992, pp. 1–6.

Cultivation of cash crops, such as vegetables and coffee, and wage labor, both in their homeland and in far off urban centers like Mombasa and Nairobi, are the major sources of income for the Wataita. Small herds of cattle, goats, and sheep serve as a source of income, but cash crops and wage labor are the primary means of acquiring wealth.

Taita men are the principle landowners, and they are most often in control of those agricultural duties connected with the production of cash crops. One of these duties includes protecting the *shambas* from raids by others. Women usually concentrate on cultivating the grains, varieties of peas and beans, and the root crops used in the local diet. In general, the Wataita live in scattered nuclear and/or extended family units which are located within easy access to one or two of the many compact village communities found throughout the Taita Hills.

Descent among the Wataita is patrilineal, with many living in extended family groups consisting of brothers and their wives and children. At a higher level of social organization, the Wataita also possess a fictive kin-group they refer to as *Kichuku*. Many Wataita also use the English term "clan" when referring to *Kichuku*. Members of a *Kichuku* usually live in close proximity to each other so that they can assist one another in times of trouble.

It is in this setting, and among these people, that I experienced one of this century's most hard-fought, yet fruitless, battles. A *shamba* belonging to my friend and key informant became the ground for hostilities between man and monkey.

■ The Raid on Sikuku's *Shamba*

I had been living in the Taita Hills slightly over a month when I was initiated (*blooded*) into one of the most sacred male rituals associated with farming in this part of the world. I and a young Wataita, Sikuku, who was my key informant and friend, sat just inside of the open door of his small two-room home. We were planning our next day's research problem, drinking beer, and watching the sun accentuate the various hues of green in the valley below. His younger female cousin, Mwakio, ran past the door delivering a panicky message in a high-pitched Kitaita no one could initially understand. She was told to calm down and repeat herself. The girl managed, in a squealing voice, to relay her bulletin. I did not understand the meaning; the presentation was much too fast for my limited Kitaita at the time, but the tone indicated serious trouble.

"Quickly!" Sikuku snapped. So away we went, bolting through the door and down a narrow path toward the valley. "We must remove those ones from the *shamba*!" he shouted to me. I ran head-long down the path, trying to keep up with this younger man who had travelled this trail a thousand times in a single year. He knew it well. I, on the other hand, was moving on unfamiliar terrain.

"Remove who? What? How?" I yelled while traversing the steep path.

Sikuku said nothing. He just seemed to increase his speed as I tried to coordinate the rate of my descent with the movement of my feet. I had to keep my feet under my body or I would fall on my face. Whatever we had to remove from the *shamba*, I wanted to arrive in one piece.

Mwakio was far above us, squealing out more alarms, calling on members of Sikiku's *Kichuku* to assist at the *shamba*. A man from a nearby household joined us. He too was moving with great speed and he, like Sikuku, made it look easy. My feet, the path, and my body were still at odds with one another. We continued down and down, turning and twisting, jumping over felled trees, trying to avoid toppling head-over-heels toward God-only-knew what. I tried to maintain some dignity in my demeanor. I did not want anyone to say I did not have a "handle" on the situation.

"How many of these notorious creatures are there?" a calm voice behind me asked.

"I do not know," I replied, huffing and puffing like an old steam engine. Three of Sikuku's male cousins passed me on the right and another two men shot by on my left. "Whose *shamba* is it?" I questioned, but no one answered. Everyone was busy trying to maintain his balance as the incline steepened.

"My *shamba* is under attack," Sikuku finally answered.

Immediately I began to gear down, trying to slow my descent, but to no avail. "Under attack?" Noticing that none of the men carried weapons of any kind, no bows and arrows, not even the all-purpose *ponga* (machete). I simply asked, "By what?"

"By nasty baboons," one of the men explained.

After descending approximately three-quarters of a mile, we reached a small hillock overlooking Sikuku's larger *shamba*. He was growing maize and beans on a little less than half an acre of prime bottom land. Scattered throughout the *shamba* was a troop of baboons. There were seven of us on the hillock. We picked up rocks, sticks, bits and pieces of decaying palm-leaves, or anything we thought suitable as a weapon. I still wondered why the men did not bring *pongas* or bows and arrows, but I thought it best not to ask. I had already made a fool of myself coming down the path. This was war time. Quickly devised estimates of the enemy's number came forth. Some of the men calculated perhaps 25 to 30 baboons in the *shamba*, with 6 or 7 on the outskirts of the plot. Others guessed the creatures were at least 30 to 40 strong, including some 20 adult males, because they believed this troop had raided the *shamba* in the past. I figured there were in the neighborhood of several hundred, probably because I had never been so close to baboons before, and they were larger than I had thought they would be.

Of course, as with most military campaigns, no one was really sure of the enemy's numbers. The confusion, coupled with fear and panic, caused an inflation in the estimates of enemy strength. If we had taken the time to count their correct numbers, we would have found only 19 of the "nasty creatures," as my Taita mates called them. Most of the enemy, it later turned out, were females and their offspring. There were four alpha males and five or six adolescent beta-sized males trying to stay out of everyone else's way. These little details were not available to us until after the battle. But, knowing how war stories have a tendency to grow with the passage of time, my original guess of several hundred baboons on the field of honor that bygone day seems nearer the correct number as the years pass. Their strengths increase at each retelling of the event.

Sikuku's oldest cousin and a man from his *Kichuku* came up behind us. "What do we do?" I wished to know. I was hoping for some definite answer steeped in the wisdom of traditionally proven strategies, an answer that came from Wataita ancestors, an answer that was handed down from the ancient gods of the Old Ones. I wanted something that would allow us to best these animals and evict them from the *shamba*. My knees were hurting from the rapid descent, and I missed the comfort of Sikuku's house. I was not ready for any major exertion.

Instead, I got puzzled looks and the most wonderful of East African rationales for an answer: "Of course, we must remove these rascals from the *shamba*." I was now sure this man, Sikuku's cousin, thought me a fool. The logic was masterful. If only I could say as much for the question.

The nine of us were simply going to attack. We moved toward the *shamba* secure in the knowledge of our ten thousand years or so of experience expelling unwanted pests from cultivated lands and millions of years of evolution. We advanced with determination and a sense of quick victory.

"Charge them, but do not go directly at them or chase one for any long time," Sikuku advised me over the shouts and yells of the other men.

As we stormed the *shamba*, I shouted back to him, "Why not?"

"They will bite you," Sikuku warned just before disappearing into a row of maize plants.

My pace immediately slowed to a cautious walk. I suddenly realized that the baboons had also been evolving for millions of years, and they also had thousands of years of experience to count upon. I crept slowly into the maize row. An adolescent male faked an attack: I yelled. There we were, two horrified combatants trying to decide what came next. I continued yelling, threw one of the small rocks I had brought from the hillock, and he retreated out of sight. Round one was mine, and my confidence was building. Deeper in the maize field, I encountered two small females and another adolescent male. They retreated without any challenge from me. As I continued to the next row, a large alpha male shot past me like a bullet.

"Baboons," I thought aloud, "are not supposed to move that fast." I froze in fear, unable to retreat or go forward. Fortunately, one of the fellows came up behind me and, with a proper shove, got me moving again.

We were nine representatives of the earth's most dominant primate species, running back and forth, in and out of maize rows, chasing baboons that barked, displayed their canines, flashed their eye-lids, engaged in mock attacks, or simply sat on their haunches yawning. In short, they were handling us better than we were controlling them. Some of the braver animals actually retrieved the smaller stones thrown at them to see if they were edible.

We had been stumbling around for five or ten minutes, a lifetime it seemed, in an effort to wrest Sikuku's fields and crops from these primates, who should have, in my estimation, run at our first appearance. Since they did not, we continued to score direct hits, only on each other, with our rocks and sticks. One of our party had been beaten over the head by another member with a dead palm-branch by mistake. The victim refused to speak to his attacker for several days. After being struck twice with missiles myself, I developed a quick appreciation for the absence of bows and arrows, *pongas*, and spears in this endeavor.

We pulled back to the hillock for a bit of rest and regrouping. It was, "Really not a retreat," I was informed by one of the men. I suppose one could say it was a strategic withdrawal to assess the damage and to reevaluate the course of action. At the time, I believed it to be a retreat not fully completed. I felt that we should have returned to the village, and not stopped at the hillock. I knew that safety and rest were further up the mountain-side.

Most of the baboons collected in the open area of the *shamba*, where the beans grew, and where they could see us more clearly. Still, many of them continued to eat some of the crops. They were, however, very agitated and began snapping at one another as they watched us. The largest of the alpha males, and the one who was clearly the leader, was exerting his dominance over the others within a five yard radius. We humans seemed as agitated as the baboons. Two of the men, exhibiting a paroxysmal fear, blamed the rest of us for not adhering to their verbal commands during the first phase of the battle. It became our collective fault that the baboons remained in the *shamba*. We, like the enemy, were short tempered and confused about the next tactic to be employed. Each time failures were cited, my name was mentioned and my maneuvers were metaphorically likened to cow dung.

Sikuku and his cousin, Mwandawa, devised a plan whereby we would form a semi-circle of sorts and progress into the *shamba* in three teams of three men each. This plan called for three men to flank the baboons on the right, three men on the left, and three men to come at them straight-on. This would force the animals out of the *shamba* and push them further down into the valley. Loading up with more ammunition, we set out to drive the enemy from "our" land.

The baboons became more agitated as we drew near their position in the *shamba*. We divided ourselves into our three-man teams and proceeded with our flanking movement. As we came closer, the females with infants clustered around the leader. Three alpha males spread out so that one was confronting each of our teams. They could keep our separate units under intense scrutiny. As we approached, adolescent males moved toward us in mock attacks. Then, the second phase of the campaign was underway. Again, two primate species were in full combat.

The men, yelling and screaming, inched forward. Rocks and sticks were thrown in every direction. The baboons barked, bared their teeth, and bounced on all fours with furor. Both sides meant serious business. I sensed that saving the crops was no longer the point of our spirited charge. Demonstrating our dominance over the arrogant little "beasties" was the rationale of the contest. How dare they refuse to run before their superiors!

Within a matter of minutes, our superior strategy and tactics gave way to confusion and panic. Baboons, except for three females and their infants, bolted in alarm and scattered throughout the *shamba*. This sudden movement was so unexpected that we too scattered in fright. Again, we humans pelted one another with stones. All five of the adolescent males had broken through our lines and threatened our retreat to the hillock. We were out-maneuvered and, seemingly, out-smarted. The more the enemy scampered about, criss-crossing in front and behind us, the less able we were to secure clear targets. Fortunately, the adolescent males at our rear were not confident enough, or large and mature enough, to charge us. The alpha males in front of us, however, were getting closer with each of their mock attacks. It was time for another strategic withdrawal. We had to fight our way past the adolescent males, while holding the three alpha males at a safe distance, and keeping an eye on the few females who had tried to join the engagement. At a time like this, one's senses increase ten-fold. Colors became more vivid, sounds increased in clarity, and the air seemed alive with differing odors that were concentrated just in the *shamba*. It was one of those moments when time is motionless, when one is at once part of, and apart from, the action that is taking place. One is a participant and, yet, one can view one's performance from a distance at the same time.

On Sikuku's cousin's command, we ran for home base (the hillock). My heart was pumping, my mouth was dry, and my legs worked only half as well as they should have. But, I managed to reach the hillock and collapse with the other men. My wind was lost somewhere back in the *shamba*. My head throbbed, my throat was raw, and my body felt like it had been crushed by an eighteen-wheeler. We lay on the hillock for what seemed forever.

Finally, after about 15 or 20 minutes, an additional four men from Sikuku's *Kichuku* arrived to help. We prepared for another attack. One of the new arrivals noticed the baboons departing down the slope toward the deeper reaches of' the valley floor. "Let us give chase!" exclaimed another of the new men.

"No brother," Sikuku replied, "let them go."

Another of the newly arrived warriors looked us

over carefully, saw our dusty appearance, noticed our fatigue, lack of fighting spirit, and said, "Ahy! You have let those ones defeat you!" Not one of us contradicted him.

Almost one-third of Sikuku's crops were eaten or destroyed. Nine of us had formed an alliance, a partnership with each other, and a covenant with the ancestors to battle another species to save our food resources. We had pledged to defend "our" land from the enemy, and to maintain dominance over so-called "lesser creatures." All had not gone quite the way we had envisioned. We had not really wrested the *shamba* from the baboons. They left in their own good time. However, two-thirds of Sikuku's crops were saved from destruction and damage, which counted for something. That alone keeps us humans ahead on over all points, and maybe that is how it has been for millennia in this region.

■ Conclusion

The events in Sikuku's *shamba* are a continuation of a centuries-old struggle in this part of the world between those that have and those that have not. Man and beast alike are the offended and offender in this ritual of life and survival. The very nature of farming in East Africa, during the past ten thousand years or so, would have been marked by such encounters. Human primates toil in the sun, turn the land, plant and weed the fields, and wait for the earth to bring forth food. These crops are a means of securing the survival of the species *Homo sapiens* and, in some instances, the excess food produced is employed to maintain economic and political ties to other human populations. Once in a while mankind's more distant relatives claim some of the fruits of this difficult labor.

In the past, the farmers of the Taita Hills lost portions of their production efforts to nomadic herders like the Maasai and some Galla groups. The baboon, perhaps the most persistent of the local animal population to raid their *shambas*, added to these losses as well. Today, an occasional human family may steal from a lowland garden, or one midway up into the foothills, but the baboon continues to pillage *shambas* throughout large areas of the Taita Hills. Baboons, like their human counterparts, have the right to exploit the environment. After all, each species views the world as theirs to control. Conflict mounts when the one cannot maintain control over the other. Humans have infringed on baboon territory in the Taita region for ten or more millennia, and it only seems fair that baboons exploit the labors of their human invaders in return.

6.6 Exercise: What Would You Do?

Put yourself into one of the following situations and describe how you would react.

1. You are in Guatemala studying infant nutrition and feeding behaviors and you come across a two-year old boy dying of malnutrition. The family has plenty of money, and there is food available for the boy to eat. It is the practice in this village to allow children (and adults) to eat as much as they want whenever they want it; there are no standard "meal times" in this culture. The boy is starving to death because he simply does not care to eat.

2. You are in Western Mongolia studying adult dental eruption patterns and relating your results to nutrition. To do this, you must examine the mouth of each adult for eruption and occlusion of the third molars (wisdom teeth.) There are no toothbrushes or other dental care devices in the village, and several people have large dental abscesses and rotting teeth. The smell from each mouth is terrible.

3. You are collecting data on the variation between actual and reported heights for a forensic anthropology course. You measure the height of all of your volunteers, and record the age, sex and race information from their driver's licenses. Your results show a correlation between differences in reported height and actual height by race. While presenting your results, some students label you as a racist.

4. You are in the Australian outback studying native populations. You come across a young girl dying of an infection received through a cut on her hand. You have just enough antibiotics available for your use throughout the field season.

5. You are in West Africa studying breast-feeding behavior in a nomadic tribe. You have brought along your ten-year old daughter and an undergraduate research assistant. You are all taking anti-malaria drugs because malaria is prevalent in this area. Your daughter and the research assistant contract severe cases of malaria, too severe for them to be flown to the United States.

6.7 Introduction to "Race"

It is apparent to anthropologists that the human species is not composed of a finite number of distinct populations that can easily be distinguished from one another by physical traits. Due to trading, warfare, migration, and other social exchanges, human groups are seldom genetically isolated. Therefore, biologically defining groups into 'races' has proven meaningless and unscientific as a means of explaining variation. In turn, most physical anthropologists prefer to describe human variation in terms of distribution and adaptive significance for a particular trait.

Read through the American Anthropological Association Statement on Race. The following questions will be discussed in class:

6.8 American Anthropological Association Statement on "Race"

The following statement was adopted by the Executive Board of the American Anthropological Association, acting on a draft prepared by a committee of representative American anthropologists. It does not reflect a consensus of all members of the AAA, as individuals vary in their approaches to the study of "race." We believe that it represents generally the contemporary thinking and scholarly positions of a majority of anthropologists.

In the United States both scholars and the general public have been conditioned to viewing human races as natural and separate divisions within the human species based on visible physical differences. With the vast expansion of scientific knowledge in this century, however, it has become clear that human populations are not unambiguous, clearly demarcated, biologically distinct groups. Evidence from the analysis of genetics (e.g., DNA) indicates that most physical variation, about 94%, lies *within* so-called racial groups. Conventional geographic "racial" groupings differ from one another only in about 6% of their genes. This means that there is greater variation within "racial" groups than between them. In neighboring populations there is much overlapping of genes and their phenotypic (physical) expressions. Throughout history whenever different groups have come into contact, they have interbred. The continued sharing of genetic materials has maintained all of humankind as a single species.

Physical variations in any given trait tend to occur gradually rather than abruptly over geographic areas. And because physical traits are inherited independently of one another, knowing the range of one trait does not predict the presence of others. For example, skin color varies largely from light in the temperate areas in the north to dark in the tropical areas in the south; its intensity is not related to nose shape or hair texture. Dark skin may be associated with frizzy or kinky hair or curly or wavy or straight hair, all of which are found among different indigenous peoples in tropical regions. These facts render any attempt to establish lines of division among biological populations both arbitrary and subjective.

Historical research has shown that the idea of "race" has always carried more meanings than mere physical differences; indeed, physical variations in the human species have no meaning except the social ones that humans put on them. Today scholars in many fields argue that "race" as it is understood in the United States of America was a social mechanism invented during the 18th century to refer to those populations brought together in colonial America: the English and other European settlers, the conquered Indian peoples, and those peoples of Africa brought in to provide slave labor.

From its inception, this modern concept of "race" was modeled after an ancient theorem of the Great Chain of Being, which posited natural categories on a hierarchy established by God or nature. Thus "race" was a mode of classification linked specifically to peoples in the colonial situation. It subsumed a growing ideology of inequality devised to rationalize European attitudes and treatment of the conquered and enslaved peoples. Proponents of slavery in particular during the 19th century used "race" to justify the retention of slavery. The ideology magnified the differences among Europeans, Africans, and Indians, established a rigid hierarchy of socially exclusive categories underscored and bolstered unequal rank and status differences, and provided the rationalization that the inequality was natural or God-given. The different physical traits of African-Americans and Indians became markers or symbols of their status differences.

As they were constructing US society, leaders among European-Americans fabricated the cultural/behavioral characteristics associated with each "race," linking superior traits with Europeans and negative and inferior ones to blacks and Indians. Numerous arbitrary and fictitious beliefs about the different peoples were institutionalized and deeply embedded in American thought.

Early in the 19th century the growing fields of science began to reflect the public consciousness about human differences. Differences among the "racial" categories were projected to their greatest extreme when the argument was posed that Africans, Indians, and Europeans were separate species, with Africans the least human and closer taxonomically to apes.

Ultimately "race" as an ideology about human differences was subsequently spread to other areas of the world. It became a strategy for dividing, ranking, and controlling colonized people used by colonial powers everywhere. But it was not limited to the colonial situation. In the latter part of the 19th century it was employed by Europeans to rank one another and to justify social, economic, and political inequalities among their peoples. During World War II, the Nazis under Adolf Hitler enjoined the expanded ideology of "race" and "racial" differences and took them to a logical end: the extermination of 11 million people of "inferior races" (e.g., Jews, Gypsies, Africans, homosexuals, and so forth) and other unspeakable brutalities of the Holocaust.

"Race" thus evolved as a worldview, a body of prejudgments that distorts our ideas about human differences and group behavior. Racial beliefs constitute myths about the diversity in the human species and about the abilities and behavior of people homogenized into "racial" categories. The myths fused behavior and physical features together in the public mind, impeding our comprehension of both biological variations and cultural behavior, implying that both are genetically determined. Racial myths bear no relationship to the reality of human capabilities or behavior. Scientists today find that reliance on such folk beliefs about human differences in research has led to countless errors.

At the end of the 20th century, we now understand that human cultural behavior is learned, conditioned into infants beginning at birth, and always subject to modification. No human is born with a built-in culture or language. Our temperaments, dispositions, and personalities, regardless of genetic propensities, are developed within sets of meanings and values that we call "culture." Studies of infant and early childhood learning and behavior attest to the reality of our cultures in forming who we are.

It is a basic tenet of anthropological knowledge that all normal human beings have the capacity to learn any cultural behavior. The American experience with immigrants from hundreds of different language and cultural backgrounds who have acquired some version of American culture traits and behavior is the clearest evidence of this fact. Moreover, people of all physical variations have learned different cultural behaviors and continue to do so as modern transportation moves millions of immigrants around the world.

How people have been accepted and treated within the context of a given society or culture has a direct impact on how they perform in that society. The "racial" worldview was invented to assign some groups to perpetual low status, while others were permitted access to privilege, power, and wealth. The tragedy in the United States has been that the policies and practices stemming from this worldview succeeded all too well in constructing unequal populations among Europeans, Native Americans, and peoples of African descent. Given what we know about the capacity of normal humans to achieve and function within any culture, we conclude that present-day inequalities between so-called "racial" groups are not consequences of their biological inheritance but products of historical and contemporary social, economic, educational, and political circumstances.

[*Note: For further information on human biological variations, see the statement prepared and issued by the American Association of Physical Anthropologists, 1996 (AJPA 101:569-570).*]

AAA Position Paper on "Race": Comments?

As a result of public confusion about the meaning of "race," claims as to major biological differences among "races" continue to be advanced. Stemming from past AAA actions designed to address public misconceptions on race and intelligence, the need was apparent for a clear AAA statement on the biology and politics of race that would be educational and informational. Rather than wait for each spurious claim to be raised, the AAA Executive Board determined that the Association should prepare a statement for approval by the Association and elicit member input.

Commissioned by the Executive Board of the American Anthropological Association, a position paper on race was authored by Audrey Smedley (*Race in North America: Origin and Evolution of a Worldview,*

1993) and thrice reviewed by a working group of prominent anthropologists: George Armelagos, Michael Blakey, C. Loring Brace, Alan Goodman, Faye Harrison, Jonathan Marks, Yolanda Moses, and Carol Mukhopadhyay. A draft of the current paper was published in the September 1997 *Anthropology Newsletter* and posted ont the AAA website http://www.ameranthassn.org for a number of months, and member comments were requested. While Smedley assumed authorship of the final draft, she received comments not only from the working group but also from the AAA membership and other interested readers. The paper above was adopted by the AAA Executive Board on May 17, 1998, as an official statement of AAA's position on "race."

As the paper is considered a *living statement*, AAA members', other anthropologists', and public comments are invited. Your comments may be sent via mail or e-mail to Patsy Evans, Director of Academic Relations, American Anthropological Association, 4350 N. Fairfax Dr., Suite 640, Arlington, VA 22203-1620.

6.9 Exercise: Race-Related Issues

Break up into five groups. Introduce yourselves to each other and choose a spokesperson and a recorder. The instructor will assign each group one of the following questions. After group members have reached a consensus, each spokesperson will present the solution to the class for discussion.

1. What biological criteria would you use to separate human populations into groups? How do you assure scientific validity? Why is this classification important?

2. We can observe that groups of individuals share certain phenotypic traits, and that these characteristics have been used to justify the separation of humans into "races." Do these "races" represent variation attributable to genetic history or environment?

3. How do you feel about the following statement: Certain groups of people are naturally better at certain types of activities and are thus inclined to enter certain professions or to live in certain places, depending upon the group to which they belong. Is this statement true? Why or why not?

4. Carlton Coon, an anthropologist working in 1965, divided people into five pure races, each of which he believed evolved from five centers of human population that were so isolated that there was almost no mixing (interbreeding) of genetic material. After 1500CE, Europeans started sailing the world, leaving their genetic material behind at numerous ports. At about the same time period, thousands of Africans were captured and forced to settle in many parts of the New World. That meant the end of pure races. However, Coon and other experts held the belief that this did not necessarily rule out the idea of distinct races. This notion suggests that there are still distinctions among races; it is just that people do not fit into these categories well anymore. What do you think of this idea? Why?

5. In recent years, we have heard about "ethnic cleansing" in Rwanda, Somalia, Yugoslavia, Bosnia, Croatia, and so forth. We have similar examples from our past, for instance, Hitler's Germany. In your opinion, are ethnic groups equivalent to races? What are the distinctions? Can ethnic cleansing ever accomplish what its proponents set out to accomplish? Why or why not?

6.10 Ancient DNA Studies

Erika Hagelberg

Now that the hype surrounding Jurassic Park *has settled down and we have become relatively used to dramatic headlines announcing the recovery of DNA from exotic fossilized remains, scientists working on ancient DNA are beginning to reflect on the long-term prospects and implications of the subject.*[1] *The science of ancient DNA has grown exponentially since its birth only ten years ago, and despite serious technical difficulties, it promises to become a revolutionary research tool in anthropology and molecular evolution. The use of bone DNA typing in particular has already yielded useful insights into Polynesian prehistory as well as spectacular applications in the forensic identification of skeletal remains.*

The Emergence of a Field

Early Studies on Ancient Molecules

Ancient DNA celebrates its tenth birthday this year: In 1984, Russell Higuchi, Allan Wilson, and colleagues the University of California, Berkeley, published a remarkable article describing the extraction of DNA from a small piece of the 140-year-old skin of a quagga, a member of the horse family hunted to extinction more than a century ago. Although most of the DNA had disappeared from the animal's tissue, and what little was left was contaminated by microbial DNA, Higuchi and his colleagues succeeded in cloning and sequencing two short fragments of mitochondrial DNA, which were found to be extremely similar to the orthologous regions in zebras and other equids.[2]

Before development of the molecular biology techniques that made this result feasible, evolutionary studies had relied either on traditional analyses of the anatomical features of living and fossil organisms or on the extrapolation of molecular data from extant species to the geological past. For several decades, however, evolutionary biologists had attempted to supplement these studies with molecular information gained directly from extinct organisms by using biochemical methods. The application of amino acid sequencing techniques to the remnants of proteins in fossils had proven unsuccessful, so attention turned to immunological methods such as radioimmunoassay to try to characterize tiny quantities of protein in the skin, teeth, or bones of fossils and preserved museum specimens. In one of these studies, although serum albumin from the muscle tissue of a 40,000-year-old mammoth had undergone considerable postmortem change, enough intact molecules survived to permit comparison with modern elephant albumin.[3]

On a more recent time scale, material extracted from a skull fragment of a Steller's sea cow, hunted to extinction by 1768, was used to show the close relationship between this species and the extant Pacific dugong.[4] In addition, radioimmunoassay of albumin from the skin of a Tasmanian wolf, or thylacine, the last of which died in a zoo in 1933, grouped this species with other Australian marsupial carnivores rather than with the remarkably similar extinct South American borhyenids.[5] However, structural proteins such as collagen and albumin are not particularly informative. Their analysis would have limited value in, say, intraspecies comparisons. In contrast, the DNA in each cell of an organism contains the entire genetic information for the organism. Consequently, by looking at the linear sequence of DNA we can potentially gain a handle on any of the tens of hundreds of genes that code for that particular individual.

Following the first successful retrieval of DNA from an extinct animal by Wilson's team, another report appeared on the cloning of ancient DNA. This time the DNA was of a human, a predynastic Egyptian mummy, analyzed by Svante Pääbo, a research student at the University of Uppsala, Sweden. Pääbo sampled 23 different mummies and examined the tissues under the microscope, discovering wide fluctuations in the state of preservation of the cellular structures.[6] The best preservation was observed in the superficial areas of the body, presumably because these had become dehydrated faster than the internal parts during mummification, inhibiting the natural autolytic degradation of the tissues. Because the cloning efficiency of the ancient DNA extracts was poor, Pääbo only managed to clone DNA from one of these mummies. However, it was clear that original human DNA has survived although, once again, it was very damaged and contaminated.

Technical Problems in Cloning Ancient DNA

It was apparent that it would be extremely hard to obtain significant amounts of genetic information from ancient remains, as most of the DNA extracted from the tissues was from microbial contamination. Moreover, the tiny amounts of original DNA were shown to be broken down into small pieces and both physically and chemically modified. This created cloning artifacts, false DNA sequences that are made when repair mechanisms in the bacterial cloning vectors salvage the damaged DNA molecules of the template. Alterations such as these could present problems in the phylogenetic analysis of the sequences.[7] This scenario prompted Jeffreys to write, in 1984, that "any hopes that molecular biology and palaeontology can be fused into a grand evolutionary synthesis by studying fossil DNA still look like nothing more than a glorious dream."[8]

Ancient DNA and the Polymerase Chain Reaction

Soon afterward, this dream came closer to reality with the invention of a new technique that allows DNA to be multiplied quickly and easily in vitro, rather than by cloning in bacteria. This technique, the polymerase chain reaction (PCR), depends on the ability of certain naturally occurring enzymes, the DNA polymerases, to copy or replicate DNA strands.[9] When a sample containing DNA is heated, its two complementary strands separate. On cooling, short pieces of synthetic single-stranded DNA, called primers, can anneal to the DNA strands. The two primers used in the PCR are designed to anneal to specific regions of DNA flanking the length of the sequence to be copied. Starting at each primer, the polymerase copies the DNA by incorporating single nucleotides, the DNA building blocks, present in the reaction mixture. The result is an identical copy of the DNA fragment bounded by the primers. Each time the reaction is repeated, there is a doubling in the DNA between the primers, with a millionfold increase in the number of original DNA sequences after 30 or 40 cycles of heating and cooling.

The PCR has several features that make it useful for ancient DNA analysis. First, the primers can be designed to define any DNA region of interest—for example, a sequence carrying an anthropologically informative polymorphism. The result is an enrichment of this particular segment, which subsequently can be analyzed by electrophoresis or sequencing. Second, only undamaged molecules of the template DNA are amplified in the PCR; this overcomes the problem of cloning artifacts caused when damaged ancient sequences are replicated in bacteria.[10] Third, extracts of many different biological materials can be used in the PCR, even if they contain only tiny amounts of DNA or if the DNA is modified or broken down. In theory, just a single copy of the target sequence is enough to start the reaction. Suitable materials for the PCR analysis include hair, blood, desiccated tissues, and frozen remains.[11-14]

The potential applications of the PCR to ancient DNA research soon became apparent. Pääbo joined Wilson's laboratory in Berkeley, where the PCR technique was beginning to be applied and, in 1988, reported the first amplification of an ancient human DNA sequence. The source of the DNA was a 7,000-year-old brain from a skeleton that had been buried in a peat bog. It was one of several human brains associated with skeletons preserved in neutral peat bogs at a site in Windover, Florida. Although previous studies on this preserved brain tissue had shown good preservation of the cellular structure and the presence of some human DNA, the DNA could not be analyzed by conventional techniques because it was contaminated with plant DNA from the surrounding peat.[15] However, using the PCR with primers specific for human DNA, Pääbo and coworkers were able to amplify short fragments of mitochondrial DNA from one of the brains and to identify two markers that defined a mitochondrial type not observed before in Native Americans.[16]

Mitochondrial DNA

Since this report, the PCR has been used in numerous ancient DNA projects, many involving the amplification of mitochondrial DNA (mtDNA).[17,18] Mitochondria are cellular organelles that contain their own complement of DNA. This type of DNA has been used widely in phylogenetic and evolutionary studies because it has useful characteristics, including a rate of evolution five to ten times faster than that of nuclear DNA, as well as maternal inheritance and small size (16,569 base pairs in humans). The complete mtDNA genomes of a human and a number of other vertebrates have been sequenced; much information also exists on other animal species.[19-22] Moreover, mammalian cells have an average of several thousand copies of mtDNA, making it much easier to recover a given mtDNA sequence than it is to obtain a single-copy nuclear sequence from a degraded sample. MtDNA information provides a simple picture of the maternal lineage as it is inherited maternally without recombination, whereas nuclear DNA represents both the male and female ancestry of an individual. In addition, nuclear DNA contains the bulk of the genetic information of the cell (3×10^9 base pairs versus the 16 kilobases of mtDNA).[23]

Although most studies of ancient DNA from human remains have used mtDNA, the first reports of the analysis of nuclear sequences from ancient remains are beginning to appear. For example, Lawlor and colleagues have amplified highly polymorphic human leukocyte antigen (HLA) genes from 7,500-year-old brain tissue from the Windover site.[24] Their study involved cloning a large number of different alleles after amplification from the tissue extracts. This particular approach is very laborious and therefore may not be generally applicable to ancient population surveys. Analyses of the highly polymorphic HLA genes are generally best done as haplotype frequencies, whereas population-specific markers are better suited to ancient DNA studies for which only limited numbers of samples may be available.

Bone Hard

A technical advance that permitted the wider application of ancient DNA to population and evolutionary studies was the discovery, in 1989, that DNA can be amplified from ancient bones. It was originally thought that DNA would not survive well, if at all, in bone. For this reason, all the early studies on ancient DNA used soft tissue remains preserved in peat bogs or by dehydration, mummification, or freezing. In late 1987, I began to experiment with different methods to extract DNA from human archeological bone. It took about a year before some of the bones finally yielded amplifiable DNA and another year for me to convince myself that I was looking at 5,000-year-old human DNA rather than some artifact.[25] Two other laboratories reported similar results from analysis of ancient human skeletal remains.[26,27] These three reports had in common the analysis of ancient human skeletal remains. Soon the question was raised of the authenticity of the amplified sequences. How did we know that we were not sequencing some of our own DNA, introduced in minute quantities into laboratory reagents?

Kosher Laboratory

To address this question, I decided to recover DNA from animals bones. In one of the earliest experiments, I extracted DNA from a pig bone recovered from the wreck of the *Mary Rose*, the flagship of Henry VIII that sank in the English Channel in 1545, causing the loss of more than 400 lives. Many animal bones are associated with the wreckage. The pig bone was originally a leg of pork from a large quantity of salted pig meat that constituted part of the diet on board. Using conserved mtDNA primers that allow amplification of a fragment of the cytochrome *b* gene in vertebrates,[12] I amplified a piece of DNA about 400 base pairs long, which, on sequencing, proved to be unequivocably porcine. As modern pig DNA had never been handled in the laboratory, this was the first unambiguous proof that DNA could be recovered from ancient bones. The publication of this result in 1991[28] was greeted by an English newspaper with the headline "Pig brings home the bacon on DNA."

Forensic Applications

About the time this work was done, we became involved in the first practical applications of bone DNA typing, which turned out, perhaps not surprisingly, to be in forensic identification. In 1990, the British police asked Alec Jeffreys of Leicester and me to help confirm the identity of the 8-year-old skeleton of a murder victim. As I had not yet finished the work on the *Mary Rose* pig sample, I was fairly apprehensive about taking on such a case, still fearing that we might be dealing with PCR artifacts rather than genuine bone DNA. Provided with a small fragment of femur from the alleged murder victim, I soon discovered that mtDNA fragments could be amplified from a bone extract. Moreover, after testing many different combinations of primers provided by colleagues in nearby laboratories, I realized that small fragments of single-copy nuclear DNA could also be amplified from the extracts. With this information, we felt justified in requesting blood samples from the murder victim's parents to permit the identification to be carried out.

The nuclear markers used for the identification had to be small; the DNA extracted from bone was too degraded for analysis by conventional DNA fingerprinting techniques. Microsatellites are only on the order of 100 base pairs in length and consist of a tandem repeat of a di-, tri-, or tetranucleotide motif, with the number of repeats being fairly variable between individuals. These types of variable tandem repeats are abundant in the human genome. New loci have been described with increasing frequency in recent years.[19] Jeffreys analyzed six different microsatellite loci in the bone extract and in the blood of the presumed parents of the victim. In every case, he observed a result that was compatible with the bone DNA being that of a child of this couple, with odds of less than 1 in 1,000 against a match by chance alone.[30] This case pioneered the use of bone DNA typing in criminal cases, forensic use of nuclear microsatellite DNA, and acceptance of PCR data as evidence in British courts. The Karen Price case was tried in January 1991, resulting in the conviction of the two murder suspects.

About this time Jeffreys and I were also involved in the identification of the skeleton alleged to be that of Nazi doctor Josef Mengele. Once again, the identity of the skeleton was confirmed by the amplification of microsatellite DNA from bone extracts and comparison with DNA from Mengele's surviving relatives.[31] This time 10 different microsatellite loci were analyzed, with odds of less than 1 in 1,800 of an inclusion by chance alone. Such odds strongly suggested that the DNA extracted from the bones was authentic; chance contamination would almost certainly have caused an exclusion. These results gave further valuable support to the validity of the bone typing techniques.

Identification using mtDNA and comparison with surviving maternal relatives has also been carried out successfully using bone[32] and teeth.[33] Very recently, both mtDNA and nuclear DNA markers were used by scientists at the Home Office Forensic Service in England to identify the skeletal remains of the Romanov family and its attendants.[34]

Human Migrations

Despite the considerable social and historical interest of these forensic cases, the main reason for looking for DNA in human bones is to gain a glimpse at prehistory relatively unclouded by the effects of recent migrations, population bottlenecks, and genetic drift, all of which affect the interpretation of data obtained from modern populations. At the MRC Unit of Molecular Haematology in Oxford, John Clegg and his colleagues have analyzed polymorphisms in the human α-globin genes that are associated with resistance to malaria in present-day Pacific populations.[35] They have found that certain of these polymorphisms have unexpected anthropological applications as population markers for extrapolating the migration route of the proto-Polynesian voyagers. We thought it would be valuable to augment these studies with the analysis of mtDNA polymorphisms in skeletal remains from archeological sites in the Pacific.

Polynesian Origins

Although linguists and prehistorians generally agree that modern Polynesians originated in the islands of Southeast Asia, there is still considerable debate about the route of colonization and the degree of admixture of these relatively recent Pacific migrants with the much earlier settlers of the islands of Melanesia. Australia and New Guinea were first settled at least 40,000 years ago, during low Pleistocene sea levels.[36,37] There is archeological evidence of prehistoric settlement dating to 28,000 years bp as far east as Buka in the Solomons.[38] Further east, there is a gap of about 25,000 years in the archeological record. The earliest human occupation of the central Pacific is associated with the "Lapita Cultural Complex," which extended from the Bismarck Archipelago to the central Pacific in the period from 3,600 to 2,500 years bp. The Lapita culture, characterized by ornate pottery, domesticated animals, and skills in agriculture and navigation, was thought to have been carried into the Pacific by Austronesian language speakers from Southeast Asia. These people, the ancestors of the modern Polynesians, reached the most distant islands of remote Oceania, Hawaii, New Zealand, and Easter Island, during the last millennium, with dates for the settlement of New Zealand being as recent as the 12th century AD.[39]

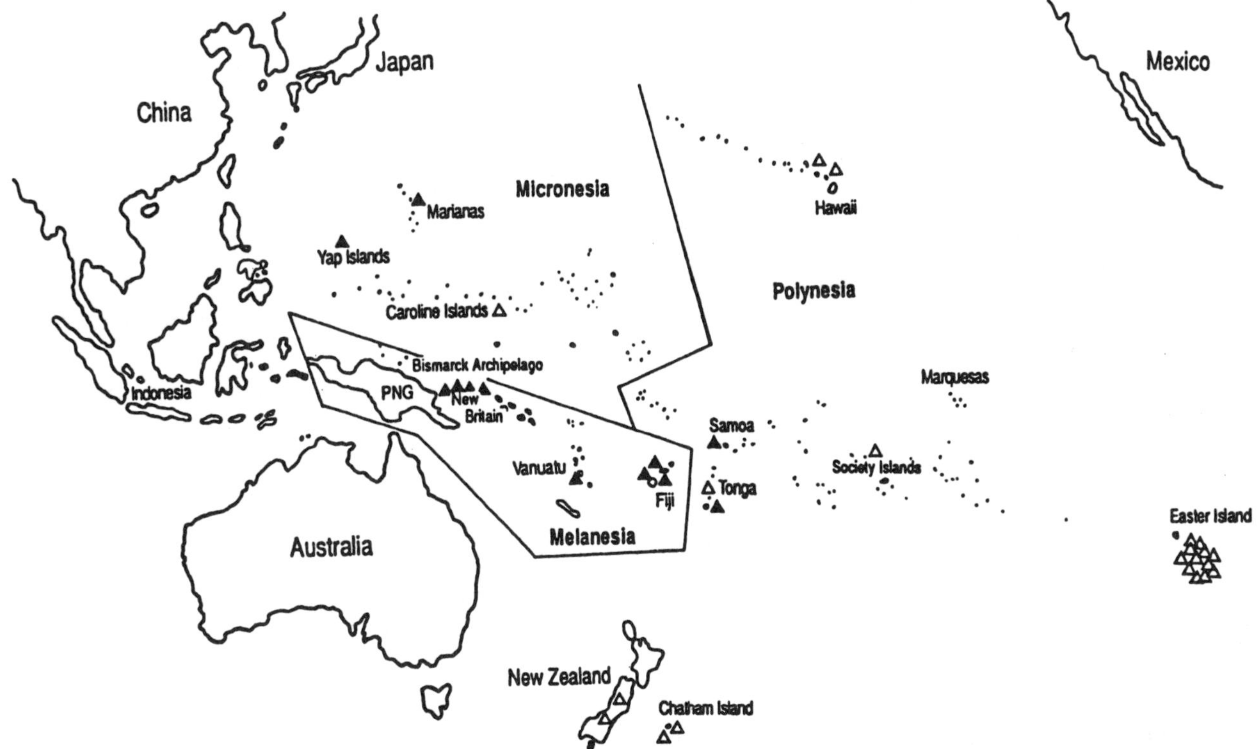

Figure 1. Map of Oceania, showing the locations of prehistoric human bones from which DNA could be extracted. Open triangles: individuals with the Asian mtDNA deletion. Solid triangles: individuals lacking the deletion.

Some prehistorians argue that there is enough archeological evidence to suggest local development of the Lapita culture in island Melanesia.[40] Some evidence from physical anthropology supports this view: morphometrical studies of early Lapita skeletons of the central Pacific seem to group them with Melanesians rather than Polynesians.[41] Genetic studies on present-day populations agree with the view of the Southeast Asian origin of modern Polynesians. The globin gene evidence points to significant genetic admixture between Melanesians and the newcomers,[42] whereas the mtDNA data support what is known as the "fast train to Polynesia" model of rapid colonization by the Lapita people and relatively little admixture with the inhabitants of island Melanesia.[43, 44]

John Clegg and I looked at mtDNA mutation that is found at high frequencies (5 to 40%) in modern populations of Asian origin and that has reached fixation in some Polynesian archipelagos.[43] This mutation is commonly known as the nine base pair deletion because it is characterized by the loss of nine bases from a small noncoding region of mtDNA. It is almost invariably present in modern Polynesians, in conjunction with three characteristic base substitutions in the hypervariable portion of mtDNA. These markers constitute a useful "Polynesian haplotype" that we hoped to use to identify prehistoric Lapita people. In an initial survey of prehistoric human skeletal remains from a range of archeological contexts in Oceania, including some of the oldest material from the central Pacific, we detected the Polynesian mtDNA markers in the bones of prehistoric Polynesians (Hawaii, Chatham Islands, Society Islands), but not in the bones of Lapitas. Our results, although very preliminary, suggest that the earliest inhabitants of the central Pacific could have come from Melanesia rather than Southeast Asia (Figure 1).[41]

Remote Easter Island

In the course of our survey of mtDNA polymorphisms in ancient and modern Polynesians, we detected just one major mtDNA lineage throughout this vast geographical expanse. It was characterized by the nine base pair deletion and the three base substitutions of mtDNA. The presence of this "Polynesian haplotype" in prehistoric Easter Islanders would support the widely held view that these people originated in Polynesia rather than South America, as held by Thor Heyerdahl, and help shed light on a question that has aroused the curiosity of scientists and lay people alike.[46, 47] To test the Polynesian origins hypothesis, we analyzed the skeletal remains of 12 individuals from two archeological contexts in Easter Island and detected the Polynesian haplotype in every single one, confirming the Polynesian ancestry of these people.[48] This is an example of a study that could not be conducted on living descendants of the prehistoric people, for Easter Island was almost completely depopulated following European contact. The majority of the present-day islanders are of Chilean origin.

■ Ancient DNA of Prehistoric Amerinds

Typing of ancient bone DNA is also being used to throw light on the colonization of the Americas. Although the route of colonization into the New World through Beringia is not questioned, there is considerable debate regarding the time of colonization, the number of different migration waves, and the existence of a genetic bottleneck.[49] Most mtDNA types found in modern Amerindian populations fall into four groups defined by a combination of mtDNA markers. It is therefore thought that a significant reduction in genetic diversity occurred as a consequence of bottlenecks during the initial colonization.[50, 51] Alternatively, a reduction in diversity may have been the consequence of demographic collapse after European contact. To test this hypothesis, Stone and Stoneking analyzed the mtDNA of 50 individuals of a pre-Columbian archeological site in Illinois. They found no appreciable difference in the levels of diversity between the ancient and contemporary populations. This suggested that European contact probably did not significantly alter the levels of mtDNA variation in Amerinds and that the diversity observed reflects the patterns of migration.[52]

■ Antediluvian DNA

These examples demonstrate the potential uses of DNA typing of ancient human remains to provide information about fundamental questions regarding the past. However, the samples studied have been, at most, only a few thousand years old, as were those from the Windover site. How about much older DNA? In 1990, Edward Golenberg and his colleagues broke the longevity record for ancient DNA with their report of a chloroplast DNA sequence from a 17- to 20-million-year-old compression fossil of a magnolia leaf recovered from an anoxic Miocene lake bed in Clarkia, Idaho.[53] In turn, this record was broken by the publication of phylogenetically informative sequences amplified from a 30-million-year-old fossil termite preserved in Dominican amber,[54] and then again by the recent sequencing of DNA from a 120-million-year-old weevil from Middle Eastern amber.[55]

Controversy has surrounded this work from the outset, as this length of time is considered by some as theoretically too long to permit the survival of DNA.[56, 57] In a recent comprehensive review on DNA instability, Thomas Lindahl describes the hydrolytic and oxidative decomposition processes that rapidly degrade the DNA of dead organisms once the repair mechanisms present in living cells cease to function.[58] Lindahl writes that survival of DNA under hydrated conditions like the Clarkia deposit "is incompatible with the known properties of the chemical structure of DNA," although he admits that amber might provide a particularly good environment for the preservation of DNA because the DNA is largely dehydrated and protected to a certain extent from oxidation and microbial degradation. Lindahl claims that the spectacular reports of the recovery of DNA from materials many millions of years old have overshadowed the important studies on moderately ancient DNA, and suggested that scientists should concentrate on the "amplification of small DNA fragments, say, 100,000 years old."[59] Poinar[60] and Golenberg[61] argue that their empirical results should have precedence over any theoretical constraints on DNA longevity. The resolution of this debate must await the laborious accumulation of a body of well controlled and phylogenetically meaningful sequences from these extraordinarily old sources of DNA.

■ Ancient DNA is Damaged

DNA extracted from ancient samples can be difficult to amplify, either because it is too damaged or because contaminating substances can inhibit the PCR. Hydrolytic and oxidative damage causes DNA to break into small fragments until eventually no intact fragments are left.[18] DNA extracted from ancient materials is also frequently contaminated by microbial DNA and compounds, notably humic acids, taken up from the surrounding burial environment. Ancient specimens can be affected by glues, consolidants, and preservatives used in museum conservation. Even when amplification is successful, the length of the amplified fragment is generally limited to just a few hundred base pairs. Despite these problems, PCR is still the method of choice for analyz-

Genetic Affinities of Prehistoric Easter Islanders

Easter Island, also known by its Polynesian name, Rapanui, is one of the most isolated inhabited islands on earth, being about 2,250 km away from Pitcairn, its nearest inhabited neighbor. This tiny island is thought to have been settled only once in prehistory, probably from the Marquesas Islands, and as early as the fourth century AD, although the earliest reliable radiocarbon date is 690 ± 130 years AD.[78,79] It is likely that the island remained isolated for at least a millennium until the first European contact in 1722. Accounts of Easter Island culture by early European visitors include descriptions of sophisticated stoneworks, including ceremonial platforms (ahu) and several hundred characteristic giant statues (moai), as well as widespread horticulture and the only written language in Polynesia (rongorongo script).

The prehistoric population probably numbered several thousand individuals, but ecological degradation caused by deforestation and overpopulation led to war and demographic collapse well before European contact. Infectious diseases and raids by Peruvian slavers had virtually depopulated the island by the end of the 19th century, helped by the environmental impact of the introduction of several thousand sheep. The island now belongs to Chile and is populated by about 2,000 individuals, mostly newcomers from the mainland.

Although most archeological, anthropological, and linguistic evidence points to a Polynesian origin of the prehistoric Easter Island people, certain cranial traits are found at relatively unusual frequencies, possibly as a result of genetic founder events in the original settlement of the island and its isolation from the rest of Polynesia.[80,81] However, Heyerdahl [46,82] suggests that the island was settled twice, first by a group of Caucasoid migrants from Peru who brought with them stoneworking skills and American crops like the sweet potato (the staple diet of islanders during prehistoric times), and later by Polynesians from the west. There is little archeological evidence for this view, but intriguing anomalies in culture and morphology, coupled with the general aura of mystery that imbues the island, will ensure that the debate about Easter Island origins will continue for some time.

The analysis of prehistoric human bones by PCR amplification and sequencing would help shed light on this question, for genetic information from present-day Easter Islanders is hard to interpret as a result of the high level of admixture with migrants from the mainland. We carded out such an analysis on bones excavated by Heyerdahl's Norwegian Archaeological Expedition of 1955–56.[46] The bones were from two spatially and temporally distinct archeological contexts in the island. In all, 12 individuals were examined, four from Ahu Tepeu on the west coast (1100–1680 AD) and eight from Ahu Vinapu on the south coast (1680–1868 AD). In every case we identified mtDNA markers characteristic of Polynesians.[48] Our results indicate that relatively recent prehistoric inhabitants of Easter Island were undoubtedly Polynesians. Although in the absence of well-characterized skeletal material from early sites we cannot refute Heyerdahl's idea of an initial non-Polynesian settlement, the lack of plausible evidence for the multiple migration hypothesis suggests that the first Easter Islanders were indeed from Polynesia.

ing ancient DNA because it selects the molecules specified by the primers, even in the presence of a vast excess of microbial DNA, and requires so little template DNA.

Nightmare of Contamination

As if these technical problems were not sufficiently discouraging, scientists working on ancient DNA are confronted with the hazards of contamination by modern DNA. The exquisite sensitivity of the PCR means that tiny quantities of contaminating DNA in the reagents or equipment can cause false-positive reactions. One main source of contamination is from people handling the specimens; another is ordinary household dust (mainly dead skin cells).

In addition, millions of copies of a given DNA sequence are made in each experiment and can inadvertently be spread around the laboratory. Such contamination is difficult to control and presents a major hazard because these products of earlier amplification reactions can easily creep into new extraction experiments or PCR reactions. When this occurs, it is difficult to distinguish between the original DNA in a sample and a contaminating sequence, for both will be amplified in PCR experiments.

A number of sensible precautions can be taken to minimize the problems of contamination, including the separation of pre- and post-PCR work in the laboratory and the use of dedicated reagents and equipment to prepare the ancient DNA samples. Contamination can be monitored by the use of suitable blanks and controls for the extractions and amplifications.[62] Finally, the correctness of the amplified sequences can sometimes be verified by phylogenetic inference. In any event, the work must be carried out with enormous care so that contamination does not lead to hopeless ambiguities in the results.

This was vividly illustrated by Bryan Sykes of Oxford at the First International Conference on Ancient DNA held at the University of Nottingham, England, in July 1991.[63-65] Sykes described a series of experiments on extracts of human and animal bones in which a human DNA segment was amplified from ancient horse and cow bones, while a pig sequence was recovered from a human bone. Obviously, the products of previous amplification reactions had randomly crept into the various experiments. Several of the results presented at this meeting, which was attended by about 70 scientists from different countries, would eventually turn out to be contamination artifacts. Despite this somber message, the meeting was a great success, marking the transition of ancient DNA from a curiosity to a full-fledged scientific discipline.[66, 67]

Growth of a Discipline

Nowhere has the expansion of this subject been more evident than at the Second International Conference on Ancient DNA held at the Smithsonian Institution in Washington DC in October 1993.[68, 69] This meeting was attended by 170 researchers; many more were turned away. Two main points had arisen from the 1991 meeting. One was the importance of frequently neglected museum collections as future sources of genetic information. The other was the relevance of methodological aspects such as DNA damage and contamination in ancient DNA research. This issue in particular was covered extensively at the 1993 meeting, where much of the first day was devoted to discussions on the biochemistry of ancient DNA, DNA damage, and contamination.

Edward Golenberg of Wayne State University chaired the "Million Plus Club." He discussed the problems of authenticating old DNA by phylogenetic inference and the importance of calibrating molecular clocks. Because all the longevity records for ancient DNA belong to insects in amber, different explanations were proposed for the preservative properties of tree resin. Raul Cano gave an impressive presentation of the quality assurance procedures in the work on DNA from amber in his laboratory at the California Polytechnic Institute. These procedures included performing 20 blank amplifications with different primers once a week to monitor PCR product "carryover." At the other end of the time spectrum, Bob Wayne of the Institute of Zoology, London, discussed the fact that although most studies of ancient DNA are done on extinct animals, the study of extant species based on museum collections and surviving populations can give valuable insights into genetic variability and inbreeding depression in endangered species.

Latest Developments

Since I started to write this article there have been exciting new results in studies of ancient DNA. Svante Pääbo and colleagues have extracted and sequenced mtDNA from the 5,000-year-old mummified human body found in September 1991 in the Tyrolean Alps.[70] In an article that will undoubtedly become a classic of ancient DNA research, these workers describe the painstaking precautions taken to ensure that they were analysing DNA of the Ice Man and not of one of the many Europeans who had handled the body since its retrieval from the ice. Although contamination by DNA of several different individuals was detected, the consensus mtDNA sequence matched the sequence determined independently by a different research team. The sequence also matched mtDNA of contemporary central and northern Europeans, whereas it differed significantly from the mtDNA sequences of Africans and Native Americans. This removed the lingering suspicion that the Ice Man was a fraud, that is a South American or Egyptian mummy placed recently in the melting ice.

A new landmark for the longevity of ancient DNA from vertebrates has also been reached: In separate communications, both Pääbo's and my research group addressed the suggestion by Thomas Lindahl that ancient samples of a moderate age, say 100,000 years, should be targeted for analysis.[59] To show that it is possible to obtain reproducible results from Pleistocene faunal remains, Pääbo and his colleagues extracted DNA from soft tissues of five different Siberian mammoths between 9,700 and 50,000 years old. Amplification of a 93 base pair fragment of mtDNA was possible from four to five individuals.[71] Completely independently, my colleagues and I amplified a 375 base pair fragment of the mtDNA cytochrome *b* gene from two samples of Siberian mammoth, from bone rather than soft tissue. We subsampled the two mammoth specimens for accelerator mass spectrometry dating, and both gave a date beyond the range of finite radiocarbon dating, 47,000 years or older. Stratigraphic evidence suggested that one of the mammoths must have been at least 150,000 years old. To our knowledge, these are the oldest dated vertebrate remains from which DNA has been amplified.[72]

Conclusion

All in all, it has been an exciting decade for ancient DNA research. Moreover, the teenage years of this young science hold much promise. Of particular interest to anthropologists is the DNA typing of skeletal remains for the study of many aspects of human evolutionary history including migrations, lineage extinctions, population structure, and the emergence of agriculture and farming. The amplification of sex-specific sequences from skeletal remains already offers particular promise for studies of the social organization of past societies,[73, 74] as well as being applicable in forensic science.[34] There is little doubt that ancient DNA will gradually become a routine research tool in archeology, anthropology, and biological conservation.

The understanding of human genetic diversity is becoming increasingly important as local populations vanish or merge with their neighbors, and much information on present populations will be gathered under the auspices of the Human Genome Diversity Project.[75] Ancient DNA studies clearly will have an important role to play in this initiative by providing a direct source of evidence on past populations and, possibly, the only insight into the genetic affinities of vanished peoples. However, this type of research will undoubtedly also be a source of contention as access to the remains of ancient peoples becomes a political or ethical issue.[76, 77]

Acknowledgments

I thank John Fleagle for inviting me to write this review and his patience in waiting for the final manuscript. My warmest thanks to John Clegg for his help and intellectual support, Mary Ganczakowski for the Easter Island photographs, and Jerry Hagelberg and Chuck Cook for comments on the manuscript. I gratefully acknowledge the financial support of the NERC Special Topic in Biomolecular Palaeontology and the Wellcome Trust.

References

1 Morrell V (1993) Dino DNA: The hunt and the hype. Science *261*:160–162.

2 Higuchi R, Bowman B, Freiberger M, Ryder OA, Wilson AC (1984) DNA sequences from the quagga, an extinct member of the horse family. Nature *312*:282–284.

3 Prager EM, Wilson AC, Lowenstein JM, Sarich VM (1980) Mammoth albumin. Science *209*:287–289.

4 Rainey WE, Lowenstein JM, Sarich VM, Magor BM (1984) Sirenian molecular systematics—including the extinct Stellar's sea cow (*Hydrodamilis gigas*). Naturwissenschaften *67*:343–346.

5 Lowenstein JM, Sarich VM, Richardson BJ (1981) Albumin systematics of the extinct mammoth and Tasmanian wolf. Nature *291*:409-411.

6 Pääbo S (1985) Molecular cloning of ancient Egyptian mummy DNA. Nature *314*:644–645.

7 Higuchi RG, Wrischnick LA, Oakes E, George M, Tong B, Wilson AC (1987) Mitochondrial DNA of the extinct quagga: Relatedness and extent of postmortem change. J Mol Evol *25*:283-287.

8 Jeffreys AC (1984)Raising the dead and buried. Nature *312*:198.

9 Saiki RK, Scharf S, Faloona F, Mullis KB, Horn GT, Erlich HA, Arnheim N (1985) Enzymatic amplification of β-globin genomic sequences and restriction site analysis for diagnosis of sickle cell anemia. Science *230*:1350–1354.

10 Pääbo S, Wilson AC (1988) Polymerase chain reaction reveals cloning artefacts. Nature *334*:387–388.

11 Higuchi R, von Beroldingen CH, Sensabaugh GF, Erlich HA (1988) DNA typing from single hairs. Nature *332*:543–546.

12 Kocher TD, Thomas WK, Meyer A, Edwards SV, Pääbo S, Villablanca FX, Wilson AC (1989) Dynamics of mitochondrial DNA evolution in animals: Amplification and sequencing with conserved primers. Proc Natl Acad Sci USA *86*:6196–6200.

13 Thomas RH, Schaffner W, Wilson AC, Pääbo S (1989) DNA phylogeny of the extinct marsupial wolf. Nature *340*:465–467.

14 Thomas WK, Pääbo S, Villablanca FX, Wilson AC (1990) Spacial and temporal continuity of kangaroo rat populations. J Mol Evol *31*:101–112.

15 Doran GH, Dickel DN, Ballinger WE Jr., Agee OF, Laipis PJ, Hauswirth WW (1986) Anatomical, cellular and molecular analysis of 8,000-yr-old human brain tissue from the Windover archaeological site. Nature *323*:803-806.

16 Pääbo S, Gifford JA, Wilson AC (1988) Mitochondrial DNA sequences from a 7000-year-old brain. Nucleic Acids Res *16*:9775–9787.

17 Pääbo S, Higuchi RG, Wilson AC (1989) Ancient DNA and the polymerase chain reaction. J Biol Chem *264*:9709–9712.

18 Pääbo S (1989) Ancient DNA: Extraction, characterization, molecular cloning and enzymatic amplification. Prac Natl Acad Sci USA *86*:1939–1943.

19 Anderson, S, Bankier AT, Barrell DG, de Bruiin MHL, Coulson AR, Drouin J, Eperon IC, Nierlich DP, Roe BA, Sanger F, Schreier PH, Smith AJH, Staden R, Young IG (1981) Sequence organisation of the human mitochondrial genome. Nature *290*:457–465.

20 Bibb MJ, van Etten RA, Wright CT, Walberg MW, Clayton DA (1981) Sequence and gene organization of mouse mitochondrial DNA. Cell *26*:167–180.

21 Anderson S, de Bruiin MHL, Coulson AR, Eperon IC, Sanger F, Young IG (1982) Complete sequence of bovine mitochondrial DNA. Conserved features of the mammalian mitochondrial genome. J Mol Biol *156*:683–717.

22 Irwin DM, Kocher TD, Wilson AC (1991) Evolution of the cytochrome b gene of mammals. J Mol Evol *32*:128–144.

23 Stoneking M (1993) DNA and recent human evolution. Evol Anthropol 2:60–73.

24 Lawlor DA, Dickel CD, Hauswirth WW, Parham P (1991) Ancient HLA genes from 7500-year-old archaeological remains. Nature *349*:785–788.

25 Hagelberg E, Sykes B, Hedges R (1989) Ancient bone DNA amplified. Nature *342*:485.

26 Horal S, Hayaska K, Murayama K, Wate N, Koike H, Nakai N (1989) DNA amplification of ancient human skeletal remains and their sequence analysis. Proc Jpn Acad Ser B *65*:229–233.

27 Hänni C, Laudet V, Sakka M, Begue A, Stehelin D (1990) Amplification of mitochondrial DNA fragments from ancient human teeth and bones. Cr Acad Sci Paris Series III *310*:365–370.

28 Hagelberg E, Clegg JB (1991) Isolation and characterisation of DNA from archaeological bone. Proc R Soc Lond B *244*:45–50.

29 Tautz D (1990) Genomic fingerprinting goes simple. BioEssays *12*:44–46.

30 Hagelberg E, Gray IC, Jeffreys AJ (1991) Identification of the skeletal remains of a murder victim by DNA analysis. Nature *352*:427–429.

31 Jeffreys AJ, Allen M, Hagelberg E, Sonnberg A (1992) Identification of the skeletal remains of Josef Mengele by DNA analysis. Forensic Sci Int *56*:65–76.

32 Stoneking M, Hedgecock D, Higuchi RG, Vigilant L, Erlich HA (1991) Population variation of human mtDNA control region sequences by enzymatic amplification and sequence-specific oligonucleotide probes. Am J Hum Genet *48*:370–382.

33 Ginther C, Issel-Tarver L, King MC (1992) Identifying individuals by sequencing mitochondrial DNA from teeth, Nature Genet 2:135–138.

34 Gill F, Ivanov PL, Kimpton K, Piercy L, Benson L, Tully G, Evett I, Hagelberg E, Sullivan K (1994) Identification of the remains of the Romanov family by DNA analysis. Nature Genet *6*:130–135.

35 Flint J, Clegg JB, Boyce AJ (1992) Molecular genetics of globin genes and human population structure. In Devor EF (ed) *Molecular Applications in Biological Anthropology*, pp 103–178. Cambridge: Cambridge University Press.

36 Groube L, Chappell J, Muke J, Price D (1986) A 40,000-year-old occupation site at Huon Peninsula. Nature *324*:453–455.

37 Bellwood PS (1989) The colonization of the Pacific: Some current hypotheses. In Hill AVS, Serjeantson SW (eds) *The Colonization of the Pacific: A Genetic Trail*. pp 1–59. Oxford: Oxford University Press.

38 Wickler S, Spriggs M (1988) Pleistocene human occupation of the Solomon Islands, Melanesia. Antiquity *62*:703–706.

39 Anderson A (1991) The chronology of colonization in New Zealand. Antiquity *65*:767–795.

40 Terrell J (1986) *Prehistory in the Pacific Islands*. Cambridge: Cambridge University Press.

41 Pietrusewsky A (1985) The earliest Lapita skeleton from the Pacific: A multivariate analysis of a mandible fragment from Natunuku, Fiji. J Polynesian Soc *94*:389–414.

42 O'Shaughnessy DF, Hill AVS, Bowden DK, Weatherall, DJ, Clegg JD (1990) Globin genes in Micronesia: Origins and affinities of Pacific island peoples. Am J Hum Genet *46*:144–155.

43 Hertzberg M, Mickleson KPN, Serjeantson SW, Prior JF, Trent RJ (1989) An Asian-specific 9-bp deletion of mitochondrial DNA is frequently found in Polynesians. Am J Hum Genet *44*:504–510.

44 Stoneking M, Wilson AC (1989) Mitochondrial DNA. In Hill AVS, Serjeantson SW (eds) *The Colonization of the Pacific: A Genetic Trail*. pp 215–245. Oxford: Oxford University Press.

45 Hagelberg E. Clegg JB (1993) Genetic polymorphisms in prehistoric Pacific Islanders determined by analysis of ancient bone DNA. Proc R Soc Lond B *252*:153–160.

46 Heyerdahl T, Ferdon E Jr (1965) *Reports of the Norwegian Archaeological expedition to Easter Island and the East Pacific. Vol. 2, Miscellaneous papers*. London, Allen & Unwin.

47 Bahn P, Flenley J (1992) *Easter Island, Earth Island*. London: Thames and Hudson.

48 Hagelberg E, Quevedo S. Turbon D, Clegg JB (1994) DNA from ancient Easter Islanders. Nature *369*:25–26.

49 Meltzer DJ (1993) Pleistocene peopling of the Americas. Evol Anthropol *1*:157–168.

50 Wallace DC, Garrison K, Knowler WC (1985) Dramatic founder effects in Amerindian mitochondrial DNAs. Am J Phys J Anthropol *68*:149–155.

51 Torroni A. Schurr TG, Yang CC, Szthmary EJE, Williams RC, Schanfeld MS, Trup GA, Knowler WC, Lawrence DN, Weiss KM, Wallace DC (1992) Native American mitochondrial DNA analysis indicated that the Amerind and the Nadene populations were founded by two independent migrations. Genetics 130:153–162.

52 Stone AC, Stoneking M (1993) Ancient DNA from a pre-Columbian Amerind population. Am J Phys Anthropol *92*:463–471.

53 Golenberg EM, Giannasi DE, Clegg MT, Smiley CJ, Durbin M, Henderson D, Zurawski G (1990) Chloroplast DNA sequence from a Miocene Magnolia species. Nature *344*:656–658.

54 DeSalle R, Gatesy J, Wheller W, Grimaldi D (1992) DNA sequences from a fossil termite in Oligo-Miocene amber and their phylogenetic implications. Science *257*:1933–1936.

55 Cano RJ, Poinar HN, Pieniazek NJ, Acra A, Poinar GO (1993) Amplification and sequencing of DNA from a 120–135-million-year-old weevil. Nature *363*:536–538.

56 Pääbo S, Wilson AC (1991) Miocene DNA sequences—a dream come true? Curr Biol *1*:45–46.

57 Sidow A, Wilson AC, Pääbo S (1991) Bacterrial DNA in Clarkia fossils. Phil Trans R Soc Lond B *333*:429–433.

58 Lindahl T (1993) Instability and decay of the primary structure of DNA. Nature *362*:709–715.

59 Lindahl T (1993) Recovery of antediluvian DNA. Nature *365*:700.

60 Poinar G (1993) Recovery of antediluvian DNA. Nature *365*:700

61 Golenberg EM (1994) Antediluvian DNA research. Nature *367*:692.

62 Hagelberg E (1994) Mitochondrial DNA from ancient bones. In Herrmann B, Hummel S (eds) *Ancient DNA*. pp 195–204. New York: Springer Verlag.

63 Cherfas J (1991) Ancient DNA: Still busy after death. Science *253*:1354–1356.

64 Pääbo S (1991) Amplifying DNA from archeological remains: A meeting report. In *PCR Methods and Applications*. Cold Spring Harbor: Cold Spring Laboratory Press.

65 Sykes B (1991) The past comes alive. Nature *352*:381–382.

66 Brown TA, Brown KA (1992) Ancient DNA and the archaeologist. Antiquity *66*:10–23.

67 Pääbo S (1993) Ancient DNA. Sci Am *269*:60–66.

68 Fischman J (1993) Going for old: Ancient DNA draws a crowd. Science *262*:655–656.

69 Sykes B (1993) Less cause for grave concern. Nature *366*:513.

70 Handt O, Richards M, Tommsdorf M, Kilger C, Simanainen J, Georgiev O, Bauer K, Stone A, Hedges R, Schaffner W, Utermann G, Sykes B, Pääbo S (1994) Molecular genetic analyses of the Tyrolean Ice Man. Science *264*:1775–1778.

71 Höss M, Pääbo S, Vereshchagin NK (1994) Reproducible mammoth DNA sequences. Nature, in press.

72 Hagelberg E, Thomas MG, Cook CE, Sher AV, Baryshnikov GF, Lister AM (1994) DNA from mammoth bones. Nature, in press.

73 Hummel S, Herrmann B (1991) Y-chromosome specific DNA amplified in ancient human bone. Naturwissenschaften *78*:266–267.

74 Hummel S, Nordsiek G, Herrmann B (1992) Improved efficiency in amplification of ancient DNA and its sequence analysis. Naturwissenschaften *79*:359–360.

75 Roberts L (1992) Genome Diversity Project: Anthropologists climb (gingerly) on board. Science *258*:1300–1301.

76 Mulvaney DJ (1991) Past regained, future lost! The Kow Swamp Pleistocene burials. Antiquity *665*:12–21.

77 Hagelberg E (1990) Bones, dry bones. The Times Higher Education Supplement *945* (14 December):14.

78 Bahn PG (1993) The history of human settlement on Rapanui. In Fisher SR (ed) *Easter Island Studies*. pp 53–55. Oxford: Oxbox Books.

79 Irwin G (1992) *The Prehistoric Exploration and Colonisation of the Pacific*. Cambridge: Cambridge University Press.

80 Gill GW, Owsley DW (1993) Human osteology of Rapanui. In Fisher SR (ed) *Easter Island Studies*, pp 56–62. Oxford: Oxbow Books.

81 Wright RVS (1992) Correlation between cranial form and geography in *Homo sapiens*: CRANID—a computer program for forensic and other applications. Perspectives Hum Biol 2: Archaeology of Oceania 27,128–134.

82 Heyardahl T (1989) *Easter Island: The Mystery Solved*. London: Souvenir Press.

6.11 Whose Ancestor is He? The Case of Kennewick Man and the Science of Repatriation

Elizabeth Miller

Whose ancestor is this? Who owns the past? These are questions which have been brought to the forefront of consideration among archaeologists, physical anthropologists, Native Americans, and ethicists by the discovery of, and subsequent controversy over, the remains of a man who lived and died approximately 9,300 years ago along the Columbia River in Washington state. The individual, called "Kennewick Man" by most archaeologists (also referred to as "Richland Man") and the "Ancient One" by many Native groups, is now at the center of one of the first legal challenges of Federal interpretation of the 1990 Native American Graves Protection and Repatriation Act (NAGPRA).

NAGPRA mandates the return of Native American human remains, objects of cultural patrimony, and ceremonial objects to affiliated tribes. Unfortunately, NAGPRA does not adequately address several significant points concerning how affiliation of human remains or their ancestral/descendent relationships are to be addressed. It is this lack of definition that has led to the current controversy over interpretations of the law.

After the discovery of the Kennewick Man remains in 1996, the Army Corps of Engineers (the agency responsible for the land on which the remains were found) initiated documentation of the remains. Because it was initially unclear whether the remains were modern or not, they were given to forensic anthropologist Dr. James Chatters. Chatters determined that the individual showed many 'Caucasoid' (use of the word 'Caucasoid', and its many interpretations, is a subject of debate within the anthropological community and, unfortunately, cannot be discussed in detail in this short work) features, along with a healing wound caused by a projectile injury, in which the point was still embedded. The remains were originally interpreted as those of an historic fur-trader or pioneer. The projectile point was observed via CAT scan, and determined to be of a type in use between 9,000 and 4,500 years ago. Subsequent examination of the remains by a second forensic anthropologist, Ms. Catherine MacMillan, confirmed Chatters' documentation of 'Caucasoid' features. Because of these features, the remains were radiocarbon dated to confirm their antiquity. The radiocarbon date also indicated that Kennewick Man was alive approximately 9,300 years ago, making his remains one of a very small number of human skeletons found in North America dating to that time period. Chatters immediately recognized the importance of the remains and called in another physical anthropologist to examine them. Dr. Grover Krantz, a professor at Washington State University, examined the remains and noted characteristics common to both Europeans and Plains Indians. Krantz concluded that the remains could not be "racially or culturally associated with any existing American Indian group" (Grover Krantz, quoted in Preston, 1997:72), and that "the Native Repatriation Act has no more applicability to this skeleton than it would if an early Chinese expedition had left one of its members there." (Grover Krantz, quoted in Preston 1997:72).

Shortly after the radiocarbon results came in, the Corps of Engineers demanded that all study of the bones cease, and required the Coroner to put the skeleton in the county sheriff's evidence locker. The Corps had decided that the skeleton was Native American and that it fell under NAGPRA. Within a period of weeks, the Army Corps of Engineers advertised its intent to repatriate the Kennewick Man remains to Native American groups currently living in the area. To give some context to the brevity of this period of consideration by the Corps, NAGPRA provided a period of five years for the documentation of remains already in museums and federal institutions. During the author's tenure at the Smithsonian as Director of the Physical Anthropology Lab in the Office of Repatriation, the determination of biological affiliation from the human remains required approximately 2–5 days intensive work on

Originally appeared in the January 1998 edition of the *Southwestern Anthropological Association Newsletter* (Volume 38, Issue 3), p. 1+.

the skeletal material. The determination of cultural affiliation required a much longer period of time, with researchers examining historic maps, diaries, government documents, archaeological reports, and other sources to determine the prehistoric and historic human composition of a geographic area. All of this for relatively recent prehistoric remains! There is no precedent for the time required to determine the biological/cultural affiliation of Paleo-Indian remains.

Physical anthropologists and other scientists were dismayed. They protested the apparent decision of the Corps that biological and/or cultural affiliation were irrelevant, with some going so far as to state that it is impossible to demonstrate a relationship between a man who lived 9,300 years or so ago and modern Native groups living in that area. Dennis Stanford, Chairman of the Department of Anthropology at the Smithsonian Institution's National Museum of Natural History, is quoted as saying "Those tribes are relatively new. They pushed out other tribes that were there" (quoted in Preston, 1997:74).

Scientists across the country wrote letters to the Corps requesting access to the remains, and giving their opinions that reburial of the Kennewick Man remains would be a great loss to both science and the American people. Some cited NAGPRA themselves concerning analysis and the public good. Section 7, paragraph 5b of 25 USC 3005 (Public Law 101-601, 104 STAT. 3054) states that remains must be repatriated expeditiously "unless such items are indispensable for completion of a specific scientific study, the outcome of which would be of major benefit to the United States," and several scientists made the argument that the remains of Kennewick Man have scientific merit of national importance. United States Senator Slade Gorton (R-Wash) and U.S. Representative Doc Hastings (R-Wash) both showed an interest in the case, urging the Corps to allow scientific study of the remains and hold off on repatriation until Congress could consider the matter. Just prior to the expiration of the 30 day waiting period required by NAGPRA before repatriation, eight anthropologists filed suit against the Department of Defense, Army Corps of Engineers and named individuals involved in the decision-making process on this issue. The lawsuit was seen as a last resort by many, if not all, of these scientists.

The scientists are basing their lawsuit on several arguments, the first (and most important, in my opinion) two of which are the facts that the Corps had insufficient evidence to determine whether the remains were Native American under the law, and that the Corps had insufficient evidence to support its claim that the remains have a connection with the tribes to which they were to be repatriated (Schneider, pers. comm.). Briefly, the Corps, by agreeing to repatriate the remains to the geographically-closest tribe(s) without scientific study, appears to have decided that biological and/or cultural affinity were irrelevant; that the oral histories and religious beliefs of Native groups currently living in the area superceded the need for scientific inquiry into the affiliation of Kennewick Man. Unfortunately, this subject cannot be treated in the depth it deserves in a short piece such as this, but it bears further consideration.

The study and repatriation of Kennewick Man has now become a matter for the courts to decide. Since the discovery of the remains, the issue has become one of science vs. religion in the popular press. The Kennewick Man case can be considered as analogous to the argument between creationists and evolutionists concerning the origins of modern humans and the teaching of evolution in public schools, in fact, as illustrated in the following quotations. The Native American view is represented by the following quote (Armand Minthorn, quoted in Preston, 1997:74):

> *Our elders have taught us that once a body goes into the ground, it is meant to stay there until the end of time... If this individual is truly over 9,000 years old, that only substantiates our belief that he is Native American. From our oral histories, we know that our people have been part of this land since the beginning of time. We do not believe that our people migrated here from another continent, as the scientists do . . . Scientists believe that because the individual's head measurement does not match ours, he is not Native American. Our elders have told us that Indian people did not always look the way we look today. Some scientists say that if this individual is not studied further, we, as Indians, will be destroying evidence of our history. We already know our history. It is passed on to us through our elders and through our religious practices.*

while the scientific perspective is represented by these quotes (Robson Bonnichson, quoted in Preston, 1997:77–78):

> *There is a presumption, written into almost every textbook on prehistory, that Paleo-Americans...are the direct ancestors of today's Native Americans. But now we*

have a very limited number of skeletons from that early time, and it's not clear that that's true. We're getting some hints from people working with genetic data that these earliest populations might have some shared characteristics with latter-day European populations. A lot more research is needed to sort all this out. Now, for the first time, we have the technology to do this research, especially in molecular biology. Which is why we must study Kennewick.

and Dennis Stanford (quoted in Preston, 1997:80):

For a long time, I've held the theory that the Clovis and the Folsom (authors' note: Clovis and Folsom are the names applied to the artifacts and culture of the earliest inhabitants of North America) were overwhelmed by a migration of Asians over the Bering land bridge. It may not just have been a genetic swamping or a pushing aside.

Stanford goes on to postulate that the Archaic spear point embedded in the Kennewick Man's hip might even be evidence of warfare between the earlier populations and the later Archaic arrivals from Asia. Certainly the abruptness of the transition between Clovis/Folsom and later cultural complexes appears to indicate a replacement of one by the next, rather than an evolution of one into the other.

The important issues here are the denial by the Corps of the merit and relevance of scientific determination of biological and/or cultural affiliation and the question of religious fundamentalism overwhelming scientific endeavors. The questions remain: Will religious fundamentalism, in this case in the form of Native American religion, take precedence over scientific discovery? Are the biological and cultural affiliation of human remains irrelevant for repatriation? Comparative data depend on the discovery and analysis of Paleo-Indian remains. If the scientists lose this court battle over Kennewick Man, religious fundamentalism will have won a major battle over science.

The case of Kennewick Man is slowly winding it's way through the judicial system. So far, scientists have won some time. In October, 1996 U.S. District Court Magistrate Judge John Jelderks ordered the Army Corps of Engineers to give the anthropologists' attorney two weeks notice before the remains are turned over to any Native group. And the Corps chose not to resolve the case immediately, deciding not to repatriate "because of the intense interest in these remains by the Native American and scientific communities" (Lt. Gen. Joe Ballard, quoted in Stang, 1996: 1). In June, 1997 Judge Jelderks charged the Corps of making faulty assumptions concerning the remains by assuming they were Native American based primarily on their age and the fact the point recovered in the Kennewick Man's hip was likely of Native manufacture. The Corps was inequitable in granting access to the remains, allowing Native groups access to the remains for religious ceremonies (they also allowed access to the Asatru Folk Assembly, a religious group focusing on Norse gods, which has also laid claim to the Kennewick remains); access which shocked the scientists and their attorneys when it came to light. The Corps has now indicated all access to the remains has been halted. And finally, in October, the Corps was re-examining its original decision—an examination which might provide room for scientific study.

In his essay "The Reburial Controversy, a general overview and exploration of a method for resolution of the ethical dilemma," Pettifor (1997:2) makes several excellent points, including this one: "A significant part of Indian culture is in its spirituality. Indians did not suffer a split as Western society did at the beginning of the 17th century between science and religion." Spirituality for many Native Americans is an integral part of their scientific beliefs. And most scientists, including me, support the maintenance of Native American culture and spirituality. Most scientists, including me, support the repatriation of Native American remains if the remains can be linked culturally or biologically with existing Native groups. But these Native American spiritual beliefs, like all spiritual beliefs represented in the United States, must be held separate from law. We cannot allow religious or spiritual beliefs to supercede scientific endeavors in governmental affairs. The establishment of affiliation on the basis of biological and/or cultural evidence must take precedence over the simple geographic proximity of any *modern* Native group to sites containing prehistoric human remains. Scientists must be allowed to study the Kennewick Man remains and to have their interpretations given *at least equal* consideration by the Army Corps of Engineers as the oral histories and religious beliefs of Native groups. It is now up to the courts to decide whether or not the skeleton of Kennewick Man will be allowed to speak to all Americans, or only to a select few. And if the opinion of this anthropologist carries any weight, the bones of the "Ancient One" will be allowed to speak to us all.

Acknowledgements: I would like to thank Dr. Gentry Steele, friend and mentor, for reading and commenting on a draft of this paper. His help was appreciated. I would also like to thank Mr. Alan Schneider, Attorney for the scientists, for sharing as much as he could about the lawsuit.

References Cited:

Pettifor E (date unknown) The Reburial Controversy: A General Overview and Exploration of a Method for Resolution of the Ethical Dilemma. Retrieved from http://www.wynja.com/arch/reburial.html on 12/10/97.

Preston D (1997) The lost man. The New Yorker, *June 16, 1997:70–81.*

Schneider A (1997) Personal communication.

Stang J (1996) Burial of ancient bones put on hold. Tri-City Herald, *October 24, 1996.* Retrieved from http://www.tri-cityherald.com/bones/1024.html on 12/10/97.

The Native American Graves Protection and Repatriation Act, Public Law 101-601, 104 STAT>3054).

6.12 Web Sites

Forensic Anthropology

American Academy of Forensic Sciences
http://www.aafs.org/

American Board of Forensic Anthropology, INC.
http://www.csuchico.edu/anth/ABFA/

Osteo Interactive
Human Osteology and Forensic Anthropology information.
http://www-medlib.med.utah.edu/kw/osteo/forensics/forens.html

Forensic Anthropology at California State University, Chico
http://www.csuchico.edu/anth/PAHIL/

Forensic Anthropology at California State L.A.
http://curriculum.calstatela.edu/courses/anth454l/

Human Dentition
http://www.sscf.ucsb.edu/~walker/dentition/HumanDentition.html

6.13 *From* Living with Our Genes: *Engineering Temperament: Cloning and the Future Politics of Personality*

Dean Hamer and Peter Copeland

Andrew thought a lot about his father, if that's what you could call him. Andrew's father was a scientist who had left a respectable career at a quiet university to join a risky biotech venture in the year 2002. The risk paid off, big time, and Andrew's father became a multimillionaire. More importantly, he was able to work on the project of his dreams: cloning. The startup firm, Mirror Image, Inc., worked on the genetic cloning of animals, including humans. Wall Street loved the idea, and the stock's initial public offering set unheard-of records. Investors bet heavily on the company because the technology was relatively simple and the promise enormous. The only possible roadblock was Washington, and there was the risk that the government would try to ban cloning research. There had been congressional hearings and public handwringing after the cloning of the first sheep, named Dolly, but the concern had eased. Scientists had showed that animal cloning could help feed the world, speed medical advances, and provide other benefits. Cloning had become less scary and more acceptable.

Human cloning was a little more complicated, but only in terms of ethics and politics. The science was the same. The ethical questions were still being debated, of course, just like people still debated how many angels could fit on the head of a pin. The more practical minded people were simply going ahead and doing it. Mirror Image pursued a two-track policy. Publicly, company officials said little, to avoid scrutiny. They weren't doing anything illegal, in fact company policy was to follow the highest legal standards to avoid being tripped up by a technicality. But behind the scenes, they were funding research at powerful think tanks and courting policymakers. Changes in the campaign finance system back in the 1990s had not worked exactly as the reformers had planned, and Mirror Image and similar companies were able to quietly influence appointments to the congressional committees overseeing their industry.

The company was doing the science openly, on animals that is. Secretly, the scientists worked on human experiments, slightly altering the protocol that had been used with sheep to make it suitable, tweaking the cell growth media, testing various methods of preparing nuclei, etc. Not actually cloning any humans, yet, but doing all the tedious but necessary preliminary experiments. In case of an emergency, most likely of the political kind, the company had built an exact replica of its U.S. lab in a secret location overseas.

Andrew's father wasn't much interested in the politics or the ethics. He was an intensely focused man interested in technique and results. He wasn't naive, however, and he knew that he had to be careful. He kept a detailed record of his experiments, his lab was meticulously run, and his public behavior was exemplary. Every step was planned and projected, and recorded on videotape, when he inserted a swab into his mouth, scraped a few cells from the inside of his cheek, and dabbed them onto a petri plate. He began the cloning process.

When his cells had progressed to the ideal stage, they were treated with a chemical that arrested growth, putting them in a temporary state of suspended animation. Then the nucleus from one cell was removed and inserted into a human egg, donated by a lab assistant, that was in the same suspended state. The DNA from the egg was replaced by the DNA from the cheek scraping, but the egg had no way of knowing this. As far as the egg was concerned it had just been fertilized in the normal way, and so it began to divide and to copy the scientist's DNA. Soon the egg was reimplanted into the womb of the lab assistant, and nine months later, a bright and healthy baby boy was delivered into the world. His name was Andrew. His DNA was identical to that of the scientist. Not 50 percent the same, as would be the case for a normal child, but base-for-base the same, as if Andrew and his father were identical twins.

The birth announcement was greeted with shock and anger. While everyone knew that it was possible to clone a human, technically at least, no one expected that it actually would be done. Anticipating the reaction, Mirror Image had prepared a strong defensive strategy, and it paid off. After the initial outrage, with magazine covers comparing Andrew's father to a Nazi scientist, the coverage began to switch focus to the baby. The baby was innocent of any wrongdoing and was undeniably cute. He cooed and gurgled at the TV cameras and seemed to love the attention. Network producers fought for the rights to chronicle his every move, and Andrew became a kind of national pet. "Andrew Eats Solid Food," trumpeted the *New York Times.* A tabloid reported, "Nothing Sheepish About Our Andy!"

The coverage began to fade after a few years, mostly because Andrew did nothing extraordinary. There were only so many stories that could be done about a normal, healthy toddler. By the time he was five, his first day at school was mentioned only in passing by the major news media. He was just another kindergartner. Andrew was raised in the modest suburban home of the lab assistant, who couldn't have loved him more. She stopped working while he was small to be with him, and Mirror Image provided more than enough money to support the little family of two. Andrew's father saw him only when the boy came to the lab for tests. The father had moved on to other experiments, and like the rest of the nation, he didn't much care about Andrew after the novelty had worn off.

The only person who remained obsessed with Andrew's story was Andrew. He had indexed all the newspaper and magazine stories about his birth, as well as the scientific abstracts. Interestingly, when his father was younger he had made a similar scrapbook, collecting thousands of articles about DNA and cloning, even though in those days it was just cloning of carrots and frogs. Andrew built his massive scrapbook on a computer with all the video and digital images of his life. He used his "Clone at Home" software, a hugely popular program, to replay his creation and development. The software allowed a person to plug in different variables, genetic or environmental, to his or her life story. Then the computer predicted how the life would have developed, and a video image showed how the person would age from birth to 80 years old. Andrew's favorite game was to delete his father's DNA and replace it with the DNA of his "mother," the lab assistant. When Andrew played out the program with her genes, he preferred the virtual results to the real thing.

It was too late to delete his father's DNA, however. All of Andrew's potential, all that he ever would be, was contained in that one swab dragged across the inside of a cheek. Andrew stared at himself in the mirror and tried to see himself clearly. Who was he? He knew he was a separate person, but it was all so confusing. When he compared himself with old snapshots taken when his father was a boy, he could hardly tell the difference, for they were as alike as identical twins. And yet he didn't *feel* like his father, or at least he didn't think so. The resemblance was so eerie that he deliberately wore his hair differently from his father and experimented with pierced cars, which didn't suit him. In his face, Andrew also noticed traces of his grandfather and grandmother. Andrew did some research on the family of his father and fell in love with his great-great-grandmother, a pioneering bioethicist who had warned, unsuccessfully as it turned out, about the dangers of genetic engineering. Andrew idolized her and saw her as his true forbearer, not the man who scraped a cheek. Andrew came to see that man as merely one disposable receptacle for the long march of his genes, with about as much personality as a beaker.

Andrew could not deny, however, that there were elements of his own personality that came from his father. They shared a sense of being proper and neat; it infuriated them both that the lab assistant allowed her car to fill up with old newspapers, gum wrappers, and empty Coke cans that rolled back and forth under the seat. They both had short fuses. Andrew's father tended to blow up when things went wrong; he once threw a batch of improperly prepared gel at a cowering postdoc. Andrew also had his rages, but he controlled his anger with exercise; when he felt the pressure building, he'd go to the gym or take a run. Andrew accepted those parts of his personality as givens, unchangeable but controllable. What he did with his life was another thing; that was his choice alone. He wasn't going to follow in his father's footsteps. In fact, he vowed to use that same focused determination and intellect that made his father such a good scientist to stop the people who believed that cloning humans was no different than mass-producing sheep.

Is Andrew's story farfetched? A little, but only to make a point. Both the knowledge of human genetics, and the ability to manipulate and exploit it, are expanding at an exponential pace. By the first decade of the twenty-first century we will know the entire sequence of the human genome, every one of the more than three billion nucleotides that make up the 100,000 genes that constitute our genetic patrimony. Deciphering the meaning and function of those genes will be slower, but success is inevitable. Already, an entire new field has emerged called "functional genomics" dedicated to figuring out what genes do. At the same time, new technologies are emerging to exploit this information with drugs and by manipulating the genetic information itself. So far the manipulations are being performed only on animals, Dolly the sheep being the first well-known example, but humans are just a few steps away.

There is no turning back. Supporters of the international Human Genome Project argue convincingly that mapping the entire genome will help produce new drugs, reduce birth defects, and allow us to live longer and healthier lives. Even if the project were officially stopped, much of the most advanced, demanding research has been taken over by biotechnology start-up companies, and by the giant pharmaceutical firms that usually end up owning them. Lives are at stake. Money is at stake. That's a powerful combination anywhere, and in America it's invincible.

The focus of attention so far has been on discoveries of genes for cancer and other physical illnesses. What often goes unsaid is that the genes being discovered also include ones that define behavior. Virtually every aspect of how we act and feel that has been studied in twins shows genetic influence, and many of the individual genes have been isolated. The fact that so many behavior genes are being found is not surprising because the brain is so complex that much of our genetic information is devoted to building, developing, and maintaining it.

The combination of these two forces—the stampede to map the genome plus the decisive role of genes in behavior—means that, whether anyone thinks it's a good idea or not, we soon will have the ability to change and manipulate human behavior through genetics.

As scary as that might sound, the genetic manipulation of behavior is not new. Humans have been selectively breeding behavior in animals, such as dogs and farm animals, since before history. And whether we recognize it or not, we already are products of genetic engineering. As far back as we can see, humans have been selective about their mates. Beauty, power, and prestige have always been desirable. Clans or families sought to marry their offspring with people of high rank and stature. People from particular religions or races sought their own kind. The highest social classes, the blue bloods, sought to preserve the purity of their lines.

The difference is that in the near future science will give us the power to do it more quickly, more accurately, and more decisively. We will select mates not because of some superficial trait like a prominent family; we'll be able to read their DNA as easily as an X-ray. Nor will we settle for the randomness of sexual blending of sperm and egg, with all its billions of possible combinations, when we can build the desired combination to the letter.

It's too late to wonder whether we are going to genetically tinker with human behavior. We need to decide very quickly how we are going to do it. How will we distinguish "good" genes from "bad?" What traits will be valued and what will be discarded? Who gets to choose?

■ DNA on a Chip

The first stage of the process will be using genes for diagnosis, rather than for manipulation. Currently, most mental health experts analyze personality using very unsophisticated tools: their eyes and ears. They listen to patients, compare their symptoms with those of recognized syndromes, and make a "diagnosis." Only it isn't a diagnosis at all because it doesn't say anything about the underlying mechanism or origins of the problem. It's just a description: a matching of the patient's complaints to complaints that other people have described.

In the future, a person who complains of depression or anxiety could have a DNA test to check the serotonin genes. People with compulsive behavior such as gambling, drinking, drugs, or promiscuous sex, would be checked for dopamine genes. Eating disorder or obesity? Look at the genes for leptin, the leptin receptor, and its targets. A new technology called DNA chips, already under development by a biotech firm called Afymatrix, will make an entire DNA blueprint as easy to read as a supermarket bar code.

Doctors won't be the only ones to read this information. Insurance companies, which profit by charging based on risk factors such as smoking, would be very interested in genetic predispositions toward addiction or mental disorders. The military, which today rejects people who took medication as teenagers to control attention deficit disorder, might want to know about genes for rebellious temperament. Employers might be interested in genes for loyalty. Religious orders would be wise to discourage high novelty seekers, while the maker of sports cars would want to target them with ads. Dating services would have revealing new ways to match people. Imagine how excited certain school administrators would be to track students who are bright, troubled, or aggressive.

We will have all new ways to understand people—and to label them, discriminate against them, or help them. The technology is coming; how to use it is up to us.

Designer Drugs

The second phase will be designer drugs tailored to individual genetic needs. Today's pharmacology is so imprecise that doctors diagnose by prescribing drugs; if Prozac works, the patient must have a serotonin problem. Why not start backwards and build a drug that addresses the problem? Individual DNA sequences, combined with existing computer modeling techniques, would allow drugs to be as precise as a key in a lock.

The customized brain drugs will certainly be an improvement over today's sledgehammer method of pounding the body with chemical combinations until something works. They also will create new dangers, however. For one, we know nothing about the consequences of changing brain chemistry. The brain is so sensitive that it might respond to our manipulations in unforeseen ways. Already people are taking drugs such as Prozac for years or decades, even though the initial safety tests lasted only months. What if the brain's long-term response to the drug is to change the wiring pattern in a way that true joy, exuberance, or ecstasy were impossible? Also, imagine the possibilities of selling illegal pleasure drugs, custom-made to individual brains.

Another danger is that we will medicalize normal human behavior and variations. Some people argue that this already is happening, that Prozac is being prescribed for normal mood swings, and that Ritalin is being used to "treat" boyhood. If drugs designed to fight life-threatening obesity are used casually to drop a few pounds before prom night, why not use a behavior drug to improve your own particular mood? Why should you ever feel blue if you don't have to? Why should teachers have to tolerate disruptive behavior when they could spray kids with a calming aerosol that actually would help them learn? Maybe crime could be reduced by smoothing out the rough edges of problem youths. We wouldn't need assertiveness training if girls could take pills to cure shyness. What about that pesky gay gene? Spray it away with new "Straight-in-a-Day!"

Gene Therapy

But why bother with pills or sprays? Why treat the symptoms if you can fix the cause? If all these mental "problems"' are caused by genes, then why not change the genes themselves? This is the ultimate stage of the coming revolution: gene therapy, the deliberate manipulation of genetic makeup to repair a defective or mutant gene, to replace it with a "better" gene, or even to introduce a completely new gene.

One way of doing this would be to alter cells directly in the brain. New genes already can be delivered into cells by packaging them inside viruses, which are designed by nature to enter cells. Already there are hundreds of clinical trials underway using gene therapy to treat simple disorders caused by a single gene, such as cystic fibrosis. Much of the difficulty at this point has been getting the new genes into the cells, so scientists are looking for new genetic delivery vehicles. Inder Verma at the Salk Institute in La Jolla, California, is experimenting with the notoriously effective virus, HIV, which causes AIDS. He has managed to disarm the AIDS part of the virus and has enabled it to penetrate many types of cells. This feared virus could become the ultimate "suitcase" for carrying genes.

It's easy to imagine how gene therapy could be used on severe brain diseases such as Parkinson's and Alzheimer's. Since Parkinson's is caused by a loss of the cells that produce dopamine, it might be possible to insert a gene that results in dopamine production. In the case of Alzheimer's, in which neurons are lost because of the formation of plaques and tangles, it might be possible to induce new neuron growth by expressing the gene for nerve growth hormone, a sort of growth hormone for brain cells. The next likely target for brain gene therapy would be the severe psychiatric disorders such as schizophrenia, although everything would depend on determining the genetic blueprint of the disorders.

If gene therapy for schizophrenia worked, it would be logical to consider gene therapy for less severe conditions, such as depression or mental fatigue. If sufferers had the "wrong" form of the serotonin transporter gene, it theoretically could be swapped out for the more upbeat version. This would be an exaggerated treatment, though, since the same effect could be obtained by taking Prozac. There also could be undesirable consequences, such as the loss of sex drive. More importantly, gene therapy would be permanent. Unlike taking a drug, there would be no way to undo the treatment. A bigger concern is that genes for personality are so complicated that it's impossible to know what might happen if one were altered. The fabric woven by DNA in combination with the environment is so intricate that unravelling a single thread could destroy the whole tapestry.

Other problems with this kind of gene therapy on brain cells would arise because it usually would be used to clean up damage rather than prevent it, and it's good for only one generation. The best way to fix a gene before it is passed on to the next generation is to go into the germ cells in the sperm and eggs. One approach to this "germline" therapy has already been developed, at least in mice. New DNA is introduced into cells that are grown in a culture, then mixed together with natural cells from an early embryo. Some of the resulting babies will have the engineered genes in their germ cells and can pass them on to the next generation.

This all sounds straightforward enough, but the human genome is so large that when a new bit of DNA is introduced into a human cell, it only rarely figures out where it's supposed to go. Nobel Prize winner Paul Berg is experimenting with how to guarantee delivery and make single base changes in the mammalian genome. Berg learned from watching yeast that a certain break in a DNA molecule makes it much easier to recombine with engineered DNA. He has managed to break mouse DNA in a way that encourages it to incorporate any change that he desires, thus clearing the way for narrowly targeted genetic engineering.

Berg, however, scoffs at the idea of genetically engineered humans, not because it won't become possible but because he doubts people will want to. His own hands-on experience with human engineering occurred when he was approached by a stranger carrying a little black bag. The man said he was collecting sperm from Nobel Prize winners and wanted a sample from Berg, which then would be sold. This is an obvious kind of genetic engineering, and there's no reason it can't work, except for the fact that people simply don't want to do it. Berg sent the man packing, telling him with a laugh that the scheme would flop. "I know a lot of Nobel laureates," he told the sperm banker. "And I know their children."

The Uncertainty Principle

Even if all the formidable technical hurdles to genetic engineering were cleared, there would remain a deep, fundamental difficulty because of the very nature of genetic influences on behavior—the uncertainty principle.

As shown time and again in this book, genes may predispose toward a particular type of temperament or behavior, but they are never sure predictors. A person may have genes that predispose him to addictive behaviors like alcoholism, but he could just as well become an avid bug collector who discovers an important new species. Another person might have the genetic makeup typical of a mass murderer; but he could turn out to be the next great professional linebacker.

The problem with germline therapy is that it targets genetic "problems" before they have manifested themselves. If left alone, traits that could be regarded as problems might never develop, or they could turn out to be assets. If it's true that there is a fine line between genius and madness, or between creativity and depression, then we should be careful what we engineer for because we just might get it. A DNA map is not the same as a road map, which shows exactly how to get from one place to the next. A DNA map offers possibilities and predictions but not certainty.

The uncertainty principle also includes unintended consequences. Even if we know exactly what a gene is for, say baldness, that doesn't mean that neutralizing the gene will cure baldness. Even if it did cure baldness, the gene might also be involved in vision or smell or some other function that we could never have imagined. Consider, for example, what happened when scientists used gene surgery to improve the muscle mass in mice, research that could be of great benefit to people suffering from muscle disorders.

A gene called myostatin controls muscle growth. When the body has the normal amount of muscle, the myostatin prevents the muscle cells from growing any further. Scientists easily knocked out the gene and bred a strain of mice without myostatin, who therefore had no block on muscle production. By six weeks, the mice had developed unusually big shoulders and hips. When they were full grown, their skeletal muscles were two to three times larger than normal mice. Other types of muscle, such as in the heart and intestines, were not changed. The scientists speculated that this type of gene therapy could be used to make leaner, meatier farm animals. Some day it could also be used on humans to treat the loss of muscle that occurs in muscular dystrophy and in some types of cancer and in AIDS.

But there was another, totally unexpected result: the muscular mice were wimps, what the scientists politely referred to as "gentler." The big mice were less eager to attack other mice and less likely to react when poked or prodded by human handlers. When Alexandra McPherron, one of the scientists at Johns Hopkins University who developed the new strain, presented the mice to the world at a news conference, the mice started fighting. McPherron commented matter-of-factly, "The normal one there is beating up the big muscular one."

No one expected a personality change. The only effect on the mice was supposed to be in muscle mass, not in the brain. Everybody thought they knew exactly how myostatin works on muscle growth, and in fact they did. The mice did get bigger, but the gene must have some other still unknown role. Or perhaps taking out that gene changed the expression of another gene, or a hormone, or something else in the body that altered personality. There could be 10,000 steps between muscle mass and a passive personality, but when 1 step is removed the entire developmental process shifts.

■ Know Thyself

Despite the risks of trying to predict what genes will do, there are ways to benefit from understanding your own genetic makeup. For example, if your family has a history of heart disease or breast cancer, it would be wise to have regular checkups and lead a healthy lifestyle. If obesity is a family problem, it would make sense to develop good eating habits early in life. If your father and brothers are alcoholics, you might be better off not drinking. Those are all commonplace examples of preventive measures based solely on genetic information. They reflect the popular wisdom that physical health is in part a product of genes. The only difference with genes for personality and behavior is that the effects are more subtle and still less understood.

When you think about the genes for your own personality, you are asking, "Who am I?" The simple answer is, "You are who your brain thinks you are." And who your brain thinks you are is the result of an intricate, one-of-a-kind interaction of genes and life experiences.

In the very first days of life, perhaps from the moment of conception, a baby is learning about itself and its world. How does a baby come to know its own body? How does it know where its toes are, and how many it has? How does it distinguish between a mother's caress and a slap on the face? All the touch-sensitive cells in the body make connections through the central nervous system, up the spinal cord to the thalamus and the brain's somatosensory cortex. There the brain cells are arranged in the form of a homunculus—a "tiny man." This little man is created in our image, sort of. He's upside down, so that neurons that respond to stimulation of the face are at the bottom, and those tied to the toes are on top. And he's distorted: the regions representing the face, hands, and genitals—the most touch-sensitive regions—are disproportionately large.

If you could open up the brain and probe it with electrodes, you would find that stimulating the cells at the top of the homunculus would "feel" like someone massaging your toes, or that touching the bottom of the strip would make you "feel" something on the tip of your tongue. This is because physical feelings are nothing more than the firing of specific brain cells.

We know three important facts about the homunculus. First, its ability to develop is genetically hardwired. Imagine the confusion if it weren't: if you were born with a "little dog" up there instead of a little man you'd be barking for your dinner. Second, the proper formation of the homunculus is dependent upon experience; although the genetic instructions are necessary, they are not sufficient. For example, if a rat is shaved of all but one whisker on its snout, and therefore can't receive the expected sensations from the other whiskers, the rat cortex develops a huge bunch of cells to receive information from the one remaining whisker. The areas tied to the missing whiskers disappear from lack of use. Third, the somatosensory cortex can change throughout adult life. For example, practicing a particular violin passage over and over leads to the expansion of the neurons that receive the signal from the relevant fingers. By practicing the violin passage, you can change how the brain is shaped and how it works. Although the DNA had a general blueprint for the homunculus at conception, it is not averse to changing to meet a later need.

To understand how personality is shaped, imagine that the brain not only has a physical homunculus that registers touch but a temperamental one that registers emotions. Each person could have an individual map of what makes him or her feel good or bad, anxious or relaxed, excited or complacent. We don't yet know much about where this hypothetical emotional homunculus is located, but it's probably more spread out than the somatosensory cortex. Nor do we understand how it varies in different people, but differences in both genetic makeup and experience are probably involved. Perhaps in one person the "rage" area is exaggerated and the "altruism" area is tiny (avoid this person). Perhaps in another person it is the excitement area that is large and the fear center that is small (don't get in her car). The empathy area could be large, which means this person feels good by helping others (marry him).

Under our theory, the temperamental homunculus develops from a combination of hardwired genetic instructions and experience. Most people are born with the capacity for the full range of human emotions: fear, anger, and sadness; joy, love, and lust; surprise, disgust, and shame. But those emotions can only develop in response to experience. Without tapping those feeling centers at the right time, they cannot develop. Just like in the rats with one whisker, the unused parts of the brain could disappear.

This is why attention to childhood development is so important. Critics of behavior genetics say it limits people by defining their lives in terms of inherited traits. That would be a mistake, just as it is a mistake to judge people by the color of their skin or place they were born. But the real tragedy is that so much genetic potential is never developed. How much greatness there is in the world that is lost because of inattention and a lack of love. How many beautiful, perfect little seeds are brought to life every day without the opportunity to grow to their strong and healthy potential. In our own country, we have eliminated many of the barriers to physical growth, such as disease, but the breakdown of the family makes it that much harder to help people reach their emotional potential.

On the other hand, the story of Nicholas Scoppetta, who rose out of a broken and troubled home to become a top attorney and New York's commissioner of child welfare, shows that people are remarkably resilient. Just as a perfect upbringing is no guarantee of success, a "bad" childhood is not a predictor of failure. In fact, maybe some people only develop all their natural instincts when challenged by a difficult environment. Perhaps adversity is what hones our genes to razor sharpness. In any case, it's clear that environment is not the only cause of personality problems. Even if we somehow managed to clean up all the slums and gave every child a hot breakfast, we would not have a perfect population. We still would fight, cheat, steal, kill, sleep late, and sleep around, drink too much, be petty, cranky, and obnoxious.

As humans, we are a diverse mix of personalities, a jumble of traits so complex that we barely come to know ourselves in the course of a lifetime, let alone understand what makes other people tick. The exciting thing about the new science is that it is giving us another tool to understand ourselves. Not too long ago, people "went crazy." Today they have chemical imbalances that can be fixed easily. Suicidal depression was often untreatable. Today many people owe their lives to a simple chemical that helps their brains. The logical extension of these breakthroughs in brain chemistry is understanding the genetic roots of personality. Genes aren't scary; they are a fact of life. Gene therapy isn't scary, either, although there are risks. There are similar risks in other scientific advances, however, such as the possibility that our reliance on life-saving antibiotics will produce new strains of superbacteria. Would anybody argue that we should never have developed antibiotics? The greatest risk has always been ignorance.

So what about free will? It's alive and well, and probably genetic. Free will means taking control of your life. This is only possible when you understand who you are. As humans, we are born with instincts to survive, to love, to reproduce. As individuals we are born unique, each of us a variation on the human theme. Genes play an essential role in the overall theme and the individual variations; genes make us human and they make us unique. People cannot be mass produced, even if we tried. Every individual has too many choices and too many possibilities to ever predict the future. You are born with a pen and paper in hand, but you have to write your own story.

Andrew refused a college scholarship from Mirror Image and worked at a restaurant to put himself through school. He studied philosophy and ethics, and wrote his Ph.D. dissertation on the work of his great-great-grandmother. There wasn't much money in philosophy, but he landed a job at a small think tank in Washington. The director remembered the story of Andrew's birth, and thought it might make a good hook to pull in donations for the center. He set Andrew working on the ethical issues of genetics, a perfect fit for the think tank and for Andrew. One of the major backers of the center, however, was not amused. Mirror Image had endowed the center before Andrew's birth, and it's mission was to provide ethical protection for gene work, not question it. Andrew was soon out of a job.

There was a flurry of publicity over the firing and a series of retrospective stories about Andrew's life. The media, of course, found it fascinating that Andrew would rebel against the very technology that created him. But people with a slightly longer view realized there was nothing unusual about a boy rebelling against his father. Andrew's father had the unique experience of being rebelled against by himself. In interviews he joked about having a split personality and said he was "of two minds" about Andrew's progress. Not everybody got the joke.

Andrew knew from his own experience that the attention wouldn't last, so he had to act fast. He set up his own foundation, attracted a few major backers, and began a campaign that would lead to the first effective legislation controlling the gene industry. He became a familiar figure on the talk shows and an articulate defender of the uniqueness of the human spirit and the power of free will. He kept alive the age old questions that had been pushed aside in the excitement over cloning: Who are we? Where do we come from? What should we do with our lives?

Andrew married a woman he met in college, and they had two beautiful children. Andrew and his wife were thoroughly modern and dutiful parents, reading to their babies and playing classical music in the nursery. Before the children were conceived, Andrew and his wife had gone to their obstetrician/geneticist for routine counseling. The doctor had offered to run their DNA through the scanner and discuss any modifications they might want to consider. Andrew, of course, was opposed to genetic engineering, but they were a little concerned because Andrew's wife had a brother who was a paranoid schizophrenic, a condition with strong genetic roots. The doctor assured them that routine screening would weed out such obvious flaws in the DNA. Severe mental conditions, obesity, extreme hyperactivity, socially limiting shyness (SLS), and criminal aggression all had been virtually eliminated through routine genetic screening before conception. People no longer aborted babies with obvious problems; such babies were no longer conceived.

Andrew and his wife decided to play it safe and have the screening. Whatever their own ethical views, it wasn't fair to the child to ignore the latest medical technology. The world was a harsh enough place that it wasn't right to doom a child to a lifetime of suffering when it could be prevented. All their friends did much more refined screening, looking for football players, concert pianists, mathematicians, or chefs. Just like certain baby names would come into style periodically, so did personality traits. The hot trait these days was insouciance, which was patented by a leading perfume maker. The issue wasn't whether to check the unborn DNA, it was what to check it for. Because of his own experience, Andrew had very strong feelings about this. On the DNA screening test, they checked "yes" next to the boxes for severe retardation and Extreme Personality Profile (EPP), which in most cases led to institutionalization. But they checked "no" in the sections for musical ability and poetry.

Andrew and his wife knew more about their children than any generation of parents before them. For the first time in history, they had both nature and nurture covered. They had read everything about childhood development, and they also had the raw genetic code. Andrew understood better than anyone what this information meant: very little. The wondrous truth was that he would have no more say in the future direction of his children than he would in the flight of a bird. All he could do was open the door of the cage and say, "Fly!"

6.14 *DNA for Sale*

Mmm, Mmm, Good!

Operon's custom DNA is made from only the finest ingredients, using our classic oligonucleotide recipe. The preparation of our DNA is carefully controlled by our experienced chefs. We can serve your special requests with over *57 VARIETIES* of modifications available. Our very economical prices make Operon's DNA an exceptional value. And with our unconditional guarantee, Operon's DNA will leave you feeling satisfied. That's why Operon's DNA is *mmm, mmm, good!*

For questions or additional information, please visit our web site at www.operon.com or call customer service at 1-800-688-2248.

List Prices for Custom DNA Services

Custom DNA Synthesis Prices

Scale	Price/base	Set-up	Maximum Length
0.05 μmole	$0.60	$5.00	60-mer
0.2 μmole	$1.20	$10.00	80-mer NEW
1.0 μmole	$2.40	$20.00	100-mer

(Larger scales available)

Purification Options

Method	Price
Sephadex	free
HPLC	from $30
PAGE	from $45

(Many scales available)

Sequence Modifications

Modification	Price
Amino Modifier	$25
Biotin	$50
Fluorescein	$50
HEX, TET, 6-FAM	$70
Phosphate	$25
Cy5 and Cy3	$70

(Many other modifications available)

World's Leading Supplier of Synthetic DNA

1000 Atlantic Avenue, Suite 108 • Alameda, CA 94501
Phone: 800-688-2248 • Fax: 510-865-5255 • E-mail: dna@operon.com • Web: http://www.operon.com

Glossary

Acclimatization Physiological response to changes in the environment that occurs during an individual's lifetime. Such responses may be short-term. The capacity for acclimatization may typify an entire population or species. This capacity is under genetic influence and thus is subject to evolutionary factors such as natural selection.

Acheulian (ash'-oo-lay-en) Pertaining to a stone tool industry of the Lower and Middle Pleistocene characterized by a large proportion of bifacial tools (flaked on both sides). Acheulian tool kits are very common in Africa, Southwest Asia, and western Europe, but are nearly absent elsewhere. (Also spelled "Acheulean.")

Adaptations Physiological and/or behavioral adjustments made by organisms in response to environmental circumstances. Adaptations may be short-term or long-term, and strictly defined, they are the results of evolutionary factors.

Adaptive niche The entire way of life of an organism: where it lives, what it eats, how it gets food, etc.

Adaptive radiation The relatively rapid expansion and diversification of an evolving group of organisms as they adapt to new niches.

Allele frequency The proportion of one allele to all alleles at a given locus in a population.

Alleles Alternate forms of a gene. Alleles occur at the same locus on homologous chromosomes and thus govern the same trait. However, because they are different, their action may result in different expressions of that trait. The term is often used synonymously with *genes.*

Amino acids Small molecules that are the components of proteins.

Analogies Similarities between organisms based strictly on common function with no assumed common evolutionary descent.

Anatomically modern *H. sapiens* All modern humans and some fossil forms, perhaps dating as early as 200,000 y.a.; defined by a set of derived characteristics, including cranial architecture and lack of skeletal robusticity; usually classified at the subspecies level as *Homo sapiens sapiens.*

Anthropoids The suborder of primates including New World monkeys, Old World monkeys, apes, and humans.

Anthropology The field of inquiry that studies human culture and evolutionary aspects of human biology; includes cultural anthropology, archaeology, linguistics, and physical anthropology.

Anthropometry Measurement of human body parts. When osteologists measure skeletal elements, the term osteometry is often used.

Arboreal Tree-living: adapted to life in the trees.

Arboreal hypothesis The traditional view that primate characteristics can be explained as a consequence of primate diversification into arboreal habitats.

Archaic *H. sapiens* Earlier forms of *Homo sapiens* (including Neandertals) from the Old World that differ from *H. erectus* but lack the full set of characteristics diagnostic of modern *H. sapiens.*

Artifacts Objects or materials made or modified for use by hominids. The earliest artifacts tend to be tools made of stone or, occasionally, bone.

Aurignacian Pertaining to an Upper Paleolithic stone tool industry in Europe beginning at about 40,000 y.a.

Australopithecines (os-tral-oh-pith'-e-seens) The colloquial term for members of genus *Australopithecus.*

Australopithecus An early hominid genus, known from the Plio-Pleistocene of Africa, characterized by bipedal locomotion, a relatively small brain, and large back teeth.

Autonomic Pertaining to physiological responses not under voluntary control. An example in chimpanzees would be the erection of body hair during excitement. An example in humans is blushing. Both convey information regarding emotional states but neither is a deliberate behavior, and communication is not intended.

Autosomes All chromosomes except the sex chromosomes.

Binocular vision Vision characterized by overlapping visual fields provided by forward-facing eyes; essential to depth perception.

Binomial nomenclature (*Binomial* means "two names") In taxonomy, the convention established by Carolus Linnaeus whereby genus and species names are used to refer to species. For example, *Homo sapiens* refers to human beings.

Bicultural Pertaining to the concept that biology makes culture possible and that culture influences biology.

Biocultural evolution The mutual, interactive evolution of human biology and culture; the concept that biology makes culture possible and that culture further influences the direction of biological evolution; a basic concept in understanding the unique components of human evolution.

Biological continuum When expressions of a phenomenon continuously grade into one another so that there are no discrete categories, they are said to exist on a continuum. Color is such a phenomenon. The term *biological continuum* refers to the fact that organisms are related through common ancestry and that behaviors and traits seen in one species are also seen in others to varying degrees.

Biological determinism The concept that phenomena, including various aspects of behavior (e.g., intelligence, values, morals) are governed by biological (genetic) factors; the inaccurate association of various behavioral attributes with certain biological traits, such as skin color.

Bipedal locomotion Walking on two feet. Walking habitually on two legs is the single most distinctive feature of the hominids.

Brachiation A form of locomotion in which the body is suspended beneath the hands and support is alternated from one forelimb to the other. Arm swinging.

Breeding isolates Populations that are clearly isolated geographically and/or socially from other breeding groups.

Catastrophism The view that the earth's geological landscape is the result of violent cataclysmic events. This view was promoted by Cuvier, especially in opposition to Lamarck.

Centromere The constricted portion of a chromosome. After replication, the two strands of a double-stranded chromosome are joined at the centromere.

Cercopithecines (serk-oh-pith'-eh-seens) The subfamily of Old World monkeys that includes baboons, macaques, and guenons.

Chatelperronian Pertaining to an Upper Paleolithic tool industry containing blade tools found in France and Spain and associated with Neandertals.

Chordata (Chordates) The phylum of the animal kingdom that includes vertebrates.

Chromosomes Discrete structures composed of DNA and protein found only in the nuclei of cells. Chromosomes are visible only under magnification during certain stages of cell division.

Chronometric Referring to a dating technique that gives an estimate in actual number of years (from *chronos*, meaning "time," and *metric*, meaning "measure").

Clade A group of species sharing a common ancestor and distinct from other groups.

Cladistics The approach to taxonomy that groups species (as well as other levels of classification) on the basis of shared derived characteristics. In this way, organisms are classified solely on the basis of presumed closeness of evolutionary relationship.

Classification In biology, the ordering of organisms into categories, such as phyla, orders, and families, to show evolutionary relationship.

Cline A gradient of genotypes (usually measured as allele frequencies) over geographical space; more exactly, the depiction of allele distribution produced by connecting points of equal frequency (as on a temperature map).

Cloning An organism that is genetically identical to another organism. The term may also be used to refer to genetically identical DNA segments and molecules.

Codominance The expression of two alleles in heterozygotes. In this situation, neither is dominant or recessive, so that both influence the phenotype.

Codons The triplets of messenger RNA bases that refer to a specific amino acid during protein synthesis.

Colobines (kole'-uh-beans) The subfamily of Old World monkeys that includes the African colobus monkeys and Asian langurs.

Communication Any act that conveys information, in the form of a message, to another individual. Frequently, the result of communication is a change in the behavior of the recipient. Communication may not be deliberate but may be the result of involuntary processes or a secondary consequence of an intentional action.

Complementary Referring to the fact that DNA bases form base pairs in a precise manner. For example, adenine can bond only to thymine. These two bases are said to be *complementary* because one requires the other to form a complete DNA base pair.

Continuum A set of relationships in which all components fall along a single integrated spectrum. All life reflects a single biological continuum.

Core area The portion of a home range containing the highest concentration of resources.

Culture All aspects of human adaptation, including technology, traditions, language, and social roles. Culture is learned and transmitted from one generation to the next by nonbiological means.

Cusps The elevated portions (bumps) on the chewing surfaces of premolar and molar teeth.

Cytoplasm The portion of the cell contained within the cell membrane, excluding the nucleus. The cytoplasm consists of a semifluid material and contains numerous structures involved with cell function.

Data (sing., datum) Facts from which conclusions can be drawn; scientific information.

Deoxyribonucleic acid (DNA) The double-stranded molecule that contains the genetic code. DNA is a main component of chromosomes.

Derived Relating to a character state that is modified from the ancestral condition and reflects a more specific evolutionary line and thus more informative of precise evolutionary relationships.

Development Differentiation of cells into different types of tissues and their maturation.

Displays Sequences of repetitious behaviors that serve to communicate emotional states. Nonhuman primate displays are most frequently associated with reproductive or agonistic behavior.

Diurnal Active during the day.

Dominance hierarchies Systems of social organization wherein individuals within a group are ranked relative to one another. Higher-ranking individuals have greater access to preferred food items and mating partners than lower-ranking individuals. Dominance hierarchies are sometimes referred to as "pecking orders."

Dominant Describing a trait governed by an allele that can be expressed in the presence of another, different allele (i.e., in heterozygotes). Dominant alleles prevent the expression of recessive alleles in heterozygotes. (This is the definition of *complete* dominance.)

Ecological Pertaining to the relationship between organisms and all aspects of their environment.

Ecological niches Specific environmental settings to which organisms are adapted.

Empirical Relying on experiment or observation; from the Latin *empiricus,* meaning "experienced."

Endemically (endemic) Continuously present in a population. With regard to disease, refers to populations in which there will always be some infected individuals.

Endocast A solid impression of the inside of the skull, often preserving details relating to the size and surface features of the brain.

Endogamy Mating with others from the same group.

Enzymes Specialized proteins that initiate and direct chemical reactions in the body.

Epochs A category of the geological time scale; a subdivision of period. In the Cenozoic, epochs include the Paleocene, Eocene, Oligocene, Miocene, Pliocene (from the Tertiary period) and the Pleistocene and Holocene (from the Quaternary period).

Essential amino acids The eight (nine for infants) amino acids that must be ingested by humans for normal growth and body maintenance; include tryptophan, leucine, lysine, methionine, phenylalanine, isoleucine, valine, and threonine (plus histidine for infants).

Estrus (ess'-truss) Period of sexual receptivity in female mammals (except humans); correlated with ovulation. When used as an adjective, the word is spelled "estrous."

Ethnographies Detailed descriptive studies of human societies. In cultural anthropology, an ethnography is traditionally the study of a non-Western society.

Eugenics The philosophy of race improvement through forced sterilization of members of some groups and encouraged reproduction among others; an overly simplified, often racist view, that is now discredited.

Evolution A change in the genetic structure of a population. The term is also frequently used to refer to the appearance of a new species.

Evolutionary trends Overall characteristics of an evolving lineage, such as the primates. Such trends are useful in helping to categorize the lineage as compared to other lineages (i.e., other placental mammals).

Exogamy Mating with individuals from other groups.

Faunal Referring to animal remains; in archaeology, specifically refers to the fossil remains of animals.

Fertility Production of offspring; distinguished from fecundity, which is the ability to produce children. For example, a woman in her early 20s is probably fecund, but she is not actually fertile unless she has had children.

Fitness Pertaining to natural selection, a measure of relative reproductive success of individuals. Fitness can be measured by an individual's genetic contribution to the next generation compared to that of others.

Fixity of species (Fixed Theory of Evolution) The notion that species, once created, can never change; an idea diametrically opposed to theories of biological evolution.

Flexed The position of the body in a bent orientation, with the arms and legs drawn up to the chest.

Forensic anthropology An applied anthropological approach dealing with legal matters. Physical anthropologists use their expertise to assist coroners and others in the analysis and interpretation of human remains.

Founder effect Also called the *Sewall-Wright effect*, a type of genetic drift in which allele frequencies are altered in small populations that are taken from, or are remnants of, larger populations.

Frugivorous (fru-give'-or-us) Having a diet composed primarily of fruit.

Gametes Reproductive cells (eggs and sperm in animals) developed from precursor cells in ovaries and testes.

Gene A sequence of DNA bases that specifies the order of amino acids in an entire protein or, in some cases, a portion of a protein. A gene may be made up of hundreds or thousands of DNA bases.

Gene flow The exchange of genes between populations (also called migration).

Gene pool The total complement of genes shared by reproductive members of a population.

Genetic drift Evolutionary changes—that is, changes in allele frequencies—produced by *random* factors. Genetic drift is a result of small population size.

Genetics The study of gene structure and action and the patterns of inheritance of traits from parent to offspring. Genetic mechanisms are the underlying foundation for evolutionary change. The branch of science that deals with the inheritance of biological characteristics.

Genome The full genetic complement of an individual (or of a species). In humans, it is estimated that each individual possesses approximately 3 billion nucleotides in his or her nuclear DNA.

Genotype The genetic makeup of an individual. Genotype can refer to an organism's entire genetic makeup or to the alleles at a particular locus.

Genus A group of closely related species.

Geological time scale The organization of earth history into eras, periods, and epochs; commonly used by geologists and paleoanthropologists.

Grooming Picking through fur to remove dirt, parasites, and other materials that may be present. Social grooming is common among primates, and it reinforces social relationships.

Growth Increase in mass or number of cells.

Heterozygous Having different alleles at the same locus on members of a pair of homologous chromosomes.

Holocene The most recent epoch of the Cenozoic. Following the Pleistocene, it is estimated to have begun 10,000 years ago.

Homeostasis A condition of balance or stability within a biological system, maintained by the interaction of physiological mechanisms that compensate for changes (both external and internal).

Hominidae The taxonomic family to which humans belong; also includes other, now extinct, bipedal relatives.

Hominids Popular form of Hominidae, the family to which modern humans belong; includes all bipedal hominoids back to the divergence from African great apes.

Hominoidea The formal designation for the superfamily of anthropoids that includes apes and humans.

Homologies Similarities between organisms based on descent from a common ancestor.

Homologous Referring to members of chromosome pairs. Homologous chromosomes carry genes that govern the same traits. During meiosis, homologous chromosomes pair and exchange segments of DNA. They are alike with regard to size and also position of the centromere.

Homoplasy (*homo*, meaning "same," and *plasy*, meaning "growth") The separate evolutionary development of similar characteristics in different groups of organisms.

Homozygous Having the same allele at the same locus on both members of a pair of homologous chromosomes.

Hormones Substances (usually proteins) that are produced by specialized cells and that travel to other parts of the body, where they influence chemical reactions and regulate various cellular functions.

Human Genome Project A multinational effort designed to map (and ultimately sequence) the complete genetic complement of *Homo sapiens.*

Hybrids Offspring of mixed ancestry; heterozygotes.

Hypothesis (pl. hypotheses) A provisional explanation of a phenomenon. Hypotheses require verification.

Intelligence Mental capacity; ability to learn, reason, or comprehend and interpret information, facts, relationships, meanings, etc.; the capacity to solve problems, whether through the application of previously acquired knowledge or through insight.

Interspecific Between species. Refers to variation beyond that seen within the same species to include additional aspects seen between two different species.

Intraspecific Within species. Refers to variation seen within the same species.

Ischial callosities Patches of tough, hard skin on the buttocks of Old World monkeys and chimpanzees.

K-selected Pertaining to an adaptive strategy whereby individuals produce relatively few offspring, in whom they invest increased parental care. Although only a few infants are born, chances of survival are increased for each individual because of parental investments in time and energy. Examples of nonprimate K-selected species are birds and wild canids (e.g., wolves, coyotes, and wild dogs).

Lactating Producing and secreting milk via the mammary glands.

Lactation The production of milk in mammals.

Large-bodied hominoids Those hominoids including "great" apes (orangutans, chimpanzees, gorillas) and hominids, as well as all ancestral forms back to the time of divergence from small-bodied hominoids (i.e., the gibbon lineage).

Locus (pl., loci) (lo'-kus, lo-sigh') The position or location on a chromosome where a given gene occurs.

Macaques (muh-kaks') Group of Old World monkeys made up of several species, including rhesus monkeys.

Macroevolution Large-scale evolutionary changes (especially speciation) that may require many hundreds of generations and are usually only detectable paleontologically (in the fossil record).

Magdalenian Pertaining to the final phase (stone tool industry) of the Upper Paleolithic in Europe.

Malnutrition A diet insufficient in quality (i.e., lacking some essential component) to support normal health.

Mammalia The technical term for the formal grouping (class) of mammals.

Material culture The physical manifestations of human activities; includes tools, art, and structures. As the most durable aspects of culture, material remains make up the majority of archaeological evidence of past societies.

Meiosis Cell division in specialized cells in ovaries and testes. Meiosis involves two divisions and results in four daughter cells, each containing only half the original number of chromosomes. These cells can develop into gametes.

Mendelian traits Characteristics that are influenced by alleles at only one genetic locus. Examples include many blood types, such as ABO. Many genetic disorders, including sickle-cell anemia and Tay-Sachs disease, are also Mendelian traits.

Mesolithic The period preceding the Neolithic, during which humans increasingly exploited smaller animals (including fish), increased the variety of tools they used, and became somewhat less nomadic.

Messenger RNA (mRNA) A form of RNA that is assembled on one sequence (one strand) of DNA bases. It carries the DNA code to the ribosome during protein synthesis.

Metazoa Multicellular animals; a major division of the animal kingdom.

Microevolution Small-scale evolutionary changes that occur over the span of a few generations and can therefore be detected in living populations.

Midline An anatomical term referring to a hypothetical line that divides the body into right and left halves.

Mitochondrial DNA (mtDNA) DNA found in the mitochondria (structures found within the cytoplasm of the cell) and inherited through the maternal line.

Mitosis Simple cell division; the process by which somatic cells divide to produce two identical daughter cells.

Molecules Structures made up of two or more atoms. Molecules can combine with other molecules to form more complex structures.

Monogenism The theory that all human races are descended from one pair (Adam and Eve), but they differ from one another because they have occupied different habitats. This concept was an attempt to explain phenotypic variation between populations, but did not imply evolutionary change.

Morphology The form (shape, size) of anatomical structures; can also refer to the entire organism.

Mosaic evolution Rates of evolution in one functional system vary from those in other systems. For example, in hominid evolution, the dental system, locomotor system, and neurological system (especially the brain) all evolved at markedly different rates.

Mousterian Pertaining to the stone tool industry associated with Neandertals and some modern *H. sapiens* groups; also called Middle Paleolithic. This industry is characterized by a larger proportion of flake tools than is found in Acheulian tool kits.

Multidisciplinary Pertaining to research that involves mutual contributions and cooperation of several different experts from various scientific fields (i.e., disciplines).

Mutation A change in DNA. Technically, mutation refers to changes in DNA bases as well as changes in chromosome number and/or structure.

Natural selection The mechanism of evolutionary change first articulated by Charles Darwin. Refers to genetic change, or to changes in the frequencies of certain traits in populations due to differential reproductive success between individuals.

Neocortex The outer (cellular) portion of the cerebrum, which has expanded through evolution, particularly in primates, and most especially in humans. The neocortex is associated with higher mental function.

Neolithic The period during which humans began to domesticate plants and animals. The Neolithic is also associated with increased sedentism. Dates for the Neolithic vary from region to region, depending on when domestication occurred.

Nocturnal Active during the night.

Nucleotides Basic units of the DNA molecule, composed of a sugar, a phosphate, and one of four DNA bases.

Nucleus A structure (organelle) found in all eukaryotic cells. The nucleus contains chromosomes (nuclear DNA).

Osteology The study of skeletons. Human osteology focuses on the interpretation of the skeletal remains of past groups. The same techniques are used in paleoanthropology to study early hominids.

Paleoanthropology The interdisciplinary approach to the study of earlier hominids—their chronology, physical structure, archaeological remains, habitats, etc.

Paleopathology The branch of osteology that studies the traces of disease and injury in human skeletal (or, occasionally, mummified) remains.

Paleospecies Species defined from fossil evidence, often covering a long time span.

Paradigm A cognitive construct or framework within which we explain phenomena. Paradigms shape our world view. They can change as a result of technological and intellectual innovation.

Pathogens Substances or microorganisms, such as bacteria, fungi, or viruses, that cause disease.

Pellagra Disease resulting from a dietary deficiency of niacin (vitamin B3). Symptoms include dermatitis, diarrhea, dementia, and death (the "four Ds").

Phenotypes The observable or detectable physical characteristics of an organism; the detectable expressions of genotypes.

Phenotypic ratio The proportion of one phenotype to other phenotypes in a group of organisms. For example, Mendel observed that there were approximately three tall plants for every short plant in the F_2 generation. This is expressed as a phenotypic ratio of 3:1.

Phylogeny A schematic representation showing ancestor descendant relationships, usually in a chronological framework.

Plasticity The capacity to change; in a physiological context, the ability of systems or organisms to make alterations in order to respond to differing conditions.

Pleistocene The epoch of the Cenozoic from 1.8 m.y.a. until 10,000 y.a. Frequently referred to as the Ice Age, this epoch is associated with continental glaciations in northern latitudes.

Plio-Pleistocene The time period including the Pliocene and the first half of the Pleistocene. For early hominids, this currently covers the range 4.5–1 m.y.a.

Polyandry A mating system wherein a female continuously associates with more than one male (usually two or three) with whom she mates. Among nonhuman primates, this type of pattern is seen only in marmosets and tamarins.

Polygenic Referring to traits that are influenced by genes at two or more loci. Examples of such traits are stature, skin color, and eye color. Many polygenic traits are also influenced by environmental factors.

Polygenism A theory, opposed to monogenism, that stated that human races were not all descended from Adam and Eve. Instead, there had been several original human pairs, each giving rise to a different group. Thus, human races were considered to be separate species.

Polymorphism A genetic trait (the locus governing the trait) with more than one allele in appreciable frequency (i.e., greater than 1 percent).

Polytypic Referring to species composed of populations that differ with regard to the expression of one or more traits.

Pongids Members of the family Pongidae, including orangutans, gorillas, chimpanzees, and bonobos.

Population Within a species, the community of individuals where mates are usually found.

Postcranial (*Post*, meaning "after") Referring to that portion of the body behind the head (in a quadruped). In bipeds, *postcranial* refers to all parts of the body *beneath* the head (i.e., from the neck down).

Prehensility Grasping, as by the hands and feet of primates.

Primate A member of the order of mammals Primates (pronounced "pry-may-tees"), which includes prosimians, monkeys, apes, and humans.

Primates The mammalian order (pronounced "pry-may'-tees") that includes prosimians, monkeys, apes, and humans. When the term is used colloquially, it is pronounced "pry'-mates."

Primatologists Scientists who study the evolution, anatomy, and behavior of nonhuman primates. Those who study behavior in noncaptive animals are usually trained as physical anthropologists.

Primatology The study of the biology and behavior of nonhuman primates (prosimians, monkeys, and apes).

Primitive Referring to a trait or combination of traits present in an ancestral form.

Principle of independent assortment The distribution of one pair of alleles into gametes does not influence the distribution of another pair. The genes controlling different traits are inherited independently of one another.

Principle of segregation Genes (alleles) occur in pairs (because chromosomes occur in pairs). During gamete production, the members of each gene pair separate, so that each gamete contains one member of each pair. During fertilization, the full number of chromosomes is restored, and members of gene or allele pairs are reunited.

Prosimians The suborder of primates that traditionally includes lemurs, lorises, and tarsiers.

Proteins Three-dimensional molecules that serve a wide variety of functions through their ability to bind to other molecules.

Protein synthesis The assembly of chains of amino acids into functional protein molecules. The process is directed by DNA.

Punctuated equilibrium The concept that evolutionary change proceeds through long periods of stasis punctuated by rapid periods of change.

Quadrupedal Using all four limbs to support the body during locomotion; the basic mammalian (and primate) form of locomotion.

Quantitatively (quantitative) Pertaining to measurements of quantity and including such properties as size, number, and capacity. When data are quantified, they are expressed numerically and are capable of being tested statistically.

Racial In biology, pertaining to populations of a species that differ from other populations of the same species with regard to some aspects of outwardly expressed phenotype. Such phenotypic variation within a species is usually associated with differences in geographical location.

Recessive Describing a trait that is not expressed in heterozygotes; also refers to the allele that governs the trait. For a recessive allele to be expressed, there must be two copies of the allele (i.e., the individual must be homozygous).

Recombination The exchange of DNA between homologous chromosomes during meiosis; also called "crossing over."

Replicate To duplicate. The DNA molecule is able to make copies of itself.

Reproductive strategies The complex of behavioral patterns that contributes to individual reproductive success. The behaviors need not be deliberate, and they often vary considerably between males and females.

Reproductive success The number of offspring an individual produces and rears to reproductive age; an individual's genetic contribution to the next generation.

Restriction fragment length polymorphisms (RFLPs) Variation among individuals in the length of DNA fragments produced by enzymes that break the DNA at specific sites.

Rhinarium (rine-air'-ee-um) The moist, hairless pad at the end of the nose seen in most mammalian species. The rhinarium enhances an animal's ability to smell.

Ribonucleic acid (RNA) A single-stranded molecule, similar in structure to DNA. The three forms of RNA are essential to protein synthesis.

Ribosomes Structures composed of a specialized form of RNA and protein. Ribosomes are found in the cell's cytoplasm and are essential to protein synthesis.

r-selected Pertaining to an adaptive strategy that emphasizes relatively large numbers of offspring and reduced parental care (compared to K-selected species). (*K-selection* and *r-selection* are relative terms; i.e., mice are r-selected compared to primates but K-selected compared to many fish species.)

Science A body of knowledge gained through observation and experimentation; from the Latin *scientia,* meaning "knowledge."

Scientific method A research method whereby a problem is identified, a hypothesis (or hypothetical explanation) is stated, and the hypothesis is tested through the collection and analysis of data. If the hypothesis is verified, it becomes a theory.

Scientific testing The precise repetition of an experiment or expansion of observed data to provide verification; the procedure by which hypotheses and theories are verified, modified, or discarded.

Selective pressures Forces in the environment that influence reproductive success in individuals. In the example of the peppered moth, birds applied the selective pressure.

Sex chromosomes The X and Y chromosomes.

Sexual dimorphism Differences in physical characteristics between males and females of the same species. For example, humans are slightly sexually dimorphic for body size, with males being taller, on average, than females of the same population.

Shared derived Relating to specific character states shared in common between two forms and considered the most useful for making evolutionary interpretations.

Sites Locations of discoveries. In paleontology and archaeology, a site may refer to a region where a number of discoveries have been made.

Social structure The composition, size, and sex ratio of a group of animals. Social structures, in part, are the result of natural selection in specific habitats, and they function to guide individual interactions and social relationships.

Sociobiology The study of the relationship between behavior and natural selection. Sociobiological theory states that certain behaviors or behavioral patterns have been selected for because they increase reproductive fitness in individuals.

Socioecology The study of animals and their habitats; specifically, attempts to find patterns of relationship between the environment and social behavior.

Somatic cells Basically, all the cells in the body except those involved with reproduction.

Specialized Evolved for a particular function; usually refers to a specific trait (e.g., incisor teeth), but may also refer to the whole way of life of an organism.

Speciation The process by which new species are produced from earlier ones; the most important mechanism of macroevolutionary change.

Species A group of organisms that can interbreed to produce fertile offspring. Members of one species are reproductively isolated from members of all other species (i.e., they cannot mate with them to produce fertile offspring).

Stereoscopic vision The condition whereby visual images are, to varying degrees, superimposed on one another. This provides for depth perception, or the perception of the external environment in three dimensions. Stereoscopic vision is partly a function of structures in the brain.

Stratigraphy Sequential layering of deposits.

Stratum Geological layer (*pl.*, strata).

Stress In a physiological context, any factor that acts to disrupt homeostasis; more precisely, the body's response to any factor that threatens its ability to maintain homeostasis.

Taxonomy The branch of science concerned with the rules of classifying organisms on the basis of evolutionary relationships.

Territories Areas that will be aggressively protected against intrusion, particularly by other members of the same species.

Theory A broad statement of scientific relationships or underlying principles that has been at least partially verified.

Transfer RNA (tRNA) The type of RNA that binds to specific amino acids and transports them to the ribosome during protein synthesis.

Transmutation The change of one species to another. The term *evolution* did not assume its current meaning until the late nineteenth century.

Uniformitarianism The theory that the earth's features are the result of long-term processes that continue to operate in the present as they did in the past. Elaborated on by Lyell, this theory opposed catastrophism and provided for immense geological time.

Upper Paleolithic Pertaining to a cultural period associated with early modern humans and distinguished by technological innovation in various stone tool industries. Best known from western Europe, similar industries are also known from central and eastern Europe and Africa.

Variation Inherited (i.e., genetically influenced) differences between individuals.

Vectors Agents that serve to transmit disease from one carrier to another. Mosquitoes are vectors for malaria, just as fleas are vectors for bubonic plague.

Vertebrates Animals with bony backbones. Includes fishes, amphibians, reptiles, birds, and mammals.

Viviparous Giving birth to live young.

World view General cultural orientation or perspective shared by members of a society.

Zygote A cell formed by the union of an egg and a sperm cell. It contains the full complement of chromosomes (in humans, 46) and has the potential of developing into an entire organism.